RISING STARS
Mathematics

Year 4

Firbeck Academy
Wollaton
Nottingham
NG8 2FB

Concept developed by
Caroline Clissold and Cherri Moseley

Year 4 Author Team
Caroline Clissold, Heather Davis, Linda Glithro,
Steph King

Homework Sheets written by
Belle Cottingham

Practice Book written by
Paul Broadbent

Teacher's Guide

Every effort has been made to trace all copyright holders, but if any have been inadvertently overlooked, the Publishers will be pleased to make the necessary arrangements at the first opportunity.

Although every effort has been made to ensure that website addresses are correct at time of going to press, Rising Stars cannot be held responsible for the content of any website mentioned in this book. It is sometimes possible to find a relocated web page by typing in the address of the home page for a website in the URL window of your browser.

Hachette UK's policy is to use papers that are natural, renewable and recyclable products and made from wood grown in sustainable forests. The logging and manufacturing processes are expected to conform to the environmental regulations of the country of origin.

ISBN: 978-1-78339-531-6

Text, design and layout © Rising Stars UK Ltd 2016

First published in 2016 by
Rising Stars UK Ltd, part of Hodder Education Group

An Hachette UK Company

Carmelite House
50 Victoria Embankment
London EC4Y 0DZ

www.risingstars-uk.com

Reprinted in 2016

Authors: Caroline Clissold, Belle Cottingham, Heather Davis, Linda Glithro, Steph King

Programme consultants: Caroline Clissold, Cherri Moseley, Paul Broadbent

Publishers: Fiona Lazenby and Alexandra Riley

Editorial: Kate Baxter, Jane Carr, Sarah Chappelow, Lucy Hyde, Jane Morgan, Denise Moulton, Christine Vaughan

Answer checking: Deborah Dobson

Project manager: Sue Walton

Text design: Steve Evans and Mark Walker

Illustrations: Steve Evans

Cover design: Steve Evans and Words & Pictures

Printed by Ashford Colour Press Ltd, Gosport, Hants

A CIP record for this book is available from the British Library.

Contents

Introduction

What is *Rising Stars Mathematics*?

Rising Stars Mathematics is a primary mathematics programme developed specifically for the 2014 National Curriculum Programmes of Study. The programme offers a complete solution to primary mathematics, adapting the best teaching and learning approaches from high-performing jurisdictions such as Shanghai and Singapore, but written bespoke to develop mathematics mastery in the context of UK classrooms.

Rising Stars Mathematics has been designed, developed and written by UK mathematics experts and educators to meet the Mathematics Textbook Guidance produced by the National Centre for Excellence in the Teaching of Mathematics (NCETM).

> 'A high-quality mathematics textbook is an educational resource that can be used by pupils in lessons and independently, and that also provides both subject knowledge and pedagogy support to teachers of mathematics. It is a comprehensive learning tool, providing support for the development of both procedural fluency and conceptual understanding in mathematics.'
>
> NCETM, January 2015
> (https://www.ncetm.org.uk/files/21383193NCETM+Textbook+Guidance.pdf)

Following these guidelines, *Rising Stars Mathematics*:

- provides the rigour teachers expect from quality schemes, without the prescription of scripted day-by-day lesson plans
- contains all the resources and CPD support teachers need to design outstanding mathematics lessons
- offers a wealth of opportunities for children to explore, practise, embed and extend learning
- follows the Concrete-Pictorial-Abstract approach to deepen children's understanding of mathematical concepts
- covers all the curriculum content with a wide variety of teaching ideas whilst respecting teachers' professionalism, to enable them to decide how best to teach their classes.

The pedagogy, approach and rationale

Rising Stars Mathematics is designed to develop fluency, build conceptual understanding and embed reasoning through an enquiry-based approach. It provides a 'light touch' comprehensive structure that allows teachers to retain the control, freedom and flexibility to adapt the timing and teaching activities to meet the needs of their own class. This means that they can focus their time and skills on teaching outstanding lessons in their own way. Carefully organised to provide a clear route through the yearly programmes of study, the curriculum concepts are revisited in a spiral way to reinforce and extend understanding and make links between content areas.

The programme has been developed based on the following key pedagogical beliefs:

1. Mathematical understanding is developed through using **concrete, pictorial** and **abstract** representations.

2. High-quality **textbooks used effectively as teaching tools** support teachers in explaining mathematical concepts clearly, encourage investigative thinking, questioning, discussion and application, all while encouraging children to engage with the wonder of mathematics (see page 6).

3. Children will only fully understand topics and **master concepts** through **step-by-step teaching** and **intelligent practice**. This means teaching concepts at a slower pace and dealing with each aspect of that concept in very small steps, in order to give children time to embed understanding. To achieve mastery, therefore, it is important to spend more time on teaching fewer topics in greater depth rather than moving on to a new topic or concept every few days (see page 6).

4. Mathematics is an interconnected subject in which children need to be able to **make connections** across mathematical ideas. This enables them to develop fluency, mathematical reasoning and problem-solving skills (see page 7).

5. Using **precise mathematical vocabulary** from the beginning is vital in ensuring children's understanding. **Rich talk and discussion** between teachers and children, and amongst peers, using mathematical terminology and constant probing questioning is an essential tool in the ongoing assessment of conceptual understanding for all children (see page 7).

Each of these key points of pedagogy is expanded on and explained in the following sections.

1. Concrete-Pictorial-Abstract (CPA) approach

Rising Stars Mathematics is based on the belief that mathematical understanding is developed through using **concrete, pictorial** and **abstract** (or symbolic) representations. Children will travel along this continuum again and again, often revisiting previous stages when a concept is extended.

Children use **concrete** objects to help them make sense of the concept or problem. This could be anything from real or plastic fruit, to straws, counters, cubes or something else meaningful. Whatever the objects are, they can be moved, grouped and rearranged to illustrate the problem. As the child's experience and confidence grows, they may no longer need physical objects to actually move around. Instead, they draw them. These simple **pictures** to represent the problem could be pictures of real objects they have used in the past, objects mentioned in the problem or something else meaningful. As understanding develops, children move on to use some form of **abstract** representation. This could be giving values to rectangular bars (bar model) to identify what is known and what is unknown, using a symbol to stand for a number, or something else.

It is important to realise that these are not stages gone through once, but a continuum. There will be occasions when a particular child will use concrete, pictorial and abstract representations all in one session. A child who uses abstract representations in one area may need concrete representations in another. On a different occasion, a child may need to revisit a concrete representation before moving on to a pictorial or abstract one.

Using the CPA approach encourages children to start by modelling a problem with concrete objects, before moving on to pictorial and abstract representations. It is important to ensure that a variety of manipulatives are available in all classrooms, not just for Key Stage 1 children. This will help children to develop their understanding more quickly and securely.

A variety of representations are used throughout *Rising Stars Mathematics*. These are both the teacher's and children's toolkit for illustrating and understanding a concept or a

Introduction

particular problem. Children will need to explore the various representations for themselves and be allowed the opportunity to choose which representations they use for a particular activity. (See pages 12–14 for examples and explanations of the main concrete resources and pictorial representations used throughout the *Rising Stars Mathematics* programme.)

2. Textbooks as teaching tools

Rising Stars Mathematics follows the Singapore and Shanghai approach to the use of textbooks. In these high-performing jurisdictions the textbook is a starting point for high-quality teaching. Teachers lead the usage of the textbook with the whole class as a starting point for high-quality teaching, rather than giving a textbook to children to work through on their own. This latter misuse of published resources unfortunately became common in England over a number of years and led to textbooks being seen as synonymous with poor-quality lessons. However, when used effectively as a teaching tool, evidence shows that this is not the case. Instead textbooks provide a framework for teachers to both introduce and develop new content, as well as providing a resource for children to refer back to as required.

The *Rising Stars Mathematics* Textbooks are designed specifically to be used as a teaching tool in conjunction with the teaching guidance and ideas provided in the corresponding Teacher's Guide pages. It is not intended that the Textbooks are given to children to work through in isolation. The Teacher's Notes tabs at the bottom of each Textbook page reference the relevant Teacher's Guide pages, so that the resources can be used in tandem.

The 'Let's learn' pages in the Textbooks should be used by the teacher as a starting point to introduce, teach, model and demonstrate new concepts. To support them in doing this, they can use the ideas in the Teacher's Guide or their own activities if preferred.

The 'Let's practise' pages in the Textbooks provide initial practice opportunities. They lead from basic practice and practice in context, to investigative, open-ended practice. These guided practice activities should be introduced by the teacher. The Teacher's Guide provides suggestions on questioning and how to give targeted support to children who may need additional help in order to move on with the group. The 'Let's practise' sections can be used to provide opportunities for independent working as appropriate for different children or as assessment opportunities to identify whether children have mastered the concept. This will then enable teachers to judge how much additional practice each child requires using the *Rising Stars Mathematics* Practice Books (or other practice materials that they choose to use).

3. The mastery approach

A mastery approach underpins the 2014 National Curriculum. This approach advocates spending longer on topics in order to embed understanding and developing rich connections across topics.

NCETM has identified further principles and features that characterise a mastery approach:

> * Teachers reinforce an expectation that all pupils are capable of achieving high standards in mathematics.
> * The large majority of pupils progress through the curriculum content at the same pace. Differentiation is achieved by emphasising deep knowledge and through individual support and intervention.
> * Teaching is underpinned by methodical curriculum design and supported by carefully crafted lessons and resources to foster deep conceptual and procedural knowledge.
> * Practice and consolidation play a central role. Carefully designed variation within this builds fluency and understanding of underlying mathematical concepts in tandem.
> * Teachers use precise questioning in class to test conceptual and procedural knowledge, and assess pupils regularly to identify those requiring intervention so that all pupils keep up.
>
> NCETM, October 2014
> (https://www.ncetm.org.uk/public/files/19990433/Developing_mastery_in mathematics_october_2014.pdf)

In December 2012, The Advisory Committee on Mathematics Education (ACME) published a report called 'Raising the bar: developing able young mathematicians'. The report identified that England needs to increase the number of young mathematicians with a robust grasp of the range of mathematical ways of thinking and working, through experiencing a deep, rich, rigorous and challenging mathematics education. Children should not be accelerated through the school curriculum: 'acceleration encourages only a shallow mastery of the subject, and so promotes procedural learning at the expense of deep understanding'. Not allowing children enough time to secure deep understanding can lead to feelings of insecurity and dislike of the subject.

Consequently, there is an expectation in the 2014 National Curriculum that most children should 'move through the programmes of study at broadly the same pace'. Children should not be accelerated into a future year group's work. Instead, it is expected that children who grasp concepts rapidly should be challenged through being offered rich and sophisticated problems before any acceleration through new content. There is also the expectation that those who are not sufficiently fluent with earlier material should consolidate their understanding, including through additional practice, before moving on. The aim is for mastery, which is the approach used by many of the high-performing jurisdictions in the international league tables.

With this in mind, there are some important questions for schools to consider when teaching for mastery, which should be discussed and agreed with the whole staff:

* To support the expectation that all children are capable of achieving high standards, what are the implications for whole-class teaching, class groupings or setting within the school?

* How will differentiation be managed to enable all children to access what is being taught? How and when will intervention be given to ensure misconceptions are dealt with immediately and shared with the whole class, so that no children fall behind?

* How will questioning and scaffolding be varied to provide support as needed? What different problems will be provided so that children who grasp the concept quickly are given complex problems which deepen their knowledge of the same content?

* Is there enough focus on the important ability to recall facts and manipulate them to work out other facts, so that children develop the fluency which comes from deep knowledge and practice?

* How will enough time be allowed for different types of intelligent practice (basic practice, variations such as practice within different contexts, extended practice which goes deeper and deeper), so that longer can be spent on key concepts? Will more than one mathematics session per day be required?

* How will practice and consolidation be provided within different contexts, e.g. time, money or length, to ensure connections are made across different areas of mathematics?

* How will teaching focus on the development of deep structural knowledge and the ability to make connections?

* Is the use of precise mathematical vocabulary consistent across the school? Is correct vocabulary introduced from the beginning of teaching? Are all teaching staff comfortable with mathematical terminology?

Practice and variation

Intelligent practice underpins the mastery approach. 'Intelligent practice' is a term used to describe practice that develops procedural fluency while at the same time exposing mathematical structures, patterns and relationships in order to deepen conceptual understanding.

Intelligent practice is clearly structured and incorporates carefully-designed variations. These variations may be conceptual or procedural:

- Procedural variation can be introduced by extending a problem (e.g. varying the number, the unknown or the context), varying the processes of solving a problem or varying the application of a method (e.g. applying the same method to a group of similar problems).

- Conceptual variation can be introduced by varying the representation of a problem.

The practice in *Rising Stars Mathematics* is based on the principles of intelligent practice.

- The 'Let's practise' pages in the Textbook are clearly structured. Steps 1 and 2 comprise bare (or, decontextualised) practice and include procedural variations. Step 3 provides practice within a variety of contexts (including time, money and statistics) and Step 4 offers open-ended, investigative practice. By working their way through the practice, children will build procedural fluency across a range of question types and in a range of contexts, while also developing their understanding of the concepts covered in the 'Let's learn' pages.

- The corresponding 'Let's practise' pages in the Teacher's Guide extend the opportunities for conceptual variation by suggesting a range of physical and pictorial representations that teachers may want to use to support children's practice.

- The Practice Book offers further carefully-crafted practice exercises. These exercises have been planned to include structured variation of a number or unknown (procedural variation), a range of representations (e.g. a question on length may use a variety of visuals such as ribbons, snakes and pencils) and open questions (e.g. 'What do you notice?') that encourage children to reason and spot patterns.

Teachers can use the carefully-designed questions and exercises as a starting point to introduce intelligent practice into their teaching. However, they retain the freedom to develop their own questions and activities, incorporating variation that best suits the needs of their children.

4. Making connections

The 2014 National Curriculum states that:

> 'Mathematics is an interconnected subject in which pupils need to be able to move fluently between representations of mathematical ideas. The programmes of study are, by necessity, organised into apparently distinct domains, but pupils should make rich connections across mathematical ideas to develop fluency, mathematical reasoning and competence in solving increasingly sophisticated problems. They should also apply their mathematical knowledge to science and other subjects.'
>
> *National Curriculum in England*, Department for Education, 2013

In *Rising Stars Mathematics* there are a wide variety of opportunities to develop mathematics in other areas of the curriculum and in real life, e.g. the opening pages of each unit in the Textbook contain interesting photos and visuals to encourage children to identify instances of mathematics in the world around them, in order to make connections between what they are learning and how it might apply in real life. The programme is designed to provide opportunities to link together different areas of mathematics together, e.g. when children practise a concept, such as addition, they will have the opportunity to do this through an area of measure, e.g. length, mass, temperature or time. This has the benefit of allowing more time to be spent on the big ideas of mathematics within its everyday applications.

The units in *Rising Stars Mathematics* are structured to focus on one of four key mathematical themes: Number Sense, Additive Reasoning, Multiplicative Reasoning or Geometric Reasoning (see page 9). These cover concepts from the related Programmes of Study areas, incorporating Measurement and Statistics where appropriate. This ensures that the end-of-year statements for these areas are covered through a multitude of practice opportunities across the units.

5. Mathematical vocabulary

The 2014 National Curriculum states that:

> 'The National Curriculum for mathematics reflects the importance of spoken language in pupils' development across the whole curriculum – cognitively, socially and linguistically. The quality and variety of language that pupils hear and speak are key factors in developing their mathematical vocabulary and presenting a mathematical justification, argument or proof. They must be assisted in making their thinking clear to themselves as well as others, and teachers should ensure that pupils build secure foundations by using discussion to probe and remedy their misconceptions.'
>
> *National Curriculum in England*, Department for Education, 2013

Using correct mathematical language is crucial for thinking, learning and communicating mathematically. Children may build knowledge through remembering information that they hear, but it is only when they put these ideas into their own words that it becomes clear whether concepts have been learnt effectively. It is in listening to children talking about mathematics that teachers can best assess what they are actually learning and understanding, which in turn enables them to identify and address any misconceptions that might be developing.

Children should be encouraged to explain what they are doing and why they are doing it, through probing questioning from the teacher if necessary. Offering opportunities to use mathematical language frequently, e.g. by participating in paired activities, group discussions and games, will ensure that rich talk develops in the classroom. Spoken language in mathematics can be thought of as a rehearsal for recording, as well as an outcome in its own right. It allows children to extend and develop their reasoning skills as they explain and justify their thinking. It provides the opportunity to review existing knowledge, to explore new ideas and to extend their understanding.

The productive use of spoken language in mathematics allows children to evaluate their learning, support others' suggestions, challenge ideas, reason or justify and ask questions. Therefore, it is important to encourage children not just to learn and remember the correct vocabulary, but also to use these words regularly to communicate mathematically. Using mathematical vocabulary can help all children to make links across areas of mathematics, across the curriculum as a whole and also within real life situations. It can enable them to build confidence, communicate and problem-solve, so should be an integral part of every mathematics lesson.

Teachers need to plan the introduction of new words into lessons and provide opportunities for children to rehearse and use them on a regular basis. It is also essential that other adults working with children use mathematical vocabulary accurately and consistently. The 'Mathematical vocabulary' sections in the *Rising Stars Mathematics* Teacher's Guide identify key words that should be covered when teaching each concept. The glossary in the Textbook provides explanations for children and the glossary at the back of this Teacher's Guide offers detailed definitions on a wide variety of key mathematical terms.

Getting started with
Rising Stars Mathematics

The components

Rising Stars Mathematics includes a wealth of resources for children and teachers. The pupil materials include full-colour Textbooks, single-colour write-in Practice Books and Homework Sheets (found at the back of the Teacher's Guides). The teacher materials comprise the Teacher's Guide and a variety of additional CPD, teaching resources, and digital teaching and learning resources be found on the My Rising Stars website. The contents for each of these components is summarised below.

Textbook

- Opportunities for children to develop problem-solving and reasoning skills.
- 14 units covering all the concepts to be learnt in Year 4.
- Glossary.

Practice Books

- 14 units providing further independent practice of all the concepts to be learnt in Year 4.
- Answers can be found on the My Rising Stars website.

Homework Sheets

- 74 expansion activities to enable children to explore mathematics further outside the classroom.
- Ideal for engaging parents/carers in children's learning.

Teacher's Guide

- CPD guidance on the pedagogy, approach and how to use the *Rising Stars Mathematics* resources.
- Scope and sequence chart and curriculum mapping grids to aid planning.
- Non-prescriptive teaching guidance for all 14 units in the Textbook.
- Photocopiable Homework Sheets and answers.
- Glossary.
- Bibliography for further reading.

Website and digital resources

- **CPD resources** including:
  1. Short, sharp **CPD videos** providing bite-sized insights into key areas of importance when teaching mathematics, as well as background subject knowledge videos for every theme.
  2. Ready-made **INSET Training PowerPoint presentation** to offer a time-saving way to introduce the principles and resources of *Rising Stars Mathematics* to staff.

- **Planning resources** including:
  1. **Scope and sequence charts** and **curriculum mapping grids** for each year group.
  2. The Rising Stars *Primary Maths Planning Framework* and **posters** for long-term planning support.
  3. Editable **medium-term planning grids** including references to other useful resources.
  4. Mathematical vocabulary **glossaries**.
  5. **Bibliography** of research papers and recommended further reading, including guidance documents from NCETM.

- **Teaching resources** including:
  1. **Teacher Toolkit** containing useful digital tools, which can be used to model concepts on the interactive whiteboard. Tools include:
     - Counters
     - Numerals & Symbols
     - 100 Squares
     - Place Value & Abacus
     - Number Line
     - Clock & Timer
     - Calendar & Timezone
     - Money
     - Calculator
     - Dice, Coin & Number
     - 2D Shapes
     - Tangrams
     - 3D Shapes
     - Fraction Wall
     - Graphs & Charts
     - Geometry Instruments

  2. **eTextbook** – a digital version of the Textbook that can be displayed in the classroom on the interactive whiteboard or shared with parents/carers, so that children can access it from home. The eTextbook is enhanced with fun animations to help explain concepts.
  3. **Animations** from the eTextbook (available separately) are organised by unit, so they can be accessed quickly to play on the interactive whiteboard when required.
  4. PDFs of the **Teacher's Guide notes**, organised unit by unit, can be viewed anytime without needing the book to hand.
  5. Editable versions of the **Homework Sheets**.
  6. Printable versions of the colour **gameboards** from the Textbooks.
  7. Editable versions of the **game instructions** from the Teacher's Guide.
  8. **Answers** to the Practice Books and Homework Sheets.

- **Pupil resources** including:
  1. **eTextbook** – see Teaching resources above.
  2. **Animations** – see Teaching resources above.
  3. **Printable gameboards** and **instruction sheets** organised unit by unit.
  5. Editable versions of the **Homework Sheets** organised unit by unit.
  6. **Answers** to the Practice Books and Homework Sheets.

Themes

Rising Stars Mathematics is built around four themes: Number Sense, Additive Reasoning, Multiplicative Reasoning and Geometric Reasoning. Each covers the concepts from the related Programme of Study areas. This approach ensures that clear connections are made between areas of mathematics.

1. **Number Sense** is about understanding our number system, with a focus on how our numbers work and fit together, and applying this understanding in different contexts. Units on Additive Reasoning and Multiplicative Reasoning are usually preceded by a unit on Number Sense, which explores the understanding needed for the subsequent unit.

2. **Additive Reasoning** is about understanding addition and subtraction together and the relationship between them, and using this understanding to solve problems.

3. **Multiplicative Reasoning** is about understanding multiplication and division together and the relationship between them, and using this understanding to solve problems.

4. **Geometric Reasoning** is about understanding the properties of shapes and the relationships between them, using this understanding to solve problems related to measure and movement within space.

Measures and statistics are included throughout as contexts for all four themes. These contexts are examples and teachers may wish to select different contexts to support each concept. **Algebra** (a new domain in Year 6) appears in all themes as part of generalisation of mathematical understanding.

The unit structure

Each year level of *Rising Stars Mathematics* contains 14 units. These units all follow the same structure as explained below. The Textbook and Teacher's Guide work alongside each other. Each double-page spread in the Teacher's Guide contains a reproduction of the corresponding Textbook page for ease of reference. The Textbook has teaching notes tabs at the bottom of each page to enable teachers to quickly find the corresponding Teacher's Guide page.

Textbook and Teacher's Guide: unit opener pages

In the Textbook, each unit begins with engaging photos of mathematics in real life. These unit opener pages give children the opportunity to discuss what they see and explore what could be going on, looking for mathematics in the world around them. 'I wonder…' questions encourage thinking around the topic. This sets the scene for exploring the underlying concepts in more depth throughout the unit. Such discussions give the teacher the opportunity to check current understanding before moving on to the concept explanation, modelling, exemplification, practice and application.

The corresponding Teacher's Guide pages highlight the main mathematical focus of the unit, expected prior learning and key new learning to be covered throughout the unit. It also provides: support for making connections across areas of mathematics or between concepts; a 'Talk about' section that focuses on the use of precise mathematical vocabulary; a variety of activities and questions about the visuals in the Textbook to engage and explore with children; a list of questions for teachers to think about regarding organisation and planning. Finally, there is brief guidance to support teachers in checking understanding as the unit progresses.

Textbook and Teacher's Guide: concept pages

Each has two pages: 'Let's learn' and 'Let's practise'. The 'Let's learn' page begins with a discussion between the year group character guides, illustrating a possible misconception. The key information about the new concept to be learnt is explained, supported by relevant pictorial representations.

The 'Let's practise' section develops children's reasoning incrementally through guided practice. In *Rising Stars Mathematics*, the first steps provide bare, decontextualised practice. The third step gives practice in a context (e.g. an area of measurement or statistics), while the fourth step is a more open-ended, investigative practice of the concept.

The corresponding Teachers' Guide pages for these sections provide: a list of key mathematical vocabulary, representations and resources; useful background knowledge; activities for warming up, modelling and teaching, digging deeper through practice and follow-up activity ideas. There is also a section on ensuring progress, with ideas for supporting and broadening understanding. These are ideas which can be adapted to the needs of the class – there is no specific script. There are also notes on how to identify when the key concepts have been mastered and answers to the 'Let's practise' activities in the Textbook.

Textbook and Teacher's Guide: gameboard pages

Each unit contains fun activities to encourage children to apply their knowledge and skills, whilst consolidating conceptual understanding. The attractive colour gameboards for these are contained in the Textbooks. Two versions of games that can be played using each gameboard are provided and children are also encouraged to invent their own game using the gameboard. The invented games are often a useful means of assessing understanding.

The corresponding Teachers' Guide pages provide further detail about playing each of the games, including the mathematics focus, resources needed, instructions for how to play and support for making the game activities easier or harder. A photocopiable sheet of 'How to play' instructions is also provided, should teachers wish to send the games home as an out-of-class activity. Printable versions of the gameboards are available to download from the website.

Textbook and Teacher's Guide: 'And finally …' review pages

The final part of each unit is a review section, which provides a variety of assessment tasks. The Textbook pages include three assessment tasks, followed by a colourful 'Did you know?' fun facts section to complete the unit. (For further information about assessment see page 11.)

The corresponding Teachers' Guide review pages provide further detail of any resources needed, instructions for how to run the tasks and guidance on what to look for in children's responses, in order to evidence mastery. There is also some background knowledge about the 'Did you know?' facts and a summary list of all the concepts children are expected to have mastered by the end of the unit.

Introduction

Practice Books

The Practice Books provide further opportunities for children to consolidate understanding and explore, explain and reason through different types of practice activities. These activities include conceptual and procedural variations, in order to develop fluency and conceptual understanding. There is practice for every concept in the Textbook. The write-in format ensures that children always have a record of their work that they can refer back to,so that they can learn from their mistakes and see the progress they are making.

The relevant Practice Book pages for each concept in the Textbook are referenced at the top of the corresponding Teacher's Guide page for each new concept.

Homework Sheets

The photocopiable Homework Sheets can be found at the back of the Teacher's Guide. Editable versions are also available on the My Rising Stars website. They provide expansion activities for children to continue to explore mathematics outside the classroom. Two activities are provided for each of the concept pages in a unit.

The relevant Homework Sheets for each concept in the Textbook are referenced at the top of the corresponding Teacher's Guide page for each new concept.

Teaching a unit

Teachers are advised to begin by looking at the Teacher's Guide to familiarise themselves with the content to be covered within a particular unit and reviewing the related CPD videos on the website if necessary.

1. Develop subject knowledge

- Watch the short online CPD videos to develop background subject knowledge before planning lessons.
- Refresh knowledge by reviewing the INSET training presentations as necessary.

2. Design lessons

- Plan and design lessons using the suggested activities in the Teacher's Guide.
- Choose how much time to spend on each activity to fit the needs of each class.
- Gather all the concrete resources and visual representations needed.
- Review the recommended Teacher Toolkit tools and any relevant concept animations on the My Rising Stars website.

3. Explore new concepts

- Introduce the unit using the Textbooks as a teaching tool. Remember to check the teaching notes tab at the bottom of each page and the corresponding Teacher's Guide pages before the lesson.
- Play any relevant animations (from the eTextbook or direct from the website) to the class and discuss them together.
- Explore, model and teach new concepts to children using a variety of representations and practical resources, following the 'Let's learn' page.
- Use tools from the Teacher Toolkit to model concepts on the interactive whiteboard where appropriate.
- Embed conceptual understanding and dig deeper into concepts through intelligent practice, using the 'Let's practise' page.

4. Embed and expand understanding

- Consolidate understanding using the fun games to provide extra practice and aid mastery. Print extra copies of the game boards and instructions from the website as necessary.
- Set expansion or out-of-class activities using the Homework Sheets or Practice Books. Answers can be found on the website.
- Encourage parents/carers to engage with children's learning by sharing the eTextbook to view the pages and animations at home.
- Provide further independent practice using the Practice Books to deepen understanding of the concepts taught using the Textbooks.

5. Assess progress and mastery

- Review the content covered throughout the unit using the assessment tasks to ensure children have mastered the concepts.
- Finish the unit by finding out some fun mathematical facts in the 'Did you know?' section.
- Use *Rising Stars Assessment Half-Termly Progress Tests* to measure progress independently, if desired.

Timing

As a guide, the expectation is that each unit will take two to three weeks to teach. The length of time spent on each unit will vary depending on the topic, the number of new concepts covered within it and how quickly children master the concepts. If teachers are confident that children have mastered a concept, then it is perfectly acceptable to move on more quickly, just as it is important to allow children to spend longer on a topic if necessary to ensure that they have fully mastered it before moving on. It is better to spend more time on fewer topics to ensure that they are fully understood and children have embedded what they have learnt, so that they can remember and apply it later on.

Mixed-age classes

For schools with mixed-age classes, the *Rising Stars Mathematics* resources can be used to teach the same topic to the whole class, as long as this is done age-appropriately. The pitch should be year-group based, regardless of the perceived ability of children within those year groups. It is important that however the classroom is managed, each year group sticks to what is expected for that year in order to meet the National Curriculum Programme of Study requirements. Children should therefore all be using the Textbooks and Practice Books appropriate for their year group. As teachers in this kind of setting will know all too well, this is like teaching two or more classes. This brings huge challenges in planning and organisation, especially in small schools where there are three to four year groups per class.

However, because the units in *Rising Stars Mathematics* all have a main focus on one of four themes (Number Sense, Additive Reasoning, Multiplicative Reasoning or Geometric Reasoning), similar topics are generally covered in the same unit in each year group. Therefore corresponding units from Year 1 and Year 2, Year 3 and Year 4, Year 5 and Year 6 will work together neatly as they focus on the same themes, e.g. Unit 1 in all year groups across the *Rising Stars Mathematics* resources is focused on Number Sense, so teachers are able to focus on similar topics at a different level within mixed-age classes.

On the website, there are Medium-term Planning Grid templates which break down the units into half-termly plans. These may be useful for teachers of mixed-age classes to compare the different year groups.

Assessment

Assessment opportunities

Each unit in *Rising Stars Mathematics* provides the opportunity for teachers to check existing understanding through the opener pages. Discussions around what children can see, how they interpret what they see and their response to the 'I wonder…' questions will reveal children's current level of understanding.

Likewise, the cartoon at the beginning of each concept, provides an opportunity to check understanding through class discussion of the misconception or error. Throughout each unit, there are continual opportunities for assessment. Teachers will probe conceptual and procedural understanding through questioning and observation as they model and teach. The way children respond to the modelling and teaching provides the teacher with valuable information on what to spend a little more time and what to move through quickly, as well as information on individual needs.

The Textbook activities provide further assessment opportunities, particularly the non-routine, open-ended types of activities offered in Step 4.

The final review activities are particularly useful assessment tasks, since they are designed to give children the opportunity to demonstrate what they know and the concepts they have mastered. In this way assessment is ongoing throughout the unit, with a summative assessment at the end of each unit.

End points to be tested in Key Stage 2 national tests

Some elements of the National Curriculum cannot be assessed in statutory tests although they will need to be assessed by teachers as part of their statutory assessment of the whole National Curriculum. Over time, all the end point requirements that can be tested in the 2014 National Curriculum will be tested at the end of Key Stage 2. It is therefore important to make a note of these, particularly for teachers in Years 5 and 6, and to make sure children are up to speed with these requirements, e.g. Roman numerals need to be taught from Years 3 to 5. There is no mention of them in Year 6. However, they could be tested in the end of Year 6 tests. *Rising Stars Mathematics* suggests times when these can be rehearsed and reinforced during the warm-up activities, practice or follow-up tasks.

Measuring progress

In a new world of assessment free from levels, it is now up to teachers to decide how best to assess the progress their children are making against the new Programmes of Study. For schools who wish to do this using regular half-termly or end-of-term tests using an independent resource outside of the *Rising Stars Mathematics* teaching materials, the *Rising Stars Assessment Half-termly Progress Tests* are an ideal resource to measure progress and inform future learning. They are organised to assess the content in the same order that it is covered in the scope and sequence of the Rising Stars Mathematics units, so that teachers can be sure that children are not being tested on content that they have yet to be taught. For more information, please visit www.risingstars-uk.com.

Ensuring progress for all children

If we consider any particular concept area as a pool, some children will paddle, others will swim with armbands and others will swim freely. They are all in the same pool, but accessing it at different levels and in different ways. This is a good metaphor for how differentiation should be managed when following a mastery approach. It will ensure that the broad majority of children all move on together into a new pool, as required by the National Curriculum.

Rising Stars Mathematics assumes that all children within the class will be taught the same content and given the same opportunities to understand the concepts. The 'Let's learn: Modelling and teaching' and 'Let's practise: Digging deeper' sections both include suggestions for a variety of representations, models and images that can be used to explain the concepts. The expectation is not that all children should be able to use all representations or methods, but rather that different representations will trigger understanding for different children. By using a wide variety of representations like this and multiple ways to explain concepts, teachers give each individual child the best possible chance of finding something that works for them. Some children may fully grasp the concept being introduced using the first or second representation, however that does not mean the rest of the lesson is irrelevant for them. Seeing the concept represented in different ways will give them the opportunity to deepen their understanding and make connections between the different methods.

Rising Stars Mathematics recognises that in every class it is likely that there will be some children who will need more support than others to achieve understanding of concepts. The Teacher's Guide includes a section on 'Supporting understanding' for children who need a little more reinforcement. The same section also offers ideas for 'Broadening understanding', for those children who have a good understanding of the concept.

In order to give all children the best possible chance to make progress in mathematics, the *Rising Stars Mathematics* approach to differentiation is that it should be managed through support and intervention, not through changing the content. Difficulties and misconceptions should be addressed as they occur and children should be challenged through more demanding problems, rather than being accelerated to future curriculum content.

Some schools are organising mathematics so that there are two shorter sessions each day. The first session is used for teaching the concept, the second is for practice. Using *Rising Stars Mathematics* for this approach, teachers would focus on the 'Let's learn' part of the unit in the first session and on the 'Let's practise' section in the second session. During the second session, the teacher could work with children who have struggled to understand as a guided group, whilst others work through the three or four steps in the Textbook more independently. A further 15-minute intervention session may be offered later the same day. Intervention must be carried out immediately to ensure that the majority of children move through the materials at the same pace. Some schools may wish to pre-teach a small group of children. This 10-minute session could be used to revise what children already know about today's concept and its vocabulary, before the concept is extended in the main session.

Children with significant special needs may require an individual programme of work. Although these children are unlikely to master concepts as deeply as others, they should still aim for mastery at a level appropriate for the individual.

Fast finishers can be challenged to deepen their understanding by generalising. Depending on the concept, they might be asked if what they have just explored will always, sometimes or never be true. They might be asked to give an example of the concept in money or measures. Alternatively, some of the other strategies to embed problem solving could be used. *Rising Stars Mathematics* provides some suggestions for broadening understanding in every unit.

Resources and representations

Representations are hugely important in helping children to develop a conceptual understanding of what they are learning. *Rising Stars Mathematics* aims to encourage all teachers to make use of these with all children from Year 1 through to Year 6. In the past, manipulatives and visual representations have often only been used in Key Stage 2 for children struggling to grasp certain concepts, but they are necessary for all. There are two main types of representations: visual (pictorial) and manipulative (concrete apparatus).

The key manipulatives included in this programme are:

- Straws (Years 1-3)
- Base 10 apparatus
- Place-value counters
- Place-value cards
- Number rods
- Double-sided counters
- Bead strings
- Plates
- Digit cards
- Coins
- Counting sticks
- Interlocking cubes
- Coloured counters
- 2-D shapes
- 3-D shapes
- Clock faces
- 1–6 dice
- 1–10 dice
- Percentage cards
- Modelling clay
- Number cards
- Tangrams

See below for further details.

The key visual representations included in this programme are:

- Number tracks
- Ten frames
- 100 squares
- Number lines
- The bar model
- Place-value grids
- Gattegno charts

See below for further details.

Concrete manipulatives

Straws

Straws are a great resource to enable children to see the cardinality of numbers. They could make bundles of ten and compare tens and ones. They could put ten bundles together to make 100 and compare these. Straws are particularly useful for younger children, when they still need to see and touch quantities.

Base 10 apparatus

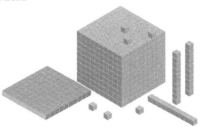

These are representations of numbers. In the first instance, the small cubes represent ones, the rods tens, the flats hundreds and the large cubes thousands. Children find these helpful because the size of the individual pieces helps to denote their value. Later, when children encounter decimals, the flats represent ones, the rods tenths and the small cubes hundredths. If children are familiar with using different manipulatives to represent numbers, it will be easy for them to make this transfer.

Place-value counters

These also represent numbers. You can see clearly what each colour represents through the values written on each (often greens are hundreds, yellows are tens, and reds are ones). They are more abstract than Base 10 apparatus because the counters are all the same size and are therefore not proportional to their value. It is recommended that these are used in late Key Stage 1 and in Key Stage 2, when children are working with larger numbers. When children have used these, you may find that they can use any coloured counters and assign their own values to them.

Number rods

Coloured number rods are excellent for helping children to become flexible in their thinking about numbers. The rods represent any number that you would want them to represent. Assign a value to one and children can work out the values of the other rods. The rods are fractions of other rods, e.g. some are halves, quarters and eighths of others. This is a great resource to use when dealing with multiplication, division and fractions.

Coloured rods can also be used as bars to support thinking when using the bar model. Using a rod to represent a bar allows bars to be changed or manipulated to illustrate the problem under consideration. See the section on the bar model for further information on this.

Double-sided counters

These are great for helping children to develop reasoning and fluency. You could give children three counters each and ask them to show you 2, then 3, then 12. Children need to consider how they could represent 12 using three counters. The only rule is that one colour needs to represent the same number. So, two yellow sides could be 5 each and a red side could be 2. Or one yellow side could be 8 and one red side 4. There are numerous ways to represent 12 or other numbers using these counters.

Bead strings

Bead strings are helpful for early calculation. When children are familiar with them and know that each string of colour is 10, they can add, subtract, multiply and divide using them and develop the ability to do this without counting one at a time, e.g. for 10 + 6, they add 6 onto 10, without the need to count ten beads, six beads and then count them all. These can be used to represent other numbers, e.g. the whole string could represent 1, each coloured section would then be one tenth and one bead would be one hundredth. This flexibility makes the bead string a very useful manipulative for fractions, decimals and percentages.

Plates

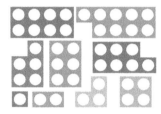

Plates like these are another manipulative which help children to move on from counting everything, e.g. if they add 5 and 9, they put the plates together. They match the result with 10 and 4 to give the answer 14. Paper 10 frames can be cut and used to represent a number in exactly the same way.

Visual representations

The bar model

The bar model is a very effective visual representation. It helps children to make sense of problems. Take missing number statements such as 35 – □ = 16. We know that 35 is the larger number, so it will be the larger bar. A smaller bar of 16 can be drawn below it. Drawing a bar from the end of the 16 bar to fill the space to the end of the 35 bar represents the missing number. We can then work out the missing number by counting back from 35 to 16 or counting on from 16 to 35.

35	
16	?

This can support children as they work out families of addition and subtraction facts.

$a = b + c$
$a = c + b$
$a - b = c$
$a - c = b$

a	
b	c

Addition and subtraction calculations can be represented using this model, e.g.

1) Samir scored 145 points on a computer game, Alex scored 76 more points. How many points did Alex score?

145	76
?	

(Alex scored 221 points.)

2) Jenny had a collection of shells. She gave her friend 123 of them. She was left with 146. How many shells did she have before giving some to her friend?

123	146
?	

(Jenny had 269 shells.)

3) Ben went for a run. He ran 12.5 km to the shop and 6.75 km back. Then he stopped to talk to a friend. How much further did he need to run to get home?

12.5 km	
?	6.75 km

(Ben has to run another 5.75 km.)

4) Ella has some cherries. She eats two. Then she eats half of what is left. She now has six. How many did she have to begin with?

?		
6	6	2

(Ella started off with 14 cherries.)

This model can be used very effectively for representing multiplication, division and fractions, as well as ratio and proportion problems. It is often helpful to use double-sided counters or coloured rods to set out the problems first and then move on to drawing them as bars, e.g.

1) There are 27 red flowers in the garden. There are three times as many red flowers as there are white flowers. How many white flowers are there?

Red flowers

White flowers

If there are 27 red flowers, each part is worth 9. So there are 9 white flowers.

2) Sam had five times as many marbles as Tom. If Sam gives 26 marbles to Tom, the two friends will have exactly the same amount. How many marbles do they have altogether?

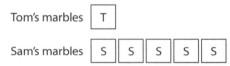

Tom's marbles | T

Sam's marbles | S | S | S | S | S

Sam gives 26 marbles to Tom.

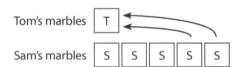

Tom's marbles | T

Sam's marbles | S | S | S | S | S

So, the model will look like this:

T	S	S
S	S	S

We now know that each part is worth 13. So they have 78 marbles altogether.

3) David spent $\frac{2}{5}$ of his money on a book. The book cost £10. How much money did he start off with?

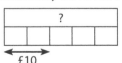

We know $\frac{2}{5}$ is equal to £10. Each part must be £5. So he started off with £25.

Introduction

4) In Class 4, 80% of children like crisps. 75% of children who like crisps also like chocolate. What percentage of Class 4 like both crisps and chocolate?

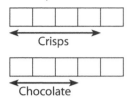

Each part in the model is worth 20%. So 60% of Class 4 like both crisps and chocolate.

5) A computer game was reduced in a sale by 20% and it now costs £48. What was the original price?

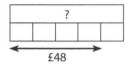

We know from this model that each part is worth £12. So, £12 is equivalent to the discount. Therefore the original cost was £60.

6) A gardener plants tulip bulbs in a flower bed. She plants 3 red bulbs for every 4 white bulbs. She plants 60 red bulbs. How many white bulbs does she plant?

If she plants 60 red tulips, each part is worth 20. Therefore she must have planted 80 white bulbs.

Ten frames

There are different types of ten frames. This is one example.

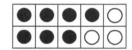

It draws out the odd and even properties of number. They are helpful for finding number bonds to 10, as well as for addition and subtraction.

These can also be used to represent fractions and decimals, e.g. if the whole frame is worth 1, what are the black counters worth? (0.7, $\frac{7}{10}$.)

Place-value grids

1000	100	10	1	.	10th	100th	1000th
				.			

Place-value grids are very useful for helping children to gain an understanding of the four main aspects of place value.

Gattegno charts

0.001	0.002	0.003	0.004	0.005	0.006	0.007	0.008	0.009
0.01	0.02	0.03	0.04	0.05	0.06	0.07	0.08	0.09
0.1	0.2	0.3	0.4	0.5	0.6	0.7	0.8	0.9
1	2	3	4	5	6	7	8	9
10	20	30	40	50	60	70	80	90
100	200	300	400	500	600	700	800	900
1000	2000	3000	4000	5000	6000	7000	8000	9000
10000	20000	30000	40000	50000	60000	70000	80000	90000

Gattegno charts are another useful resource that will help to secure children's conceptual understanding of place value.

Delivering the aims of the National Curriculum

Developing fluency

The first aim of the 2014 National Curriculum states that teachers must ensure that children: 'become fluent in the fundamentals of mathematics, including through varied and frequent practice with increasingly complex problems over time, so that pupils develop conceptual understanding and the ability to recall and apply knowledge rapidly and accurately'. Fluency includes:

- knowing number bonds for all numbers to 10, then 20 and 100.
- knowing multiplication facts up to 12×12.
- using these facts flexibly to create other facts, e.g. if you know that $6 \times 7 = 42$, you can work out that $6 \times 70 = 420$, $6 \times 35 = 210$ and so on.
- knowing efficient mental calculation strategies and written procedures for the four operations and using them efficiently.
- knowing when to use these methods appropriately. Children need to develop conceptual understanding, so that they know the facts and the procedures and how and why they work.

Developing reasoning skills

The second aim of the 2014 National Curriculum states that we should ensure that children: 'reason mathematically by following a line of enquiry, conjecturing relationships and generalisations, and developing an argument, justification or proof using mathematical language'.

Reasoning is about:

- making and testing predictions, conjectures or hypotheses
- searching for patterns and relationships
- making and investigating general statements by finding examples that satisfy them
- explaining and justifying solutions, results, conjectures, conclusions, generalisations and so on:
  - by testing
  - by reasoned argument
- disproving by finding counter-examples.

Many of the activities in *Rising Stars Mathematics* encourage reasoning. You can also provide extra activities to encourage reasoning. Only children can actually do the reasoning, but teachers can help them acquire and refine the necessary skills to do this. Teachers can also model reasoning by 'thinking out loud'.

The problem-solving strategies outlined in this introduction are useful ones to look at for developing reasoning. See also the introduction to the Textbooks, where there are some useful reminder prompts to help children think critically about reasoning and solving problems.

Strategies to embed problem solving

There are many strategies that will embed problem solving, which is the third aim of the 2014 National Curriculum. We need to ensure that children: 'can solve problems by applying their mathematics to a variety of routine and non-routine problems with increasing sophistication, including breaking down problems into a series of simpler steps and persevering in seeking solutions'.

Here are a few strategies that you might like to use, particularly when you work on activities that seek to deepen children's understanding of what you are teaching. Further guidance, detailed examples and activities using these strategies can be found in the Rising Stars *Problem Solving and Reasoning* programme developed by Tim Handley.

Always, sometimes, never

'Always, sometimes, never' is when you give children a statement and then ask whether it is always, sometimes or never true. This encourages the development of the skills of proof, generalisation and algebraic thinking. These are part of reasoning, which is the second aim of the National Curriculum. This strategy also encourages children to make connections between different areas of mathematics.

Another, another, another

'Another, another, another' is a strategy which involves giving children a statement and asking them to give you an example that matches it, and then another and another, e.g. say that $\frac{1}{2}$ and $\frac{2}{4}$ are equivalent fractions, then ask for another pair of equivalent fractions…and another…and another.

This strategy encourages children to give specific examples which meet a given general statement. It provides a good opportunity to assess children's conceptual understanding of an area of mathematics.

Convince me

'Convince me' activities are a useful way to encourage children to explore the structure of a mathematical concept. The teacher makes a statement to children and asks them to decide whether it is accurate or not, and then explain why. Their explanations to convince you allow them to develop their skills of reasoning in the context of mathematical proof, generalisation and algebraic thinking, which is the second aim of the National Curriculum.

Hard and easy

'Hard and easy' is an example of a strategy that encourages children to think closely about the structure of mathematics. It enables you to assess children's conceptual understanding of their mathematics. Ask them to give you an example of a 'hard' and 'easy' answer to a question and explain why one is 'hard' and the other is 'easy'. The choices children make when responding to this often provide valuable information about what they find difficult.

If this is the answer, what's the question?

'If this is the answer, what's the question?' activities encourage children to think creatively and explore the structure of mathematics. The strategy also allows children to develop their skills of generalisation. Give children an answer such as 25% and ask them to come up with as many questions as possible that could have that answer, e.g. 'What is $\frac{1}{4}$ of 100%?' or 'A jumper costs £15 in a sale and the original price was £20. What is the percentage discount?'

Mathematics stories

Giving children a number, geometric concept or measure and asking them to write its 'story', is a strategy that encourages children to explore everything they know about a mathematical concept. It is therefore particularly effective at developing children's subject knowledge, whilst also encouraging them to reason. Through telling a 'story', children are also likely to form and use their own generalisations and patterns, which can be a great starting point for further discussion.

Odd one out

'Odd one out' is a strategy which encourages conjecturing, making generalisations and reasoning about items in a set. All you need to do is give children a set of three or more numbers, shapes or statements and ask them to identify which is the odd one out and why. There will often be several potential responses involving each of the numbers, shapes or statements.

Peculiar, obvious, general

'Peculiar, obvious, general' is a strategy that encourages children to think about the structure of mathematics and to reason about it. Through focusing on what makes a peculiar, obvious or general example of a given statement, children have to think carefully about the statement given, the criteria needed to meet the statement, and what examples they could give.

Silly answers

'Silly answers' encourages children to make generalisations. In giving you a 'silly' answer to a question and explaining why it is such, they will have to reason about possible 'correct' answers. This will require them to consider the properties relating to the topic in the question, therefore deepening their conceptual understanding.

What do you notice?

The 'what do you notice?' strategy encourages children to look deeply at the structure of mathematics. By asking them 'What do you notice?' about a number, set of numbers, shape or mathematical statement, they will need to make their own generalisations and test them against specific examples.

What else do we know?

'What else do we know?' is a strategy that encourages children to see the links that exist in all areas of mathematics. It encourages them to reason and combine other known facts with a given statement, e.g. give children a statement such as 'If we know $8 \times 9 = 72$, what else do we know?' They could then create new statements by doubling, halving and multiplying or dividing by 10, such as $8 \times 90 = 720$, $8 \times 45 = 360$ and $4 \times 45 = 180$.

What's the same? What's different?

'What's the same? What's different?' is a strategy that encourages children to compare and contrast. Children will need to spot patterns and similarities, as well as making generalisations and connections between different aspects of mathematics.

Zooming in

'Zooming in' is a strategy that encourages children to reason about mathematical properties, e.g. give a criterion such as an odd number. Ask children to give an example that fits the criteria. Then 'zoom in' to give another criterion, e.g. an odd number which is also a multiple of 7. This strategy also encourages children to re-evaluate their decisions and helps them to try to make more reasoned choices for their initial 'answers'.

Effective questioning

Questioning is an important strategy which can help embed problem solving and reasoning into day-to-day mathematics teaching. It also allows you to assess children's conceptual understanding. Here are some examples of question structures and routines:

Can you give me an example of …?

- a prime number which is not odd
- an irregular quadrilateral
- a percentage fraction and decimal equivalence

What is the quickest or easiest way to …?

- find out if a number is prime
- find the area of a rectangle
- find out how many chairs will fit into our school hall

What are 7, 11 and 13 examples of …?

What about 36?

What about 72 cm²?

How can we be sure that …?

- all multiples of 6 are multiples of 3
- the area of a triangle $= \frac{1}{2}$ base $\times$ height
- $\frac{6}{8}$ is equal to $\frac{12}{16}$

What's the link between …?

- 12, 24 and 36
- $\frac{6}{8}$, 0.75 and 75%
- a rectangle and a square

Developing mental and written calculation skills

Mental calculation strategies

Throughout the 2014 National Curriculum Programme of Study for Mathematics, children are expected to use mental calculation strategies as appropriate. Very often, after written methods have been introduced, children tend to use these as their default methods for answering calculations, whether they are appropriate or not. It is therefore important to provide opportunities where children are given calculations and have to decide which methods would be the most efficient to solve them. This encourages them to continue using mental arithmetic as much as possible.

If schools still have copies of the 1999 National Numeracy Strategy Framework, teachers may find the section on mental calculation strategies for addition, subtraction, multiplication and division a useful reference tool for identifying key mental calculation strategies to teach and practise regularly. The 1999 QCA booklet, Teaching mental calculation strategies: guidance for teachers at key stages 1 and 2, is another useful resource.

Key mental calculation strategies include:

- Partition and recombine: $36 + 24 = 30 + 20 + 6 + 4 = 50 + 10 = 60$
- Sequencing: $135 + 78 = 135 + 70 + 8 = 205 + 8 = 213$
- Doubles and near doubles: $154 + 153 = $ double $154 - 1 = 307$
- Using number pairs to 10 and 100: $462 + 138 = 460 + 130 + 10 = 400 + 100 + 100 = 600$
- Adding near multiples of 10 and adjusting: $1458 + 2998 = 1458 + 3000 - 2 = 4456$
- Using known number facts: if we know that $12 \times 7 = 84$ then $12 \times 14 = 168$, $1.2 \times 7 = 8.4$, $2.4 \times 7 = 16.8$
- Bridging though tens, hundreds, tenths: $36 + 8 = 36 + 4 + 4 = 40 + 4 = 44$
- Using relationships between operations: if $256 + 135 = 391$, then $135 + 256$ must also be 391, $391 - 256$ must be 135 and $391 - 135$ must be 256
- Counting on: $365 - 178$, $178 + 22 = 200$, $200 + 165 = 365$, so $365 - 178 = 22 + 165 = 187$
- $\times 4$ by doubling and doubling again: 280×4, double $280 = 560$, double $560 = 1120$
- $\times 8$ by doubling, doubling and doubling again: 56×8, double $56 = 112$, double $112 = 224$, double $224 = 448$
- $\times 5$ by $\times 10$ and halving: $364 \times 10 = 3640$, half $3640 = 1820 = 364 \times 5$
- $\times 9$ by $\times 10$ then subtracting: $\times 1$ $17 \times 9 = (17 \times 10) - (17 \times 1) = 170 - 17 = 153$
- $\times 20$ by $\times 10$ and doubling: $470 \times 20 = 470 \times 10 \times 2 = 4700 \times 2 = 9400$
- $\times 25$ by $\times 100$ then halving and halving again: 37×25, $37 \times 100 = 3700$, half $3700 = 1850$, half $1850 = 925 = 37 \times 25$.

Rising Stars Mathematics encourages teachers to rehearse mental calculation strategies regularly with children during the 'Warming up' sections.

Mental strategies are often used in conjunction with written strategies, so the two do, in fact, go hand in hand. Children will use mental strategies to estimate the solution to a number statement. They will also use, e.g. their mental calculation skills in each column of a written calculation and when using an algorithm.

Approach to written algorithms

In the 2014 National Curriculum Programme of Study for Mathematics, formal written algorithms are introduced during Key Stage 2. It is not necessary to introduce any algorithms into Key Stage 1, these children should be focusing on mental calculation strategies. However, recording addition and subtraction in columns can be introduced if teachers wish to support understanding of place value and prepare for formal written methods later on.

When written algorithms are introduced, children need to develop a conceptual understanding of these and not just learn a method using a rote learning process. It is therefore very important that they use manipulatives, such as those outlined in the Resources and Representations section (see pages 12–14), when they learn a new method or use a method that they have previously learnt but are beginning to apply to larger numbers or decimals.

In Key Stage 2, Base 10 apparatus and place-value counters are very important for developing this conceptual understanding. It is useful for the teacher to model the procedure using this apparatus (which could be on the interactive whiteboard) and children follow their lead. The teacher should then model the written method and ask children to identify what is the same and what is different about the two methods. Some suggestions for how to model this for each operation are given below.

It is often a good idea, when beginning a series of lessons on one of the four operations, to write a selection of calculations on the whiteboard. Children can then discuss with a partner which methods would be the best to use. This highlights the fact that mental calculation strategies are often the most efficient methods to use.

Mental calculation uses the multiplicative property of place value and written methods use the positional property, e.g. if using the strategy of sequencing, one number needs to be partitioned, $246 + 132 = 246 + 100 + 30 + 2$. If subtracting 4567 and 1281, children will refer to the digits positioned in their columns. This is one reason that children need to have a deep conceptual knowledge of place value.

Addition

45 + 77

Encourage children to group the ones. They will have 12, 10 of which need to be changed to one ten. They then add the tens to give 12. 10 of these need changing to one hundred. Model the written method as children progress through each stage with the Base 10 apparatus.

$$\begin{array}{r} 4\ 5 \\ +\ 7\ 7 \\ \hline 1\ 2\ 2 \\ {\scriptstyle 1\ 1} \end{array}$$

How are these models different?
How are they the same?

Using the correct vocabulary is also important. With addition, the vocabulary is:

augend + addend = sum

Subtraction

182 – 147

In this example, children set out 182. When they need to subtract 7 from 2, they can see that there are not enough ones. They therefore need to exchange a ten for 10 ones. They can then take away the other numbers. Again, teachers should model the written method as children progress through the stages of the calculation using the Base 10 apparatus.

Using the correct vocabulary is also important. With subtraction, the correct vocabulary is:

minuend – subtrahend = difference

Multiplication

Arrays are a key visual representation for multiplication. They highlight the links with repeated addition and division. In this example, 38 × 3, 38 is made three times using manipulatives and then grouped. The model below shows how the physical array links to the grid method and then to the written method:

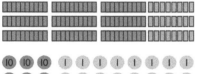

	30	8
3	90	24

$$\begin{array}{r} 38 \\ \times\ 3 \\ \hline 114 \\ {\scriptstyle 2} \end{array}$$

What's different about all these models?
What's the same?

The correct vocabulary for multiplication is:

multiplicand × multiplier = product

Division

Division is basically grouping, i.e. how many groups of the divisor can be made out of the dividend? When children set out the number (the dividend) using manipulatives, they can clearly see how many groups of the divisor (the number they are dividing by) they can make out of the numbers of each particular value.

Step 1

135 ÷ 3

We can't make any groups of 3 hundred with the 1 hundred we have. Exchange the 1 hundred for 10 tens.

$$3\overline{)135}$$

What is different about these models?
What is the same

Step 2

We now have 13 tens.

$$3\overline{)1^{1}35}$$

What is different about these models?
What is the same?

Step 3

We can make 4 groups of three 10s, leaving one 10

$$\begin{array}{r} 4 \\ 3\overline{)1^{1}35} \end{array}$$

What is different about these models?
What is the same?

Step 4

We need to exchange the one 10 for ten 1s

$$\begin{array}{r} 4 \\ 3\overline{)1^{1}3^{1}5} \end{array}$$

What is different about these models?
What is the same

Step 5

We can make 5 groups of three 1s, giving an answer of 45

$$\begin{array}{r} 45 \\ 3\overline{)1^{1}3^{1}5} \end{array}$$

What is different about these models?
What is the same

The correct vocabulary for division is:

dividend ÷ divisor = quotient

Use of calculators

The 2014 National Curriculum states that: 'Calculators should not be used as a substitute for good written and mental arithmetic. They should therefore only be introduced near the end of Key Stage 2 to support pupils' conceptual understanding and exploration of more complex number problems, if written and mental arithmetic are secure. In both primary and secondary schools, teachers should use their judgement about when ICT tools should be used'.

It is extremely important that children do not learn to rely on calculators instead of being able to use mental and written calculation methods securely. The calculations given to children as practice should be carefully chosen, so that they are able to perform them using appropriate mental or written methods. However, when working on a real life problem with a large amount of data, teachers may wish to allow children to perform calculations on a calculator, so that they focus more deeply on the problem-solving task at hand.

Calculators are also a very effective way to rehearse recognising numbers for Key Stage 1 and understanding place value in both Key Stage 1 and Key Stage 2, e.g. to rehearse place value, give children the following instructions. They must work out what operation to use at each stage:

- key in 3
- put 5 in front of the 3 (they must add 50)
- put a 2 in front of the 5 (they must add 200)
- change the 5 to a 2 (they must subtract 30)

and so on.

Mathematics outside the classroom

Homework

Rising Stars Mathematics provides a range of homework options:

1. The Textbook can be sent home for children to complete a particular step in the 'Let's practise' section. Within the Textbook, children will have access to the concept explanation, modelling, exemplification, practice and application that they have already explored in the 'Let's learn' section. This enables them to pick up where they left off in class. For schools that do not wish to send Textbooks home, eTextbook versions on the website can be shared with parents/carers, so that the content can be accessed online from home.

2. All the gameboards and game instructions can be downloaded and printed from the website and sent home for children to play with parents/carers/siblings/friends. Children can also be asked to design their own game using the game boards in the Textbook.

Introduction

3. There is a bank of Homework activities at the back of this Teacher's Guide, which can be used as expansion activities outside the classroom. There are two activities for each concept spread in the Textbook. These are also available as editable files on the website, enabling teachers to choose both the homework and its frequency.

4. The Practice Books provide a wide range of additional questions to consolidate and reinforce understanding of concepts taught using the Textbook in class. These extra practice activities can be set as homework or used as further practice within the classroom. Either way, they provide a good record for the child of their understanding and progress and will help teachers identify any misconceptions or gaps in understanding.

Engaging parents/carers

In order to engage parents/carers in their children's learning, it is important to share and explain the way in which mathematics is being taught in school and the key features and benefits of the *Rising Stars Mathematics* approach. An example of a letter to parents/carers is set out below:

Dear Parent/Carer,

As you know, mathematics is an integral part of your child's learning. We are using the innovative *Rising Stars Mathematics* programme to ensure mathematics is accessible for all children and that they achieve personal success in the subject.

Throughout the programme, there is a focus on the development of deep subject knowledge and the ability to make connections. The approach places importance on different types of practice, as well as the ability to recall facts and manipulate them to work out other facts.

The questioning in *Rising Stars Mathematics* is tailored to your child's needs, with a variety of different problems to solve. Any misconceptions are dealt with immediately. Children who grasp mathematical concepts quickly will be given complex problems which deepen their knowledge of the same content, rather than being accelerated into content from the next year level.

There is a focus on practice and spending longer on key concepts to embed understanding. This includes different types of practice, each of which requires a deeper level of understanding:

1. Basic practice, i.e. without any contexts

2. Variations or intelligent practice, this shows children patterns or helps them to make connections

3. Practice and consolidation within different contexts, e.g. time, money or length

4. Open-ended, investigative practice. This goes deeper and deeper, requiring greater reasoning.

Precise mathematical vocabulary will be taught from the start and used consistently throughout the school, including these terms:

Augend + addend = sum/total

Minuend − subtrahend = difference

Multiplicand × multiplier = product

Dividend ÷ divisor = quotient.

We are very excited to be using this unique programme and appreciate your continued support.

Yours faithfully,

The style of the *Rising Stars Mathematics* resources is clear and engaging, which will help to capture the interest of parents/carers. In the Textbook, explanations are supported by clear pictorial representations and followed by guided, step-by-step practice. This will enable parents/carers to quickly familiarise themselves with both what is being taught and how it is being approached. This is especially important if children are asked to complete activities from the Textbook as homework. Since the concepts are set out clearly in the 'Let's learn' section, children will be able to show and explain what they have been learning. Parents/carers will feel able to help without confusing their child by introducing a different method, particularly if they were taught mathematics in a different way themselves.

For schools that do not wish to send Textbooks home, online versions can be shared as eTextbooks and accessed online by parents/carers or children at home. These provide an enhanced version of the print Textbooks, with a number of pop-up animations throughout that help to explain key concepts. Parents/carers may wish to watch these with their child, to enable them to participate in their learning.

It may also be useful to share the school's Calculation Policy or the pages from this Teacher's Guide introduction on the *Rising Stars Mathematics* approach to mental arithmetic and written algorithms (see pages 16–17). This could help parents/carers understand how their child will be tackling calculations during practice or homework activities and explain how best they can support this

Planning grids

Year 4 scope and sequence

The following grid shows the concepts and objectives that are covered within each *Rising Stars Mathematics* Year 4 unit and provides page references to each of the various components.

Unit	Concept	Objectives	Textbook	Teacher's Guide	Practice Book	Homework Sheets
1	1a Counting	• Count in multiples of three, six and nine. • Count backwards through zero to include negative numbers.	12–13	26–7	4–7	182
	1b Place value	• Recognise the place value of each digit in a 4-digit number (thousands, hundreds, tens, and ones). • Identify, represent and estimate numbers using different representations. • Solve number and practical problems that involve all of the above and with increasingly large positive numbers.	14–15	28–9	8–12	183
2	2a Adding 4–digit numbers	• Add numbers with up to four digits using the formal written methods of columnar addition where appropriate. • Estimate and use inverse operations to check answers to a calculation. • Solve addition and subtraction two-step problems in contexts, deciding which operations and methods to use and why.	22–3	36–7	13–16	184
	2b Subtracting 4–digit numbers	• Subtract numbers with up to four digits using the formal written methods of columnar subtraction where appropriate. • Estimate and use inverse operations to check answers to a calculation. • Solve addition and subtraction two-step problems in contexts, deciding which operations and methods to use and why.	24–5	38–9	17–20	185
3	3a Counting	• Count in multiples of six and nine. • Recall multiplication and division facts for multiplication tables six, nine and twelve.	32–3	46–7	21–3	186
	3b Calculating mentally	• Use place value, known and derived facts to multiply and divide mentally, including multiplying together three numbers. • Recognise and using factor pairs and commutativity in mental calculations.	34–5	48–9	24–6	187
	3c Calculating on paper	• Multiply 2-digit and 3-digit numbers by a single-digit number using formal written layout. • Solve problems involving multiplying and adding, including using the distributive law to multiply 2-digit numbers by single-digit numbers.	36–7	50–1	27–30	188
4	4a Three types of triangle	• Identify acute and obtuse angles and compare and order angles up to two right angles by size.	44–5	58–9	31–4	189
	4b Triangles	• Identify acute and obtuse angles and compare and order angles up to two right angles by size. • Compare and classify geometric shapes, including quadrilaterals and triangles, based on their properties and sizes.	46–7	60–1	35–6	190
	4c Quadrilaterals	• Compare and classify geometric shapes, including quadrilaterals and triangles, based on their properties and sizes.	48–9	62–3	37–40	191
	4d Symmetry	• Compare and classify geometric shapes, including quadrilaterals and triangles, based on their properties and sizes. • Identify lines of symmetry in 2-D shapes presented in different orientations.	50–1	64–5	41–3	192
5	5a Counting in steps	• Count in multiples of seven. • Count backwards through zero to include negative numbers. • Solve number and practical problems that involve all of the above and with increasingly large positive numbers.	58–9	72–3	44–6	193
	5b Rounding, ordering and comparing	• Recognise the place value of each digit in a 4-digit number (thousands, hundreds, tens, and ones). • Order and compare numbers beyond 1000. • Identify, represent and estimate numbers using different representations. • Round any number to the nearest 10, 100 or 1000. • Solve number and practical problems that involve all of the above and with increasingly large positive numbers.	60–1	74–5	47–51	194
	5c Roman numerals	• Read Roman numerals to 100 (I to C) and know that over time, the numeral system changed to include the concept of zero and place value.	62–3	76–7	52–3	195

Introduction

Unit	Concept	Objectives	Textbook	Teacher's Guide	Practice Book	Homework Sheets
6	6a Using mental and written methods to solve problems	• Add and subtract numbers with up to four digits using the formal written methods of columnar addition and subtraction where appropriate. • Estimate and use inverse operations to check answers to a calculation. • Solve addition and subtraction two-step problems in contexts, deciding which operations and methods to use and why. • Convert between different units of measure (for example, kilometre to metre; hour to minute). • Read, write and convert time between analogue and digital 12- and 24-hour clocks. • Solve problems involving converting from hours to minutes; minutes to seconds; years to months; weeks to days.	70–1	84–5	54–8	196
	6b bar models and bar charts	• Solve addition and subtraction multi-step problems in contexts, deciding which operations and methods to use and why. • Interpret and present discrete and continuous data using appropriate graphical methods, including bar charts and time graphs. • Solve comparison, sum and difference problems using information presented in bar charts, pictograms, tables and other graphs.	72–3	86–7	59–63	197
	6c Solving problems	• Add and subtract numbers with up to four digits using the formal written methods of columnar addition and subtraction where appropriate. • Estimate and use inverse operations to check answers to a calculation. • Solve addition and subtraction two-step problems in contexts, deciding which operations and methods to use and why. • Estimate, compare and calculate using different measures, including money, in pounds and pence.	74–5	88–9	64–5	198
7	7a families of fractions	• Recognise and show, using diagrams, families of common equivalent fractions. • Solve problems involving increasingly harder fractions to calculate quantities, and fractions to divide quantities, including non-unit fractions where the answer is a whole number. • Add and subtract fractions with the same denominator.	82–3	96–7	66–70	199
	7b Decimals and equivalences	• Count up and down in hundredths; recognise that hundredths arise when dividing an object by 100 and dividing tenths by ten. • Recognise and write decimal equivalents of any number of tenths or hundredths. • Recognise and write decimal equivalents to a quarter, half and three quarters. • Find the effect of dividing a single- or 2-digit number by ten and 100, identifying the value of the digits in the answer as ones, tenths and hundredths.	84–5	98–9	71–3	200
8	8a Multiplication table facts	• Count in multiples of 7. • Recall multiplication and division facts for the 7 and 11 times tables..	92–3	106–7	74–7	201
	8b Three at once	• Use place value, known and derived facts to multiply and divide mentally, including: multiplying by 0 and 1; dividing by 1; multiplying together three numbers	94–5	108–9	78–80	202
	8c Written methods	• Multiply 2-digit numbers by a single-digit number using a formal written layout. • Solve problems involving multiplying and adding.	96–7	110–11	81–3	203
	8d Scaling	• Solve integer scaling problems.	98–9	112–13	84–6	204
9	9a Trapeziums and kites	• Compare and classify geometric shapes, including all types of quadrilaterals and triangles, based on their properties and sizes.	106–7	120–1	87–90	205
	9b Coordinates and translations	• Describe positions on a 2-D grid as coordinates in the first quadrant. • Describe movements between positions as translations of a given unit to the left/right and up/down. • Plot specified points and draw sides to complete a given polygon.	108–9	122–3	91–3	206
10	10a 25s and 1000s	• Count in multiples of 25 and 1000. • Find 1000 more or less than a given number.	116–17	130–1	94–6	207
	10b Place value and measures	• Recognise the place value of each digit in a 4-digit number (thousands, hundreds, tens, and ones). • Identify, represent and estimate numbers using different representations. • Solve number and practical problems that involve all of the above and with increasingly large positive numbers.	118–19	132–3	97–9	208
11	11a Solving problems using written methods	• Add and subtract numbers with up to four digits using the formal written methods of columnar addition and subtraction where appropriate. • Estimate and use inverse operations to check answers to a calculation. • Solve simple measure and money problems involving fractions and decimals to two decimal places. • Estimate, compare and calculate different measures including money, in pounds and pence.	126–7	140–1	100–3	209
	11b Applying methods of addition and subtraction	• Solve addition and subtraction two-step problems in contexts, deciding which operations and methods to use and why.	128–9	142–3	104–7	210

Unit	Concept	Objectives	Textbook	Teacher's Guide	Practice Book	Homework Sheets
12	12a Equivalences	• Recognise and write decimal equivalents of any number of tenths or hundredths. • Recognise and write decimal equivalents to quarter, half and three-quarters. • Recognise and show, using diagrams, families of common equivalent fractions. • Add and subtract fractions with the same denominator.	136–7	150–1	108–11	211
	12b Comparing and rounding decimals	• Round decimals with one decimal place to the nearest whole number. • Compare numbers with the same number of decimal places up to two decimal places.	138–9	152–3	112–15	212
13	13a Multiplying and dividing mentally	• Count in multiples of 25 and 1000. • Recall multiplication and division facts for multiplication tables up to 12 × 12.	146–7	160–1	116–19	213
	13b Multiplying on paper	• Multiply 2-digit and 3-digit numbers by a single-digit number using a formal written layout. • Solve problems involving multiplying and adding.	148–9	162–3	120–1	214
	13c Scaling	• Solve problems involving multiplying and adding, including integer scaling problems and harder correspondence problems such as *n* objects are connected with *m* objects.	150–1	164–5	122–4	215
14	14a Perimeter and area	• Measure and calculate the perimeter of rectilinear figures (including squares) in centimetres and metres. • Find the area of rectilinear shapes by counting squares.	158–9	172–3	125–8	216
	14b Perimeter and angles	• Measure and calculate the perimeter of a rectilinear figure (including squares) in centimetres and metres. • Identify acute and obtuse angles and compare and order angles up to two right angles by size.	160–1	174–5	129–33	217
	14c Area and symmetry	• Complete a simple symmetrical figure with respect to a specific line of symmetry. • Find the area of rectilinear shapes by counting squares.	162–3	176–7	134–7	218

Curriculum mapping grid

The following grid shows what children should be taught during Year 4, as laid out in the 2014 National Curriculum Programme of Study for Mathematics and how these are covered within the *Rising Stars Mathematics* Year 4 units.

Domain	Sub-domain	Statement	Unit 1	Unit 2	Unit 3	Unit 4	Unit 5	Unit 6	Unit 7	Unit 8	Unit 9	Unit 10	Unit 11	Unit 12	Unit 13	Unit 14
NUMBER	Number and place value	count in multiples of six, seven, nine, 25 and 1000	a		a		a			a		a			a	
		find 1000 more or less than a given number										a				
		count backwards through zero to include negative numbers	a				a									
		recognise the place value of each digit in a 4-digit number (thousands, hundreds, tens, and ones)	b				b					b				
		order and compare numbers beyond 1000					b									
		identify, represent and estimate numbers using different representations	b				b					b				
		round any number to the nearest ten, 100 or 1000					b									
		solve number and practical problems that involve all of the above and with increasingly large positive numbers	b				a, b					b				
		read Roman numerals to 100 (I to C) and know that over time, the numeral system changed to include the concept of zero and place value					c									
	Addition and subtraction	add and subtract numbers with up to four digits using the formal written methods of columnar addition and subtraction where appropriate		a, b				a, c					a			
		estimate and use inverse operations to check answers to a calculation		a, b				a, c					a			
		solve addition and subtraction two-step problems in contexts, deciding which operations and methods to use and why		a, b				a, b, c					b			
	Multiplication and division	recall multiplication and division facts for multiplication tables up to 12 × 12			a					a					a	
		use place value, known and derived facts to multiply and divide mentally, including: multiplying by zero and one; dividing by one; multiplying together three numbers			b					b						
		recognise and use factor pairs and commutativity in mental calculations			b											
		multiply 2-digit and 3-digit numbers by a single-digit number using formal written layout								c					b	
		solve problems involving multiplying and adding, including using the distributive law to multiply 2-digit numbers by a single-digit number, integer scaling problems and harder correspondence problems such as *n* objects are connected to *m* objects			c					c, d					b, c	
	Fractions (including decimals)	recognise and show, using diagrams, families of common equivalent fractions							a					a		
		count up and down in hundredths; recognise that hundredths arise when dividing an object by one hundred and dividing tenths by ten							b							
		solve problems involving increasingly harder fractions to calculate quantities, and fractions to divide quantities, including non-unit fractions where the answer is a whole number							a							
		add and subtract fractions with the same denominator							a					a		
		recognise and write decimal equivalents of any number of tenths or hundredths							b					a		
		recognise and write decimal equivalents to $\frac{1}{4}, \frac{1}{2}, \frac{3}{4}$							b					a		
		find the effect of dividing a single- or 2-digit number by ten and 100, identifying the value of the digits in the answer as ones, tenths and hundredths							b							
		round decimals with one decimal place to the nearest whole number												b		
		compare numbers with the same number of decimal places up to two decimal places												b		
		solve simple measure and money problems involving fractions and decimals to two decimal places											a			

Domain	Sub-domain	Statement	Unit 1	Unit 2	Unit 3	Unit 4	Unit 5	Unit 6	Unit 7	Unit 8	Unit 9	Unit 10	Unit 11	Unit 12	Unit 13	Unit 14
MEASUREMENT	Measurement	convert between different units of measure [e.g. kilometre to metre; hour to minute]						a								
		measure and calculate the perimeter of a rectilinear figure (including squares) in centimetres and metres														a, b
		find the area of rectilinear shapes by counting squares														a, c
		estimate, compare and calculate different measures, including money in pounds and pence						c					a			
		read, write and convert time between analogue and digital 12- and 24-hour clocks						a								
		solve problems involving converting from hours to minutes; minutes to seconds; years to months; weeks to days						a								
GEOMETRY	Properties of shapes	compare and classify geometric shapes, including quadrilaterals and triangles, based on their properties and sizes				b, c, d					a					
		identify acute and obtuse angles and compare and order angles up to two right angles by size				a, b										b
		identify lines of symmetry in 2-D shapes presented in different orientations				d										
		complete a simple symmetric figure with respect to a specific line of symmetry														c
	Position and direction	describe positions on a 2-D grid as coordinates in the first quadrant									b					
		describe movements between positions as translations of a given unit to the left/right and up/down									b					
		plot specified points and draw sides to complete a given polygon									b					
STATISTICS	Statistics	interpret and present discrete and continuous data using appropriate graphical methods, including bar charts and time graphs						b								
		solve comparison, sum and difference problems using information presented in bar charts, pictograms, tables and other graphs						b								

Number and place value

Mathematical focus

★ **Number:** number and place value, multiplication and division

★ **Measurement:** length, mass, volume/capacity, money, time, temperature

Prior learning

Children should already be able to:

- count in multiples of 4, 8, 50 and 100
- recognise the place value of each digit in a 3-digit number
- read and write numbers up to 1000 in numerals and words
- identify and represent numbers to 1000 using different representations.

Key new learning

- Count in multiples of 3, 6, 7 and 9.
- Count backwards through zero to include negative numbers.
- Recognise the place value of each digit in a 4-digit number (thousands, hundreds, tens, and ones).
- Identify, represent and estimate numbers using different representations.
- Solve number and practical problems that involve all of the above and with increasingly large positive numbers.

Making connections

- Counting in steps underpins children's ability to recall multiplication and division facts; plenty of practice in saying the multiples in order will help embed the facts. They will also find this useful when constructing or interpreting data on bar charts where the scale increases in steps, and pictograms where the symbol represents more than one.

- It is important that children explore real-life examples of negative numbers, so that these do not seem purely abstract. The obvious context is temperature. The ability to read a number line or scale involving negative numbers will support children in reading graph axes in later years.

- An understanding of place value is important so that children develop secure number sense skills. This will help them when they come to compare and order numbers beyond a thousand and round numbers to the nearest 10, 100 and 1000 in later units.

- Place value has a practical application in the context of measures. You can link 3- and 4-digit numbers to measurements of length (metres and centimetres), money (pounds and pence), mass (kilograms and grams) and volume (litres and millilitres).

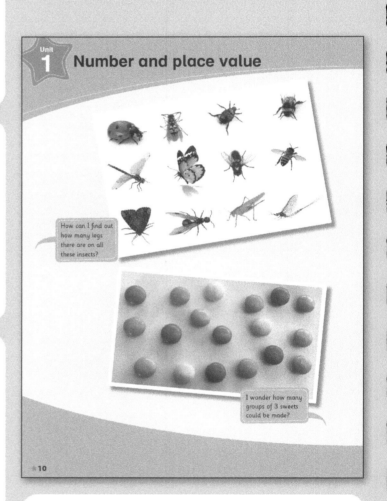

Unit 1 Number and place value

How can I find out how many legs there are on all these insects?

I wonder how many groups of 3 sweets could be made?

▲10

💬 Talk about

It is important to use precise mathematical vocabulary from the beginning. Ask children what they can remember about the properties of place value: positional, multiplicative, additive and Base 10. Ensure that they understand that positional is the position that the digit is placed in, multiplicative is what the number must be multiplied by to get its true value and that additive is when the parts are added together to get the whole. Remind them that our number system increases and decreases by powers of ten and that this is the Base 10 property of place value.

Engaging and exploring

Ask children to describe the insects shown in the first picture. Can they name them all? (Ladybird, wasp, beetle, bee, dragonfly, butterfly, bluebottle, honey bee, moth, ant, grasshopper, mayfly.) Ask them to describe what each looks like, naming the different parts. Draw on their knowledge of insects from their science lessons or general knowledge. Elicit that all insects have six legs and two antennae; those shown all have four wings, although in some cases (e.g. the honey bee) the forewings and hindwings link in flight and in others (e.g. the ladybird) one pair are hardened and protect the pair used for flying. Ask children to tell you how they could find out how many antennae there are altogether. Make links between counting in twos and the two times table. Repeat for wings and counting in fours. *How many wings would there be on four insects? On seven? 12?*

Next focus on the insects' legs. *Each insect has six, so how could we find out how many five insects have?* This could lead to a discussion on ways to multiply by five (counting, multiplication facts, multiplying by ten then halving). Ask children to find out how many legs there are altogether. Agree that they could count them all individually, but this would not be an efficient method; instead they could count in sixes or use multiplication facts. Agree that if they know their three times table, they could double the answer to 3×12.

Look at the photo of the sweets. Ask children to tell you how they could find out how many there are quickly without counting them one at a time. Listen to their suggestions. Agree that, e.g. they could subitise (perceive the number of items without counting) the six on the left, add the next two, then the other group of six and finally the last four on the right. Ask them how they could group the sweets in threes. *What will help?* Agree their multiplication facts for three. Give them counters so they can practically group them. Discuss how this could help them group into nines. Agree that because three multiplied by three equals nine, they can regroup the threes into two nines. Repeat for other multiples of nine in the same way to emphasise the link between counting in threes and nines (treble the threes to give nines).

Next look at the photo of the money box. Ask children to tell you the coins and notes that we use in our monetary system and their values in pence. Ask them to make amounts, such as 31p or £1.25, in several different ways and then using the least number of coins. Then ask them to tell you how many pence there are in different numbers of pounds and then a mixture of pounds and pence.

Draw a place-value grid that shows 100, 10 and 1 on the board. Invite children to write different amounts of pence on to it. Discuss the positional, multiplicative and additive aspects of place value using this, e.g. in the number 345 there is a three in the hundreds position so it needs multiplying by 100 to give its value, there is a four in the tens which needs multiplying by ten to get its value and a five in the ones which needs multiplying by 1; $300 + 40 + 5 = 345$. Next draw a new grid underneath the first, with headings 1, 10th and 100th. Make the link between, e.g. 345 pence and £3.45, emphasising that in the second grid the four is four tenths and the five, five hundredths.

Ask children to draw their own grids showing 100, 10 and 1 and 1, 10th and 100th and write the numbers of coins shown in the Textbook in the appropriate places. Agree that there are £4.69, or 469 pence in total. Repeat this for other amounts.

Ask children to identify the temperature on the thermometer. Agree that this is a negative number. Ask them to tell you all they know about negative numbers and where they can be seen in real life. *What time of year would we commonly have negative temperatures?* Ask children to count forwards and backwards across zero from given starting points. Ask them to draw a number line from –10 to 10 and mark –5. As a class, count on from –5 to 10 to find the increase in degrees from –5°C to 10°C. Repeat this for other pairs of temperatures that they can show on their number line.

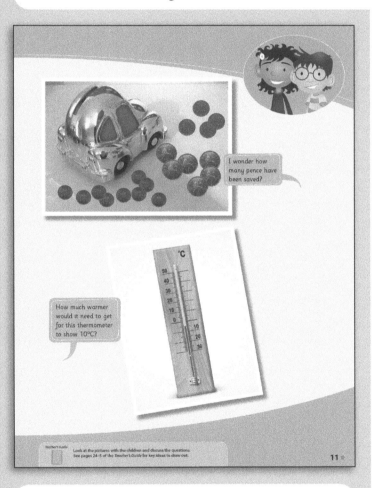

Things to think about

- How will you organise groupings for discussion and sharing ideas?

- What manipulatives and visual representations will you use to help conceptual understanding of place value with all children? Do you have enough Base 10 apparatus, place-value counters, partitioning cards and so on?

- How will you ensure children experience practical opportunities to work on place value within the contexts of measure, length and money?

Checking understanding

You will know children have mastered these concepts when they can count fluently from zero in threes, sixes and nines, and count backwards through zero to include negative numbers. They will be able to demonstrate and explain the place value of each digit in a 4-digit number and identify and represent 4-digit numbers in a variety of ways.

- **Count in multiples of three, six and nine.**
- **Count backwards through zero to include negative numbers.**

 Homework 1 and 2

 Practice Book pp 4–7

Mathematical vocabulary

Multiple, zero, positive number, negative number

Representations and resources

Clocks with movable hands, squared paper, rulers, coins, counters, number lines, calculators.

Warming up

Give each child a clock. Ask them to find different times and show you. Focus on minutes past, e.g. 45 minutes past seven, 35 minutes past 11. Each time ask children to tell you how many minutes there are to the next o'clock time. Also ask them to write down the time in 12- and 24-hour digital format.

Background knowledge

Counting in multiples is also known as skip counting. This is an important skill, particularly when children begin to learn their multiplication tables. It is helpful to encourage children to use their fingers as they count in multiples, so that, e.g. when they say 54 and show the ninth finger, they know that six multiplied by nine equals 54. In this concept they will be counting in multiples of six and nine. So, use this as an opportunity to rehearse the multiplication facts to both six and nine multiplied by 12.

Negative numbers are less than zero. They represent opposites. If a positive represents height above sea level, then negative represents depth below. If a positive represents a credit in the bank, a negative represents a debt. These numbers are quite abstract for children because you cannot have a negative amount of objects. Teach them in a context with which children are familiar, e.g. temperature. Discourage the use of 'minus' for these numbers, –7 is negative seven not minus seven.

Let's learn: Modelling and teaching

Counting in threes, sixes and nines

- Explain to children that when we count in steps, we say the multiples of a number. Use the bar models in the Textbook to revise counting in threes, then move on to counting in sixes and nines. Discuss the cartoon, establishing that zero is not a multiple of anything, so the first multiple of six is six (6×1), the second 12 (6×2) and so on. Ask questions, e.g. *What is the fourth multiple of six? What is the fifth multiple of nine?*

- Ask children to discuss with a partner any patterns they can see in the bar models. Establish that one step counted in sixes is the same as two steps counted in threes, and one step counted in nines is the same as three steps counted in threes. Then explore the digit totals of the multiples of six and nine, agreeing that the digit total for a multiple of six will always be a multiple of three, and the

digit total for a multiple of nine will always be nine.

Negative numbers

- Discuss what a negative number is and where they are used in real life, e.g. in sport, science and finance. Establish that negative numbers mirror positive numbers, going backwards from zero. Using the number line in the Textbook, or one from –20 to 20 drawn on the board, practise counting up and down from different starting numbers, including negative numbers.

- Demonstrate finding the difference between a positive or negative number by counting up, as shown in the Textbook. Ask children to choose pairs of numbers and tell you the difference between them in the same way. Record their answers.

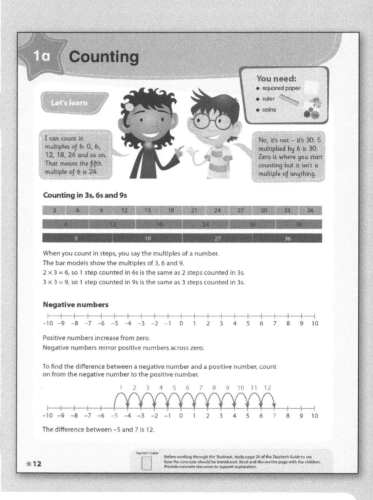

Let's practise: Digging deeper
Step 1

This task asks children to write down the first 12 multiples of three, six and nine. Check they understand that they can do this by counting in threes, sixes and nines from zero. Children then need to write down different multiples of three, six and nine. They can use the lists they have written to help them. If appropriate, you could ask them to write down the multiplication statement that fits as well (e.g. for the fifth multiple of three, $3 \times 5 = 15$).

Step 2

For this task, children need to draw an empty number line 40 squares long, and mark zero in the middle. They then mark on the given numbers. You might need to demonstrate this with other numbers first on the board. Establish that you can position each number by counting on or back from zero or another number that has already been placed. Children should check their number line by counting up from –20 to 20. They then choose pairs of numbers and find the difference between them. They should do this by counting on from the lowest number. Challenge some children to choose numbers other than those already marked on their number lines.

Step 3

This practical activity gives children the opportunity to use money to count in sixes and nines. They make groups of six pence using the fewest coins (5p and 1p) and make a line of 12 groups. They do the same for groups of nine pence (5p, 2p and 2p). They then identify the amounts that appear in both lines (common multiples). Some children will benefit from arranging their lines of coins on a piece of paper and writing the total amount at each point on the line underneath. Finally, they find the total amount of money and change the coins they have to the fewest possible for that amount.

Step 4

Encourage children to work systematically in order to find the numbers Ana could be thinking of. They should look at each clue in turn, listing the thousands and hundreds digit, then working through the even multiples of nine.

Ensuring progress
Supporting understanding

Counters and number lines can be used to support children who find counting in steps of six or nine difficult. For Step 3, you could ask children to total the groups of six pence and reduce the number of coins to ten pence and one pence coins, rather than find the overall total.

Broadening understanding

You could explore further the divisibility rules for three, six and nine. Ask children to make up some 2- and 3-digit numbers that are multiples of these numbers. They can check that their numbers are correct using a calculator. Step 3 could be extended to include multiples of 12p, or even 24p.

✓ Concept mastered

Children can count fluently in multiples of three, six and nine, and count forwards and backwards across zero.

Let's practise

1 **Count.**
Write down the first 12 multiples of these numbers:
a   3   b   6   c   9

Write down:
d   the fifth multiple of 3   e   the third multiple of 6   f   the sixth multiple of 9

2 **Draw.**
On squared paper, draw a line 40 squares long. Mark zero in the middle.
Mark on these numbers. The first one is shown for you.
a   17   c   7   e   13   g   18
b   –5   d   –12   f   –19   h   –2
Choose pairs of numbers and count on from the lowest to the highest.
Record the numbers and the difference between them. Repeat 5 times.

3 **Apply.**
Make 6p using the fewest coins.
Do this 12 times and make a line of 12 groups of coins.
Do the same for 9p.
a   What amounts appear in both lines? The first is 18p.
b   How many groups of 6p make 18p?
c   How many groups of 9p make 18p? What others can you find?
d   How much money do you have altogether?
Make the total using the fewest coins possible.

4 **Think.**
Ana is thinking of a number.
Her number has 4 digits.
The thousands digit is one less than 5.
The hundreds digit is one more than 6.
The tens and ones are an even multiple of 9.

What numbers could I be thinking of?

See page 27 of the Teacher's Guide for ideas of how to guide practice. Work through each step together as a class to develop children's conceptual understanding.

13

Follow-up ideas

- Draw a clock face on the board, write six in the middle. Point to the hour numbers in turn and then randomly. Children call out the answer when six is multiplied by the number you point to. Repeat this for seven and nine.

- Children write multiples of six and nine on cards and shuffle them. They take turns to pick a card and place it face up. If two cards are multiples of six and nine the first player to say 'snap' wins all up-turned cards.

- Children write the numbers from -15 to 15 on cards, shuffle them and place face down. They take it in turns to pick a card and place it on the table. Each new card should be placed in the correct position so that all cards are in order.

Answers

Step 1
a   3, 6, 9, 12, 15, 18, 21, 24, 27, 30, 33, 36
b   6, 12, 18, 24, 30, 36, 42, 48, 54, 60, 66, 72
c   9, 18, 27, 36, 45, 54, 63, 72, 81, 90, 99, 108
d   15
e   18
f   54

Step 3
a   18p, 36p, 54p, 72p
b   3 groups of 6p make 18p
c   2 groups of 9p make 18p
d   Total = £1.80 (£1 + 50p + 20p + 10p)

Step 4
4718, 4736, 4754, 4772, 4790

1b Place value

- Recognise the place value of each digit in a 4-digit number (thousands, hundreds, tens, and ones).
- Identify, represent and estimate numbers using different representations.
- Solve number and practical problems that involve all of the above and with increasingly large positive numbers.

Homework 3 and 4   Practice Book pp 8–12   Place Value & Abacus

Mathematical vocabulary

Place value, positional, multiplicative, additive, zero, place holder

Representations and resources

Place-value grids, digit cards, place-value cards, Base 10 apparatus, place-value counters, coloured counters, money (coins and notes).

Warming up

Rehearse multiplication facts for the six and nine times tables. You could do this by asking children to count in multiples of these numbers using their fingers. Stop children every so often and ask them to give the multiplication statement, the commutative fact and the corresponding divisions, e.g. if counting in nines, at the sixth finger they say nine multiplied by six equals 54 and six multiplied by nine equals 54, 54 divided by six equals nine and 54 divided by nine equals six. For the 11th and 12th multiple they show ten fingers and then one or two.

Background knowledge

It is important that children develop a conceptual understanding of place value. Do not assume that children have this understanding if they can partition and recombine numbers, as there is much more to place value. The following words are important: positional (where the digit is placed in the number), multiplicative (the digit is multiplied by its position to get its value) and additive (add all the individual numbers together). Ensure children have plenty of practice using visual representations such as place-value cards and place-value grids. Another important aspect of place value is the place holder where a zero holds the place in a position that has no value.

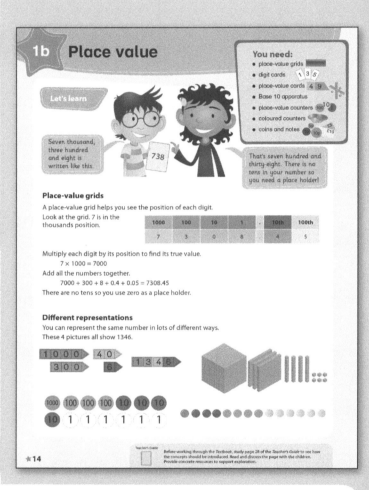

Let's learn: Modelling and teaching

Place-value grids

- Discuss Tom's error in the misconception cartoon in the Textbook. Establish that a place holder holds the position where there is no value. Ask children to identify in which position the zero is in the place-value grid (tens). Write numbers on the board with place holders and ask children to identify their positions.

- Discuss the positional, multiplicative and additional properties of the number shown in the grid in the Textbook, e.g. the four is in the tenths position so must be multiplied by one tenth to give four tenths. Once all the values are found the numbers are added together to give the whole number.

- Give children place-value grids and digit cards. Ask them to make numbers in their grids and to explain the properties of place value to a partner.

Different representations

- Discuss the fact that numbers can be represented in different ways. Ask children to identify the representations in the Textbook and find the concrete resources in the classroom. They then explain them to a partner. Encourage them to use the vocabulary associated with place value and ask them to write additive statements for the representations. Can they think of any other ways to show numbers? They might suggest using money, lengths, masses, capacities and Roman numerals. Work through a few examples, e.g. £13.46, 13 m 46 cm.

- Ask them to make different 4-digit numbers, e.g. 3517, using any equipment available. You could also give them some 2-digit numbers to represent using length in centimetres and millimetres, money and Roman numerals.

Let's practise: Digging deeper

Step 1

Understanding the role of zero as a place holder is an important aspect of place value. In this task children need to identify the position or positions the zero is holding. You could ask children to make each number with digit cards first in their place-value grids. They can then make up their own numbers with place holders and give them to a partner who identifies the position of the place holder.

Step 2

It often helps children's memories to talk about and write information in complete sentences. This task expects them to define the positional, multiplicative and additive properties of place value using given numbers. Expect children to write, e.g. 'The seven is in the hundreds position, so it is multiplied by 100 to give its true value. The six is in the tens position so must be

multiplied by ten to give its true value. The five is in the ones position and is multiplied by one. These numbers are added together to give the whole number: 700 + 60 + 5 = 765'.

Step 3

This task looks at how numbers can be represented in different, real-life contexts. For the first part, children make each amount using the least number of notes and coins and record it in two different ways (pounds/pence and pence only, e.g. £3.68 and 368p). Work through a few examples first. For the second part of the task they need to record what the numbers would be if they represented centimetres in two ways, e.g. 368 cm and 3 m 68 cm. Recap that there are 100 centimetres in one metre and rehearse some conversions between the two measurements.

Step 4

This task asks children to make up all the 4-digit numbers they can from the digits six, seven, two and four. Discuss what working systematically is and encourage children to carry out the task in this way, e.g. find all the numbers that can be made with 6000 first.

Let's practise

1 **Write.**
Write down the position of the place holder in these numbers.
a   640   c   2305   e   7630   g   16070

b   301   d   3025   f   1562.09   h   10603

Now make up 8 numbers of your own. Each number must have at least 1 place holder. Ask your partner to tell you their positions.

2 **Describe.**
Write sentences to describe the positional, multiplicative and additive properties of place value in these numbers.
a   765   c   179.38   e   8352.25

b   628.4   d   2451   f   7819.75

3 **Apply.**
Use coins and notes to represent these numbers. Use the fewest coins possible. Record the amounts in 2 different ways.
a   368   c   1050

b   986   d   1281

Write down what these numbers would be if they represented centimetres.

Now write your answers in metres and centimetres.

4 **Think.**
Use these digits to make as many 4-digit numbers as you can.

Can you find them all? How will you know that you have?

Teacher's Guide
See page 29 of the *Teacher's Guide* for ideas of how to guide practice. Work through each step together as a class to develop children's conceptual understanding.

15

Follow-up ideas

- Ask children to put sand into plastic bags. They weigh different combinations of two or more bags (total should be more than one kilogram). They record their results in different ways, e.g. grams and kilograms and grams.

- Repeat the above activity with two-litre plastic bottles and water for volume. Record measurements in millilitres and litres and millilitres.

- Children use four digit cards to make 4-digit numbers. They then make these numbers using the different representations that they have access to. Encourage them to describe the position and value of each digit and show how they are added together to make the whole number in an addition statement.

Ensuring progress

Supporting understanding

If children are unclear about the place value of 3- and 4-digit numbers and zero as a place holder, work through Steps 1 and 2 in small groups. First focus on whole numbers and use variation, e.g. ask: *What is the position of the place holder in 640, 650, 660?* Then discuss the place value of the other digits in the numbers.

Broadening understanding

In Step 3, you could extend the task so that children write the lengths in three different ways: centimetres, metres, and centimetres and metres. They could also record what the amounts would be if they represented mass and capacity/ volume.

✓ **Concept mastered**

Children can explain and demonstrate the positional, multiplicative and additive properties of place value and the role of zero as the place holder.

Answers

Step 1

a   ones   d   hundreds

b   tens   e   ones

c   tens   f   tenths

g   hundreds and ones

h   thousands and tens

Step 2

Answers will vary but should all explain the properties of place value learnt in this spread.

Step 3

a   368p, £3.68 (£2 + £1, + 50p + 10p + 5p + 2p + 1p); 368 cm, 3 m 68 cm

b   986p, £9.86 (£5 + £2 + £2 + 50p + 20p + 10p + 5p + 1p); 986 cm, 9 m 86 cm

c   1050p, £10.50 (£10 + 50p); 1050 cm, 10 m 50 cm

d   1281p, £12.81 (£10 + £2 + 50p + 20p + 10p + 1p); 1281 cm, 12 m 81 cm

Step 4

6724, 6742, 6274, 6247, 6472, 6427

7624, 7642, 7462, 7426, 7264, 7246

2674, 2647, 2764, 2746, 2476, 2467

4672, 4627, 4726, 4762, 4267, 4276

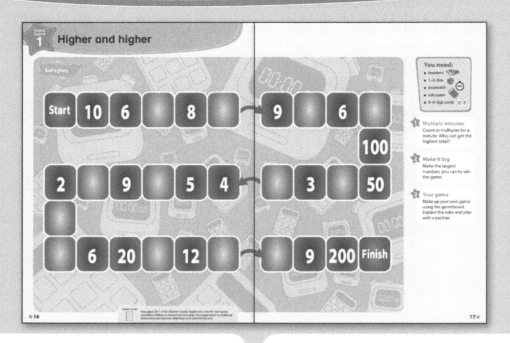

Game 1: Multiple minutes

This game gives children lots of practice in counting in multiples of different numbers, including sixes and nines.

Maths focus

- Counting in multiples

Resources

1 counter per player (1 colour per player), 1–6 dice (1), stopwatches (or minute timers), calculators.

How to play

This game should be played in pairs. Children place their counters on Start. They then take it in turns to roll the dice and move their counter that number of places. If they land on a space, they do nothing. If they land on a number, they count in multiples of that number for one minute; their partner times them and checks they are counting correctly. The final number they say in their minute is their score for their go. Play continues like this until both players reach Finish. They can use a calculator to find their final score and the winner is the player with the higher total.

Making it easier

Discuss the more challenging multiples (12, 20, 200) with children before they play, e.g. counting in 12s gives every other number in the count of sixes. Alternatively, alter the board so that children focus on the multiples they most need to rehearse.

Making it harder

Encourage children to write down their sequences as they say them so that their partner can check they are correct more easily. You could also add other multiples to the board, if appropriate (e.g. 7, 11, 150, 75).

Game 2: Make it big

This game relies on children's understanding of place value.

Maths focus

- Recognise the place value of each digit in a 4-digit number

Resources

1 counter per player (1 colour per player), 1–6 dice (1), 0–9 digit cards (two sets per pair).

How to play

This game should be played in pairs. Children shuffle the two sets of digit cards together and place them face down on the table. They place their counters on Start. They take it in turns to roll the dice and move their counter that number of places. If they land on a space with a number they do nothing. If they land on an empty space both players take four digit cards and make the highest number they can. The child who makes the higher number wins a point. They then return the cards to the pack and continue to play. The winner is the child with the most points when both have reached Finish.

Making it easier

You could ask children to take three digit cards and make 3-digit numbers.

Making it harder

You could ask children to make the highest and then the lowest number they can from four cards. They find the difference between the two. The child with the largest difference wins a point.

Game 3: Your game

Children should invent their own game, designing rules that use the concepts covered in the unit. Challenge children to make their game easier or harder.

Unit 1 Higher and higher

Choose a game to play.

Game 1: Multiple minutes

How to play

- Each player places a counter on Start.
- Take turns to roll the dice. Move your counter that number of places.
- If you land on a space, do nothing.
- If you land on a number, count in multiples of that number for 1 minute. The final number you say is your score.
- When you both reach Finish, add up your scores. Use a calculator if you need to. The winner is the player with the higher total.

You need:

- 1 counter per player (1 colour per player)
- 1–6 dice
- stopwatch
- calculator

Game 2: Make it big

How to play

- Shuffle the 2 sets of digit cards together and place them face down on the table. Each player places a counter on Start.
- Take turns to roll the dice. Move your counter that number of places.
- If you land on a number, do nothing.
- If you land on a space, both of you take 4 digit cards. Make the highest number you can with them. The player who makes the higher number wins a point. Put the cards back in the pack and continue playing.
- When you both reach Finish, add up your points. The winner is the player with the higher total.

You need:

- 1 counter per player (1 colour per player)
- 1–6 dice
- 0–9 digit cards (2 sets)

Game 3: Your game

- Make up your own game using the gameboard.
- Will you need to use a stopwatch?
- What are the rules for your game? Explain them to someone.

Please help your child by reading the instructions and playing the game together.

Assessment task 1

Resources

100 squares, yellow and blue pencils.

Running the task

Before children begin the task, recap what multiples are. Agree that they are numbers that occur when counting from zero in steps of different sizes. Agree that counting in multiples helps us to learn and make sense of multiplication tables. Practise counting together in multiples of three, six and nine in preparation for the task.

The task asks children to circle the multiples of three on a 100 square, then colour the multiples of six yellow and the multiples of nine blue. The patterns children see in the 100 square and the numbers they write in answer to the questions in the Textbook should help reinforce the fact that all multiples of six and nine are also multiples of three. Can children explain this? (Six and nine are themselves multiples of three.) Related to this, they may also tell you that every other multiple of three is also a multiple of six and every third multiple of three is also a multiple of nine. If appropriate, you could relate this to the six and nine times tables (doubling the three times table gives the six times table; trebling the three times table gives the nine times table).

Children should also spot that every other multiple of nine is also a multiple of six. If children talk about a 'diagonal line' in relation to the multiples of nine, see if they can tell you why this happens (each row in the square has ten numbers, and nine is one less than ten).

Evidencing mastery

If children can fluently count in multiples of six and nine they are evidencing mastery. Those with a particularly strong grasp of the concept will be able to describe and explain patterns and relationships between the multiples of three, six and nine.

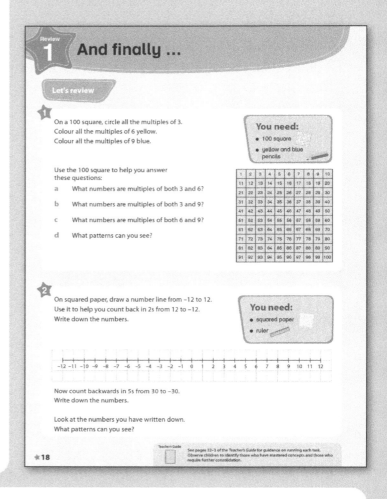

Assessment task 2

Resources

Squared paper, ruler.

Running the task

Before children begin the task, draw a −20 to 20 number line on the board and practise counting backwards and forwards from different starting numbers, including negative numbers. Then count in twos from zero to 20, drawing the 'hops' on the line on the board. Count back from 20 to zero and discuss how the count could be continued into the negative numbers with further 'hops' of two.

During the task, children draw a number line and use it to help them count back in twos from 12 to −12, writing down the numbers. They then count backwards in fives from 30 to −30, again writing down the numbers. They could draw a number line for this, too, if they are not confident counting back without one. They then look at the numbers they have written down and describe any patterns they see. They should notice that in each case the negative numbers mirror the positive numbers.

You could extend the task by asking them to predict what will happen if they count back from zero in threes, sixes or nines, then draw a number line to help them check whether they were correct (the numbers will be the same as the positive multiples, but negative). Alternatively, you could ask them to find the difference between a negative and positive multiple of five (e.g. −15 and 10) by counting up. Observe whether they do this by counting in ones (1, 2, 3, … 23, 24, 25) or in steps of five (5, 10, 15, 20, 25).

Evidencing mastery

Children who can fluently count backwards through zero, to include negative numbers, have mastered this concept. They should understand that negative numbers mirror positive numbers but they go backwards from zero.

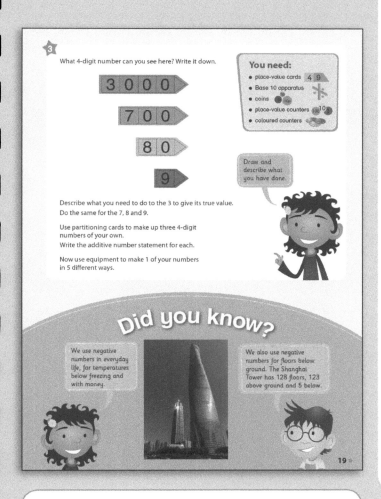

Concepts mastered

☑ Children can count fluently in multiples of three, six and nine, and count forwards and backwards across zero.

☑ Children can explain and demonstrate the positional, multiplicative and additive properties of place value and the role of zero as the place holder.

Assessment task 3

Resources

Place-value cards, Base 10 apparatus, coins, place-value counters, coloured counters.

Running the task

The task asks children to identify the number shown by the place-value cards (3789). They then need to describe how each digit in the number gets its value. Encourage those that can to write an explanation; ask those who may struggle with the writing to explain verbally. Use their explanations to assess whether they have understood the positional and multiplicative aspects of place value, e.g. they should say that the three in 3789 represents three thousands, so you need to multiply it by 1000 to get its true value, 3000 (as shown on the place-value card).

Children then need to use place-value cards to make up 4-digit numbers, recording the additive number statement for each to demonstrate that they understand the additive property of place value (e.g. 4000 + 300 + 70 + 3 = 4373).

Finally, children choose one of their numbers and use equipment to make it in five different ways. The resources list suggests place-value cards, Base 10 apparatus, coins, place-value counters and coloured counters, but you could discuss other possibilities, e.g. bottles containing different volumes of water that add up to the total. Encourage them to include one number which uses zero as a place holder.

You could extend the task by asking children to repeat the final part for one of the other numbers they made up, or ask them to represent smaller numbers in more creative ways (e.g. using Roman numerals or knuckles on their fingers).

Evidencing mastery

Children who have achieved mastery of place value will be able to explain and demonstrate the positional, multiplicative and additive properties of 4-digit numbers, and how to represent such numbers in different ways.

Did you know?

Negative numbers can seem somewhat abstract to children at first, so it is a good idea to discuss real-life examples with them. *Does our outside temperature ever drop below freezing?* Have any of the children visited a place where the temperature is regularly below zero? You could also talk about negative numbers in the context of money, perhaps demonstrating the various different ways negative amounts can be presented in a spreadsheet.

Children often enjoy questions involving lifts, e.g. *Ana got in the lift at floor zero. She went up two floors, then down four. What floor did she end up on?* (–2) Most buildings only have one, or perhaps two floors below ground. However, the Shanghai Tower, the tallest building in China, has five floors below ground. You could discuss with children what these might be called. In some buildings, 'floor zero' is called the ground floor, and floors below ground might be called B1, B2, etc. (B for 'basement'). You could draw a number line on the board to demonstrate this.

Addition and subtraction

Mathematical focus

★ **Number: addition and subtraction, number and place value**

★ **Measurement: money, time, volume, capacity**

★ **Statistics: interpret and present data, solve problems**

Prior learning

Children should already be able to:

- add and subtract numbers mentally, including: a 3-digit number and ones
- add and subtract numbers with up to three digits
- recognise the place value of each digit in a 4-digit number (thousands, hundreds, tens, and ones)
- find 10, 100 and 1000 more or less than a given number.

Key new learning

- Add and subtract numbers with up to four digits using the formal written methods of columnar addition and subtraction where appropriate.
- Estimate and use inverse operations to check answers to a calculation.
- Solve addition and subtraction two-step problems in contexts, deciding which operations and methods to use and why.

Making connections

- Children need to know when they will need to apply methods of addition and subtraction in other areas of the mathematics curriculum and in real life. Learning in this unit is linked to calculating with different measures, and making decisions about which methods to use. Children will need to draw on the relationship between units of measurement to help them make decisions when calculating.
- The unit opener also provides an opportunity to convert time between analogue and a digital 12-clock to solve a problem.
- You could link this unit with a history topic. Familiarity with 4-digit numbers could help children to understand dates in history and to find out how long ago events happened.

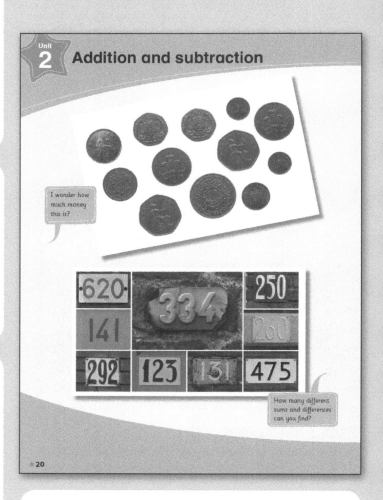

Talk about

It is important to use precise mathematical vocabulary from the beginning so that children refer to the place value of numbers when they estimate and calculate. Continue to use the words 'positional' (where the digit is placed in the number), 'multiplicative' (the digit is multiplied by its position to get its value) and 'additive' (add all the individual numbers together) when talking about place value. Remember to include the position of the place holder, zero, as this is also vital to calculating.

Engaging and exploring

Look together at the first photo. Discuss and match the different coins with physical coins in the classroom. Ask: *How many of each coin are there?* Think about sensible estimates for the total amount of money shown. Ask children to also give you 'silly answers', explaining why they would not be sensible, e.g. *An estimate of £1 is a silly answer because I can see a £2 coin in the picture.*

Challenge children to think about different ways to count the coins. Prompt by asking: *What would be a good starting point?* Discuss other useful strategies for counting and adding, e.g. making groups of ten or 100, or in this case groups of 10p and £1. Explore other amounts that can be made by grouping the coins to help count and calculate, e.g. 20p + 20p + 10p = 50p and 2p + 2p + 1p = 5p. Look at the relationship between the values of the groups of coins here, i.e. one set (50p) is ten times larger than the other

(5p). Agree that there is £4 and 65p in total, which can also be written as 465p because there are 100 pennies in each pound.

Look at the numbers in the next photo and discuss where children would see numbers like this, i.e. on house doors. Discuss the different methods that children can use to find sums and differences, relating the vocabulary to addition and subtraction. Suggest that some pairs of numbers can be added and subtracted using a mental method. Children should discuss possible pairs and methods they can use, e.g. 141 – 123 because the numbers are close together on the number line; 141 – 131 because they are close together and have the same number of ones; 260 + 250 because they are both multiples of ten and 260 is only ten more than 250 so double 250 + 10, etc.

For the theatre time and clock photos, discuss the differences and similarities between the ways that the times are displayed, including the use of Roman numerals. Revisit some of the language used to describe times shown on an analogue clock, e.g. past, to, fractions of hours and the way that digital times are expressed as a number of minutes past the hour, e.g. 3:45 as three forty-five.

Suggest that the next performance will take place after midnight. Ask children to explain why you have made a mistake. They should refer to the fact that the time is given as p.m. not just that it is unusual for a performance to start so late. Return to the question and discuss how long it is before the start of the next performance. Suggest children write the time on the analogue watch as a digital time to compare. They should calculate that there are still 19 minutes before the start of the next performance. Establish that they have found the difference between the 12:21 p.m. and 12:40 p.m.

For the cycle chart, discuss the different ways that children have seen data presented, e.g. pictograms, bar charts, tables, tallies, etc. Ask them to consider why we represent data in these ways rather than just writing it all down. They should understand that a lot of information can be shown in a small space and can be compared easily, and these representations are easily understood all over the world because they use very few words.

Hide or ignore the scale to begin with, and discuss the possible values of a square of four, e.g. worth four bikes or 12 bikes or 40 bikes or 400 bikes. *What would be the value of a single square (quarter of the larger square) each time?* Establish that we need to know the scale of the pictogram if we are to know exactly what the data represents. Challenge children to work out the number of road bikes sold. How can their counting help them here? Discuss the fraction of a full square that is also shown for this bike. Agree that value must be 50 because it is half of the larger square. Establish that a single square is 25 and relate this to counting in steps of 25 to help find the value of different fractions of the whole square of four. Ask children to make up a different scale for the pictogram and represent the given data using this scale.

Things to think about

- How will you model and encourage the use of precise mathematical vocabulary when talking and reasoning about number and measurement?

- How will you share the language requirements with other adults before the start of a lesson?

- What will be the best use of manipulatives and visual representations to help all children with their conceptual understanding of adding and subtracting 4-digit numbers?

- How will you group children so they can learn from each other and practise applying a range of concepts in a positive environment?

Checking understanding

You will know children have mastered these concepts when they can solve addition and subtraction problems in different contexts, appropriately choosing and using number facts, showing understanding of place value and counting and mental and written methods. They can explain their decision making and justify their solutions.

- Add numbers with up to four digits using the formal written methods of columnar addition where appropriate.
- Estimate and use inverse operations to check answers to a calculation.
- Solve addition and subtraction two-step problems in contexts, deciding which operations and methods to use and why.

Homework 5 and 6   Practice Book pp 13–16

Representations and resources

Place-value counters, place-value cards, Base 10 apparatus, 0–9 digit cards, calculators.

Mathematical vocabulary

Addition, total, sum, altogether, equal, estimate, inverse, subtraction

Warming up

Rehearse rounding numbers to the nearest 100 and the nearest 1000. Discuss the rules for rounding. Quickly round a range of 3-digit numbers to the nearest hundred, e.g. 349, 708, 965, 111 and 4-digit numbers to the nearest thousand, e.g. 1099, 1999, 3450, 5800, etc. Give examples of some of the rounding you have done, e.g. *I rounded a number to the nearest 100 and it rounded to 700, what number was it? I rounded a number to the nearest 1000 and it rounded to 5000, what number was it?* Children can play a similar game with a partner.

Background knowledge

In this concept you will build on the mental strategies developed in Year 3 and connect counting to calculating. Number bonds will underpin mental calculation strategies for addition. Ensure that you make available a range of representations to help secure understanding, e.g. use Base 10 apparatus to make the place value in each addition calculation explicit.

Let's learn: Modelling and teaching
Mental methods of addition

- Discuss the misconception cartoon, asking children to suggest some large number additions that would be best carried out using a mental method and those that would not.

- Look at the two numbers 2300 and 4500. Make the numbers using place-value cards. Using the place-value cards and the images in the Textbook, discuss the additive property of each number. Move on to discuss the positional and multiplicative aspect of each digit and the role of zero. Children should notice that both numbers only have digits greater than zero in the thousands and hundreds position. Elicit that this makes it easier to use a mental method as we can treat the numbers as 2-digit numbers while remembering their place value, i.e. 23 hundreds and 45 hundreds. Explore strategies that can be used to add these mentally, including partitioning and sequencing on a number line as modelled in the Textbook.

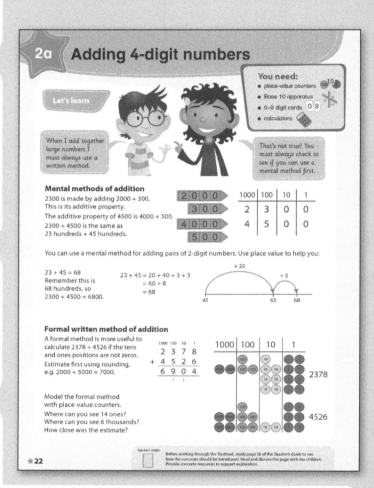

Formal written method of addition

- Ask: *What is the same and what is different about the numbers 2378 and 4526 and the numbers 2300 and 4500?*

- Explain that a mental method would be trickier here because the additive properties of each number mean they have more parts to deal with. 2378 = 2000 + 300 + 70 + 8 and 4526 = 4000 + 500 + 20 + 6. Encourage children to estimate the answer to 2378 + 4526.

- Model the calculation using place-value counters and the written method, discussing differences and similarities. Establish that the columns and headings in the formal method determine the position and value of each digit. The place-value counters help to make this explicit. Return to the estimate and use a calculator to check the answer using the inverse, subtraction.

Let's practise: Digging deeper

Step 1

Children are required to add pairs of 4-digit numbers with up to two significant figures using mental methods of their choice. The calculations build on the expectations for Year 3. Children explain their choice of method with reference to place value.

Step 2

Children make an estimate first and reason about why a written method should be used for these calculations. Then they use manipulatives to model each of the calculations so that place value is explicit, e.g. saying 'four hundreds + three hundreds or 400 + 300 equals seven hundreds or 700', rather than referring only to single digits (4 + 3). Observe how accurate children's estimates were.

Step 3

In this practical task children apply methods of written calculation within the context of capacity. As before, they should make an estimate first and check the calculations using the inverse, subtraction. Ask them to record the subtraction statement each time. They continue making other 4-digit number additions using millilitres, and measuring out the appropriate amounts into the containers. Read Tom's challenge together. Encourage children to reason about the values in the most significant positions.

Step 4

This problem is set in the context of money and statistics. Children should recognise where they can add pairs of 2-digit numbers to help them and then apply place value, e.g. £5400 + £3300, and also as possible calculations with a total £7800. For Charity C, look for children who quickly recognise that the last three digits of both numbers are the same, and again, can be solved mentally. Children can explore a range of calculations with the total £7800, perhaps starting with a simple calculation £4000 + £3800 and then adapting it, e.g. £4100 + £3900.

Let's practise

1

Calculate.
Add using a mental method. Explain to your partner how your method works.

a   3600 + 2400 =   c   5000 + 2800 =   e   2060 + 2020 =

b   6700 + 2000 =   d   6000 + 3000 =   f   6007 + 1005 =

2

Calculate.
Estimate the answers to these questions.
Explain why it would be difficult to calculate the answers using a mental method.

a   3417 + 1346 =   b   2374 + 1251 =   c   3843 + 1726 =

Now complete the calculations using the formal method of addition. Use place-value counters or Base 10 apparatus to help you. How close were your estimates?

3

Apply.
Pick 4 digit cards. Make a number. This is the amount of water for the 1st container.

Rearrange the digits to make another 4-digit number. This is the amount of water for the 2nd container.

Calculate the total amount of water in the containers. Estimate first then use the formal written method.

Check your answer on a calculator using subtraction.

Can you pick 4 different digit cards and arrange them so that the total amount of water in the 2 containers is between 5500 ml and 6000 ml?

4

Think.
The table shows money donated to 4 charities. The charities have shops and also receive other donations, e.g. schools collecting money.

	Shop donations	Other donations	Total
Charity A	£5400	£3300	
Charity B	£6347	£2408	
Charity C	£4325		£8325
Charity D			£7800

a   Copy and complete the table for Charities A, B and C.

b   Charity D is given £7800 in total donations. Find some possible amounts to make this true.

Teacher's Guide
See page 37 of the Teacher's Guide for ideas of how to guide practice. Work through each step together as a class to develop children's conceptual understanding.

23

Ensuring progress

Supporting understanding

You may wish to focus on adding pairs of numbers that do not require any exchanging initially, or where exchanging is limited to the ones column only. It is important that children can talk about the place value of each digit in a 4-digit number and refer to this when adding before they are involved with more complex calculations. Continue to use manipulatives alongside a mental or written method.

Broadening understanding

In Step 4, children can further explore more complex additions with the total £7800 which would be more appropriately solved using a written method, e.g. £4176 + £3624. They should use a calculator to check their workings using subtraction, but also explain that the ones digits must always total ten so they immediately know that a calculation such as £4176 + £3625 is not possible.

✓ Concept mastered

Children can explain when a mental method is more appropriate than a written method and fluently apply knowledge of number facts and place value to support mental work. They can explain the positional, multiplicative and additive properties of numbers and refer to these when using a formal written method. Children use rounding to help make estimates and recognise that subtraction can be used to check an addition calculation.

Follow-up ideas

- Look at other statistical representations, e.g. bar charts with scales with larger intervals, e.g. 200, 400, 500 or 1000. Children use the information to solve sum and difference problems. With the numbers and scales involved, the majority of calculations will warrant a mental method.

- Use catalogues or online price lists that give the cost of different items in pounds. Explore the price of, e.g. buying a new small car with an optional extra, keeping the total price below £10 000.

- Explore distances between different major airports in cities in the world, e.g. London and Cairo (approximately 3536 km from Heathrow), Cairo and Dubai (approximately 2418 km). Challenge children to calculate the total distance an aeroplane would fly from London to Dubai with a stopover in Cairo.

Answers

Step 1

a	6000	d	9000
b	8700	e	4080
c	7800	f	7012

Step 2

a	4763	c	5569
b	3625		

Step 4

a   Charity A: £5400 + £3300 = £8700

Charity B: £6347 + £2408 = £8755

Charity C: £4325 + 4000 = £8325

b   Possible answers, e.g. £6000 + £1800, £6500 + £1300, £4000 + £3800 etc.

- Subtract numbers with up to four digits using the formal written methods of columnar subtraction where appropriate.
- Estimate and use inverse operations to check answers to a calculation.
- Solve addition and subtraction two-step problems in contexts, deciding which operations and methods to use and why.

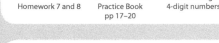

Homework 7 and 8   Practice Book pp 17–20   Subtracting 4-digit numbers

Representations and resources

Base 10 apparatus, place-value counters, number lines, tape measures.

Mathematical vocabulary

Subtract, difference, equal, equivalent, partition, estimate, inverse, addition, millimetre, centimetre

Warming up

Practise counting on and back in steps of ten, 100 and 1000 from different numbers. Challenge children to see how far they can count on in hundreds from 875 in a minute or back in tens from 2015 in a minute. *How far can you each get? How much more or less is your last number in your count than your first number?* Discuss numbers that they know will not be in the count, e.g. *All these counts must end in a five, and all the numbers in the hundreds count will end in 75.*

Background knowledge

Continue to build on mental subtraction strategies from Year 3, connecting counting to calculating. Partitioning in different ways will help children to make sense of decomposition. The minuend is re-partitioned to accommodate subtracting a larger digit, e.g. for 4672 – 1348, the minuend is partitioned into 4000 + 600 + 60 + 12 so the eight ones can be subtracted.

Let's learn: Modelling and teaching
Mental methods of subtraction

- Focus on a range of subtraction calculations that can be solved using a mental method of subtracting multiples of ten, 100 or 1000, or a single digit, e.g. 3260 – 1000, 3500 – 400, 1075 – 9, etc. Discuss why a written method is not appropriate. Relate the example 7500 – 2100 to the subtraction 75 – 21, carefully discussing the place value, i.e. 75 hundreds – 21 hundreds.

- Discuss how mental methods can be used to subtract numbers that are close together on the number line, using the calculation 2000 – 1878 (as shown in the Textbook) as a starting point. Model the concept using bars and solve using the number line. Highlight the use of number bonds.

- Ask children to work in pairs to solve similar calculations using a bar model and number line.

Formal written method of subtraction

- Compare the calculation 3652 – 1437 with subtractions they made with the door numbers in the unit opener. Children should recognise that they are now working with 4-digit

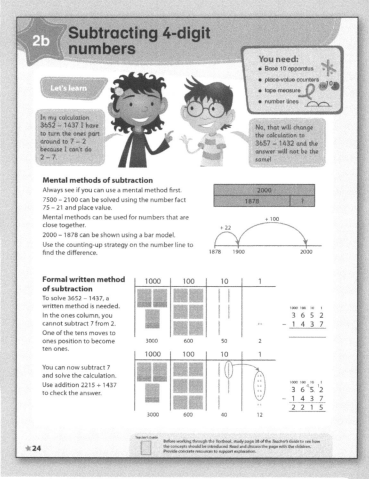

numbers, neither are multiples of ten and they are not really close together on the number line. A formal written method would, therefore, be appropriate. Discuss a useful estimate using rounding, e.g. 4000 – 1000 or 3700 – 1400.

- Use the first representations to help discuss the error in the misconception cartoon. Look at the first two Base 10 representations in the Textbook and explore equivalence so that children understand that both 3000 + 600 + 50 + 2 and 3000 + 600 + 40 + 12 have the same value, but do not look the same. Explain that the numbers have been partitioned in different ways and this can help us with the problem.

- Model the formal written method alongside the Base 10 representations, taking away the relevant number of ones, tens, hundreds and thousands to complete the calculation.

Let's practise: Digging deeper

Step 1

All calculations in this task should be solved mentally, and children should relate the method to the numbers involved, e.g. finding the difference because the numbers are close together, rounding and adjusting a near multiple. Focus on the calculation 8300 – 1200, making sure that children relate this to place value and the related fact, 83 – 12.

Step 2

The minuend in each of these calculations is the same so that children can focus on exchanging values in different positions (thousands, hundreds, tens and ones). Only one exchange is needed each time and the first calculation requires no exchanging. Each time children should represent 4374 and partition the number in different ways as required by the subtrahend. They should use the manipulatives to support the formal written method, matching the values.

Step 3

Revisit the relationship between centimetres and millimetres first so that children recognise that the value in millimetres is always ten times larger than the same measurement in centimetres. They should choose to use mental or written methods and explain their choices.

Step 4

This task requires children to apply their knowledge of addition as the inverse of subtraction. They use the addition calculation that Tom used to check a subtraction to find his original subtraction. Provide manipulatives, e.g. Base 10 apparatus and place-value counters, to confirm decisions. They make up word problems to match the calculation. The task becomes more open as children find possible subtraction calculations to suit Ana's 'checking' addition, drawing on mental and written strategies. Ask children to reason about values, e.g. *When the answer to Ana's checking calculation is 3000, what is the value of the empty box? What do you know about the size of the answer to the checking calculation if the empty box is a 2-digit number?*

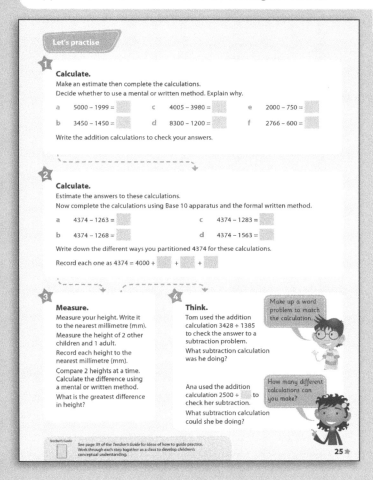

Ensuring progress

Supporting understanding

You may wish to focus on subtraction calculations that do not require any exchanging initially, or where exchanging is limited to the ones column only. It is important that children can talk about the place value of each digit in a 4-digit number and refer to this when subtracting before they are involved with more complex calculations.

Broadening understanding

Children apply addition and subtraction to sort and solve sets of one- and two-step problems, deciding which operation to use and whether a mental or written method is more appropriate. Calculations can be sorted into a Carroll Diagram with headings: one-step problem, two-step problem, mental method and written method.

✓ Concept mastered

Children can explain when a mental method is more appropriate than a written method and fluently apply knowledge of number facts and place value to support mental work. They use representations and the written method to subtract 4-digit numbers and use knowledge of partitioning in different ways to support exchanging. Children use rounding to help make estimates and recognise that addition can be used to check a subtraction calculation.

Follow-up ideas

- Children can solve a range of word problems that require them to use mental and written methods. Problems should be set in the context of measurement, including money and time. Focus on the use of the number line to work with time problems.

- Return to the pictogram in the unit opener and explore sums and differences as the scale is changed, e.g. change the scale so that a square of four now represents 600 or 1000. Calculate sums and differences between the sales of the different bikes using mental methods. Show the same information on a bar chart, deciding carefully about the intervals on the scale, i.e. for 1000 bikes per symbol, label the bar chart in thousands with intervals of 250 (labelled or unlabelled).

Answers

Step 1

a	3001	d	7100
b	2000	e	1250
c	25	f	2166

For checking: 3001 + 1999; 2000 + 1450; 3980 + 25; 7100 + 1200; 1250 + 750; 2166 + 600.

Step 2

a	3111	c	3091
b	3106	d	2811

4374 = 4000 + 300 + 70 + 4
4374 = 4000 + 300 + 60 + 14
4374 = 4000 + 200 + 170 + 4
4374 = 3000 + 1300 + 70 + 4

Step 4

4813 – 3428 or 4813 – 1385.

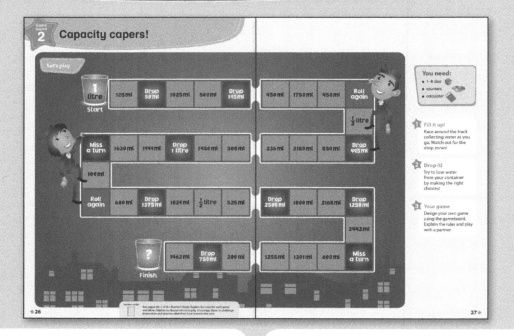

Game 1: Fill it up!

This game provides children with the opportunity to add and subtract values in the context of capacity, deciding when to use a mental or written method.

Maths focus

- Addition and subtraction
- Measurement

Resources

1–6 dice (1), 1 counter per player (1 colour per player), calculators, place-value apparatus.

How to play

Play in pairs. Players start with one litre of water in their 'containers' and take it in turns to collect more water as they move around the board. They roll the dice and add the amount of water shown in the space they land on to the amount already in the container, using a mental or written calculation. They must subtract an amount if they land on a 'drop' space.

If a player reaches 10 000 ml (ten litres), they must start a new container but the ten litres collected still counts towards their score. Players should check each other's calculations using a calculator. The winner is the player who finishes the game with the greatest capacity of water.

Making it easier

Play in groups so a player has a partner to work with. The game could be played using place-value counters or Base 10 apparatus so that children can practically add and subtract as they move around the board. Players can convert all the litre capacities to millilitres before they start so the amounts are all in the same unit of measurement.

Making it harder

Introduce two dice so that children make decisions about which number to use, e.g. at the beginning of the game, are they better to choose a three or a five? The five would move them further around the board but they have to drop water, whereas the three will result in collecting more water.

Game 2: Drop it!

This game provides children with the opportunity to add and subtract values in the context of capacity, using mental or written methods as appropriate. They must also use their reasoning skills.

Maths focus

- Addition and subtraction
- Measurement

Resources

1–6 dice (2), 1 counter per player (1 colour per player), calculators, place-value apparatus.

How to play

Players must finish the race with the least amount of water in the 'container'. Play in pairs. Each player starts with one litre of water and takes it in turns to roll two dice. They choose which of the two numbers to use. If a player reaches 10 000 ml (ten litres), they must start a new container but the ten litres collected still counts towards their score. Players should use calculators to check each other's calculations. If a player runs out of water during the game, they are the winner.

Making it easier

Play in groups so children can discuss strategies and the dice to choose each time. Use place-value counters or Base 10 apparatus.

Making it harder

Throwing a double means you have to add three-quarters of a litre of water to the container before moving on the number of spaces shown by one of the dice.

Game 3: Your game

Children should invent their own game designing rules that use the concepts covered in the unit. Challenge children to make their game easier or harder.

Unit 2 Capacity capers!

Choose a game to play.

Game 1: Fill it up!

How to play

- Start with 1 litre of water in each of your 'containers'.
- Take it in turns to roll the dice and move the number of spaces shown.
- 'Collect' the water and add it to the amount of water already in your container. Use a mental or written calculation.
- You must subtract the amount if you land on a 'drop' space.
- Check each other's calculations using a calculator.
- The winner is the player who finishes the game with the greatest capacity of water.

You need:

- 1–6 dice
- 1 counter per player (1 colour per player)
- calculator
- pencil and paper

Game 2: Drop it!

How to play

- Start with 1 litre of water in each of your 'containers'.
- Take it in turns to roll 2 dice and choose the number of spaces to move on. Think carefully!
- Add or drop the water from your container using a mental or written calculation.
- Check each other's calculations using a calculator.
- The winner is the player who finishes the game with the least water in their container or who runs out of water first!

You need:

- two 1–6 dice
- 1 counter per player (1 colour per player)
- calculator
- pencil and paper

Game 3: Your game

- Make up your own game using the gameboard.
- You could make up a rule where throwing a 6 with the dice means you carry out a special instruction.
- What are the rules for your game? Explain them to someone.

Please help your child by reading the instructions and playing the game together.

Assessment task 1

Running the task

Encourage children to discuss some of the mental and written calculations they have been doing recently, giving examples of calculations that would best suit a mental method and those that would not. They should recognise that a subtraction with numbers that are close together on the number line can be more easily calculated using a mental method of counting on.

Children can work in pairs or in a group to make up different addition and subtraction calculations that are best solved using a mental method. They should explain the decisions they have made and then complete the calculation, remembering to make an estimate first. Look for children who fluently add and subtract multiples of a hundred or a thousand, and draw on related facts and place value to make calculations easier to do. Discuss a checking calculation each time.

The task continues as children are now required to make up some written calculations. As the majority of numbers were chosen to influence mental calculation, the question mark can also be used each time as any number of their choice.

Evidencing mastery

Children are showing mastery when they readily describe calculations that are best solved using a mental method and can explain their decisions, linking this to some of the counting they have done, related facts that they know and place value. They use a range of strategies, including sequencing on a number line, partitioning, etc. to help them. They recognise calculations that are more complex and are best solved using a written method.

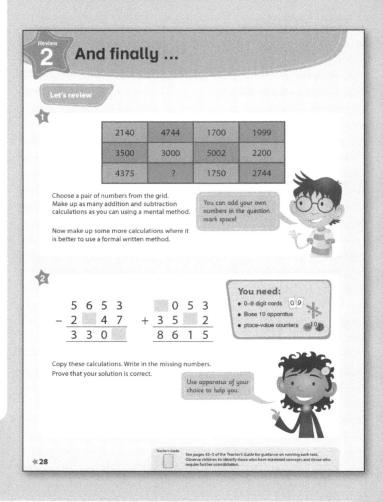

Assessment task 2

Resources

Sticky notes, 0–9 digit cards, Base 10 apparatus, place-value counters.

Running the task

It would be useful for children to complete an addition and subtraction calculation first using the formal written method so they are already thinking about the value of the columns and the procedure they will use.

Look together at the calculations with missing digits and ensure that children understand what the task is asking. It may be worth sticking one or two sticky notes over the calculations they have just completed so that they know that the empty boxes have a hidden value.

The task can be represented using digit cards and place-value apparatus (e.g. Base 10 or counters), allowing children to make sense of the steps and reason about the size of the missing digits.

Discuss which inverse operation calculations can be used to check solutions.

Evidencing mastery

Children show mastery when they can model and explain the steps in the formal written methods of addition and subtraction and recognise how a total in a column or difference in a column can be made. They draw on number bonds to 20 to aid calculations. Children identify the inverse operation and the calculation that can be used to check working.

Assessment task 3

Running the task

Discuss some of the word problems that children have been solving using different operations. Ask them to think about some of the words that are useful to look out for and may give them clues about the operation to use. Discuss why the phrases 'more than' and 'less than' can be tricky as it will depend on the question being asked. 'More than' does not always mean you have to add and 'less than' does not always mean you have to subtract. Discuss some examples.

Ask children to work with a partner, perhaps pairing more confident readers with less confident readers, so they can solve the problem together. Part a has two steps but only involves addition. A formal written method should be used and children should explain why this is the case. Children can choose to use representations to help them, e.g. the bar model, remembering to make estimates first. Encourage children to use a mental method for part b of the problem and to recognise that the hundreds, tens and ones value of both numbers is the same.

Evidencing mastery

Children display mastery when they recognise that part a involves two steps of addition and part b involves two steps of subtraction. Representing the calculations in their own way, e.g. the bar model, Base 10 apparatus, also indicates mastery. Children can can explain why the column method is useful here as the numbers involved require more steps to be taken. They make useful estimates using place value to help them.

Did you know?

Encourage children to find out about a discovery made in 1949 by the mathematician D.R. Kaprekar from Devlali in India. He devised a process that is now known as 'Kaprekar's operation' and involves the number 6174. Have a go at using the process with children as it is a great way to reinforce place value and apply the formal written method of subtraction:

- Choose any 4-digit number where the digits are not all the same, e.g. 2175. Rearrange the digits to make the largest and smallest number possible: 7521 and 1275. Use the numbers to make the subtraction 7521 – 1275 = 6246.

- Now do the same with the digits from 6246 to make the subtraction 6642 – 2466 = 4176 with the largest and smallest numbers. Repeat with the subtraction 7641 – 1467 = 6174 to find the mysterious number. You cannot go any further because rearranging the digits would give the same calculation 7641 – 1467 = 6174.

Investigate other numbers using the same process and find out how quickly number 6174 appears. When numbers with zeros are used, e.g. for 3056 the largest number is 6530 and the smallest is 0356; for 7005, the largest number is 7500 and the smallest is 0057. 6174 is known as the kernel of 'Kaprekar's operation' as it is the central or most important part.

Concepts mastered

☑ Children can explain when a mental method is more appropriate than a written method and fluently apply knowledge of number facts and place value to support mental work. They can explain the positional, multiplicative and additive properties of numbers and refer to these when using a formal written method. Children use rounding to help make estimates and recognise that subtraction can be used to check an addition calculation.

☑ Children can explain when a mental method is more appropriate than a written method and fluently apply knowledge of number facts and place value to support mental work. They use representations and the written method to subtract 4-digit numbers and use knowledge of partitioning in different ways to support exchanging. Children use rounding to help make estimates and recognise that addition can be used to check a subtraction calculation.

Factors and calculating

Mathematical focus

★ **Number: number and place value, multiplication and division**

★ **Measurement: money, time, mass, capacity/volume, length**

Prior learning

Children should already be able to:

- recall multiplication and division facts for multiplication tables two, three, four, five and eight

- use the language of factors and multiples

- recall facts about units of time.

Key new learning

- Count in multiples of six and nine.

- Recall multiplication and division facts for multiplication tables six, nine and 12.

- Use place value, known and derived facts to multiply and divide mentally, including multiplying together three numbers, recognising and using factor pairs and commutativity in mental calculations.

- Solve problems involving multiplying and adding, including using the distributive law to multiply 2-digit numbers by single-digit numbers.

Making connections

- Working on the multiplication facts for six will develop fluency in calculation with seconds, minutes and hours.

- There are 12 months in a year. Being able to multiply and divide by 12 supports work on calendar facts and solving problems involving conversion between months and years.

- Many children will use measures of length in later life, as well as in many other subjects in school. The questions using metric units of length prepare for these and also allow children to apply their knowledge and understanding of multiplying and dividing by powers of ten.

- Many children are familiar with imperial units of length, such as feet and inches, from everyday life. These have links outside the classroom. There is also cross-curricular work that can be done with History about the origins of these measures. In RE you can investigate biblical measures and how they relate to imperial ones. There may also be measures from other religions.

- Money is an obvious opportunity to use multiplication and addition. Many children will be familiar with the process of spending money.

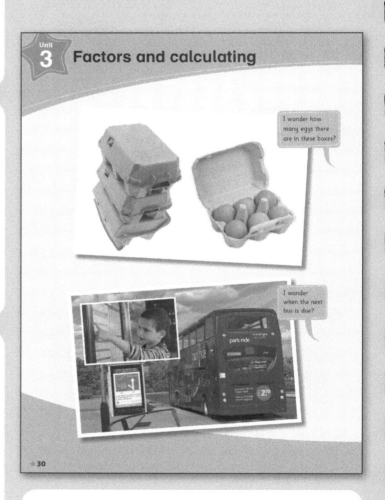

Talk about

Children should use the term 'multiply', rather than 'times'. They should know the terms 'factor' and 'multiple' and be clear that a factor divides a number and a multiple is the result of multiplying a number by a whole number. It is very common for children to confuse the terms. 'Factor' leads to factorising later in algebra. Use discussion to draw out the difference between the cardinal value of a number and its ordinal nature.

Engaging and exploring

You could ask if children have seen boxes containing six eggs and also if they have seen other sizes of egg box. You could discuss why six is the usual capacity of an egg box. Ask: *What other situations can you think of where you might count in 6s?* Possible examples could be because there are six in a family, we have six cats, baking cakes or puddings and so on. You could ask: *How many eggs will there be in 5 of those boxes?* This could be done by counting in sixes or by recalling their multiplication facts for five and working it out that way.

Children will have seen buses and many will have travelled on them. Ask: *Have you ever been on a bus journey? How did you know when to arrive at the bus stop?* You could show examples from local bus timetables – some display when the first bus leaves and then 'every 12 minutes until …', so some calculation is required. Pose questions, e.g. *The first bus is at 8 a.m and they go every 12 minutes. Which is the first bus after 10 a.m.?* Since 12 is a factor of 60, this should be straightforward. You could go on to every nine minutes and so on. Support the discussion by drawing a number line of times, e.g. 9 o'clock, 10 o'clock, etc. You can use this to count on in order to calculate the times.

Filling goodie bags presents many mathematical problems. Party blowers may come in packs of six. Balloons might come in packs of 20. Other items will have to be bought individually. Working out the number of each to buy and then the cost requires plenty of multiplication and adding. Design a class goodie bag. Ask children to suggest the items and research their costs, either in the local shop or online. Ask them to discuss in groups how to work out the total cost of nine goodie bags. Take feedback from each group by asking questions such as: *How did you work it out? Which approach is most efficient?*

Metric and imperial units are both still used today. Many adults and children know their height in feet and inches, but not in metres and centimetres. Ask children if they have heard of inches and if they know how long a foot is. This could lead to a discussion on the historical origins of feet as a measure. You could ask children to research this further on the Internet and produce a poster of their findings. Ask if anyone knows their height in feet and inches. Measure each child in the class and model how to use facts from the 12 times table to work out the height in inches. Work together to record all the heights in a table. Invite children to suggest an appropriate chart that might help them to compare the heights, e.g. a bar chart with vertical bars.

Most schools have productions, so children will have seen the hall set out with chairs in rows. Knowing how many will fit is crucial. Ask children how they could work it out. Ask questions such as: *Would they count each one every time a few more chairs were added? Would they count up the rows?* If they know the number of rows and the number of chairs in each row, ask how they would find the total number of chairs. Let them discuss it and their ideas could go on a working wall to refer to as the unit progresses.

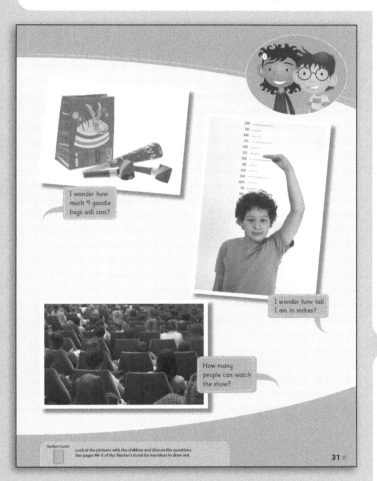

I wonder how much 9 goodie bags will cost?

I wonder how tall I am in inches?

How many people can watch the show?

Look at the pictures with the children and discuss the questions. See pages 44–5 of the Teacher's Guide for key ideas to draw out.

31

Checking understanding

You will know children have mastered these concepts when they can explain the relationships between multiplication table facts, factors and counting in steps of the same size. They can use the associative and commutative properties to do multiplications mentally. They can use distributivity to support written methods for multiplying 2-digit numbers by single-digit numbers.

Things to think about

- How will you decide whether to allow children to use calculators to check their work?

- How will you decide how much recording of their methods you will ask children to do?

- How will you use discussion between children to evaluate effectiveness of methods used?

- How will you develop fluency? Will you use games and thinking questions? Will you seek other opportunities such as problem-solving tasks?

- How will you check for understanding during each lesson? Will you ask children to explain their thinking?

- How will you check for deep learning as the topic progresses? Will you use same/different questions?

- How will you use concrete resources and images, and which will you use when presenting tasks and ideas to children?

- How will you ensure you spend enough time on the unit opener to engage children?

- How will you revisit the unit opener at the end of the topic?

- **Count in multiples of six and nine.**
- **Recall multiplication and division facts for multiplication tables six, nine and 12.**

Homework 9 and 10   Practice Book pp 21–3   Number Line; 100 Squares

Mathematical vocabulary

Multiple, multiplication, division

Warming up

Ask questions about intervals of time, e.g. *It is 10 to 2, what time will it be in 25 minutes? It is quarter past 3. What time was it 32 minutes ago?*

Practise counting up and down in threes from different numbers, then move on to counting up and down in fours from different numbers.

Background knowledge

Grouping is an important model for multiplication because it connects ordinal and cardinal representations of numbers for children. It is important that they link the amount or size of the group (cardinal) with its position of the number on the number line (ordinal). This links counting and measuring. We use the two concepts interchangeably, whereas they are in fact different ideas. The size of the jump is the cardinal number, where it 'lands' is the ordinal number. Children will have been encouraged to link the two, four and eight multiplication facts, as well as the fives and tens, in the same way as they now link the threes, sixes, nines and 12s.

Let's learn: Modelling and teaching

Counting in sixes and nines

- Give children bead strings. Together, group the beads in threes and count aloud: 3, 6, 9, 12, 15, 18. Show children the number line in the Textbook. Ask: *What is the same and what is different about the number line and bead string?*

- Repeat the count in threes, only saying alternate numbers. Ask children what they notice. Elicit that they are now counting in sixes. Count in sixes again, using the bead string for support. Again, compare the bead string to the number line in the Textbook.

- Repeat the exercise for counting in nines. This time, ask children to guide you to draw the corresponding number line. Compare your number line to the one in the Textbook.

- Ask questions such as: *Why can we use steps of 3 to go up in steps of 6 and 9? What happens if we start with a number other than zero?* Draw out the idea that the steps are the same, even if the starting point is different.

Representations and resources

Number lines, bead strings, coloured rods, cubes, sticky notes, place-value counters, 100 squares, multiplication squares.

Multiplication facts for six, nine and 12

- Model 2 × 3 and 1 × 6 using cubes. Ask children what they notice. Elicit that two groups of three is equal to one group of six. Repeat for 4 × 3 and 2 × 6. Ask children to continue by making 6 × 3 and 3 × 6 with cubes. Record the multiplication facts on sticky notes under each.

- Repeat the exercise for multiplication facts for nine and 12, e.g. show 12 as four groups of three and two groups of six.

- Discuss the bar models in the Textbook. Model them using number rods. Ask questions such as: *What is the same and different about the bar model, number rods and cubes? Which representation do you find most helpful? Why?*

Let's practise: Digging deeper

Step 1

Some children will answer these questions mentally. Others will need to write down the numbers they count to keep track of where they are.

Step 2

It is important that children continue to move between multiplication and division forms of the same multiplication table fact. Asking: *Can you write that as a multiplication/division calculation?* helps children relate these forms and embed the knowledge of the number fact. Children may need extra support for parts a to d as they involve new multiplication facts. If appropriate, work through parts a and b together using bead strings and number lines then allow children to complete c and d independently. After completing parts e, f and g, ask: *What do you notice?* Elicit the idea that more than one multiplication

results in 48 or 72. Dig deeper by asking: *What other facts with answers of 48 or 72 can you write down?*

Step 3

Support children in solving the problems through targeted questioning, e.g. *Which time fact do you need for this question? Which multiplication table can you use to calculate the answer?* Encourage children to use place-value counters or a number line as an additional support. For part e, a time number line could be particularly useful.

Step 4

Odd and even numbers are important in developing children's understanding of the structure of the number system. Starting with an odd number and adding an even number each time always results in odd numbers, and starting with an even number and adding even numbers always results in even numbers. Use questioning to encourage children to notice this. Some may spot that starting with a multiple of three means you always get multiples of three but it doesn't work with multiples of five, for example. The second question lays the foundation for later work on common multiples.

Ensuring progress

Supporting understanding

Children can continue to use a number line or 100 square to regulate their counting. They can use a multiplication square to support recall of the number facts. Alternatively, a multiplication square with the six, nine and 12 rows and columns empty could be used.

Broadening understanding

Ask children to pose their own questions similar to Step 1 parts a and b. Ask them to find a more efficient method than counting back and to connect this with the appropriate multiplication tables. Ask further questions, e.g. *How can you use the multiplication tables to see if 300 is in the sequence obtained when starting with 13 and counting in steps of nine?*

Concept mastered

Children can count in steps of six and nine. They can recall and use multiplication table facts for six, nine and 12.

Let's practise

1 Answer these.

a Count in 6s from 6. Do you land on 90?

b Count in 9s from 2. Do you land on 91?

c Count back in 6 from 100. How many numbers do you count before you pass zero?

d Count back in 9s from 125. Which single-digit number do you count on?

2 Answer these.

What do you notice about your answers to b, f and g?

a $6 \times 8 =$

b $6 \times 12 =$

c $9 \times 7 =$

d $9 \times 12 =$

e $12 \times \boxed{} = 48$

f $72 \div \boxed{} = 6$

g $12 \times \boxed{} = 72$

Copy and complete:

h $48 = 6 \times \boxed{}$

i $63 = 9 \times \boxed{}$

j $72 \div 9 = \boxed{}$

3 Solve.

a How many minutes are in 3 hours?

b A dozen means 12 items. How many bread rolls are in 8 dozen?

c Ana ran for 720 seconds. How many minutes did she run for?

d Tom has 72 counters. How many groups of 9 counters can he make?

e The first bus leaves the town centre at 5 past 8 in the morning. After that, buses leave every 9 minutes. Ana catches the last bus to leave before 9 o'clock in the morning. What time does it leave?

f Tom reads that depth of water is measured in fathoms. He discovers there are 6 feet in a fathom. How many inches is that? (There are 12 inches in a foot).

4 Think.

a Count in 6s from 1. What do you notice about the numbers you land on? What if you count in 6s from 2? What is different about the numbers you land on?

Count in 6s from different starting numbers. Explain the patterns you notice.

b Which numbers appear in the multiplication tables for both 6 and 9? Why is that? Predict which numbers are in the multiplication tables for both 9 and 12. Were you right?

Teacher's Guide See page 47 of the Teacher's Guide for ideas of how to guide practice. Work through each step together as a class to develop children's conceptual understanding.

33

Follow-up ideas

- Explore the number patterns of multiples of six, nine and 12 on a 100 square with the usual rows of ten. Then use a different length of row, perhaps six, nine or 12, to reveal the relationship between these multiplication tables.

- Use percussion instruments to beat out time in sixes, nines and 12s, with a background beat of two or three. Experiment with other background beats.

- Measure distances in and around the classroom in feet and inches, to practise the multiplication facts for 12.

Answers

Step 1

a Yes

b No

c 16

d 8

Step 2

a 48

b 72

c 63

d 108

e $12 \times 4 = 48$

f $72 \div 12 = 6$

g $12 \times 6 = 72$

h 8

i 7

j 8

They are all number sentences of $6 \times 12 = 72$.

Step 3

a 180 minutes

b 96 bread rolls

c 12 minutes

d 8

e 08:59

f 72 inches

Step 4

a 1, 7, 13, 19, 25, 31… all odd, some are prime. 2, 8, 14, 20, 26, 32… all even numbers will be the same distance up or down from a multiple of 6 each time.

b Individual answers. Pupils should spot common multiples of each pair of numbers.

- **Use place value, known and derived facts to multiply and divide mentally, including multiplying together three numbers, recognising and using factor pairs and commutativity in mental calculations.**

Homework 11 and 12   Practice Book pp 24–6

Representations and resources

Counters, digit cards, cards showing ×, sticky notes.

Mathematical vocabulary

Commutative, associative, factor, factor pair, product

Warming up

Practise the 9 and 12 multiplication table facts. Ask questions, e.g. *Give me an example of a number that is in the 9 and 12 multiplication tables. If I know that $3 \times 12 = 36$ what else do I know? Count on in 12s from 9. Count back in 9s from 120.*

Background knowledge

Multiplication is commutative, e.g. $3 \times 4 = 4 \times 3$. Division is not commutative, e.g. three divided by four is not equal to four divided by three. The same is true for associativity. Multiplication is associative, e.g. $(12 \times 3) \times 2 = 12 \times (3 \times 2)$, but division is not, e.g. $(12 \div 3) \div 2 = 4 \div 2 = 2$ but $12 \div (3 \div 2) = 12 \div 1.5 = 8$. Children used commutative and associative laws in Year 3 to do mental calculations with increasing efficiency. You will develop these skills now that children have a greater range of multiplication table facts to draw on. At this point children should be fluent in multiplication table facts for all numbers up to 12, except sevens and 11s.

Factor pairs are pairs of numbers that multiply together to make a given product. One product may have several different factor pairs. Recognising factor pairs supports mental calculation.

Let's learn: Modelling and teaching

Pairing and swapping

- Ask children to work out $2 \times 9 \times 5$ and record how they worked it out, without sharing their answer or method. Then collect their responses on the whiteboard. Have any made the same error as in the misconception cartoon?

- Remind them about the commutative law of multiplication. Ask: *What other ways can we put 2, 9 and 5 in order, to work out their product?* Discuss the six possible ways.

- Remind children that the associative law means that for each of those arrangements we can work out the product of the first pair, or the second pair, first. That gives 12 different ways to work out the answer. Ask children to do those 12 calculations, modelling them using 90 counters. Write the workings on the whiteboard, e.g. $2 \times 5 \times 9 = 10 \times 9$, or 2×45 and so on. Ask questions, e.g. *What do you notice? Which ways are most efficient?*

- Compare these methods with children's own and the method shown in the Textbook. Encourage them to pursue the method that is most efficient for them.

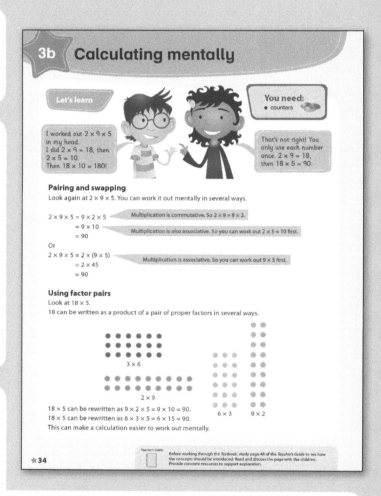

Using factor pairs

- Ask children to show 18 as the product of two factors in as many ways as possible using counters set out in arrays. Note that children should not use a multiplication square as a support.

- Compare their arrays to the images in the Textbook. Ask: *Which are the same as your counters?* Write out the calculations and label each array model with a sticky note. Order the arrays sequentially.

- Ask questions such as: *Work out 18×5 using all the ways you have found to rewrite 18. Which ways work best?* Discuss which factor pairs make the calculation easier. Draw out the idea that finding 2×5 in a calculation is helpful as multiplying by ten is easy.

Let's practise: Digging deeper
Step 1

Prompt children to spot the numbers that can make the calculation easier. Discuss what was helpful when they worked out $2 \times 9 \times 5$. Draw attention to five as one of the numbers in the product. Ask: *This 5 could be helpful – why is that?* Then highlight the even number, as this will multiply by five to give a multiple of ten.

Step 2

Allow children time to make sense of these questions. Writing down the calculations allows children to rearrange or replace numbers to determine the factors that are involved. Suggest working through the calculation to see if they could use 3×2 or 4×5. Encourage them to reflect on their answers, so they notice that if a calculation does not involve a number with five as a factor then 4×5 cannot be used.

Step 3

The first three questions involve recall of time and calendar facts. Children do not need to convert the metric measures in parts c and d although some will do this. Children are only required to go from larger to smaller units in Year 4. Drawing pictures or diagrams of the situation when a question is set in context is usually helpful.

Step 4

Working in groups enables discussion and checking results. A selection of answers are given to allow children to check some results, however the checking is best when it can be agreed within the group. You could extend by asking children how many ways there are of writing 360 as a product of four factors.

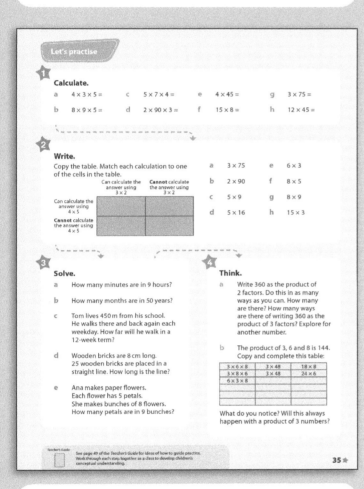

Ensuring progress
Supporting understanding

Give children digit cards and cards showing the multiplication sign. Ask them to make the calculation using the cards. Prompt children to change the order of the numbers by moving the cards. Prompt them to swap numbers for a factor pair of that number and then arrange the cards in different ways for the calculation.

Broadening understanding

Children could draw a flowchart for deciding the best approach to a mental calculation. This encourages generalisation of approaches after reflecting upon them.

 ## Concept mastered

Children can use factor pairs and commutativity to do mental calculations involving multiplication.

Follow-up ideas

- Children make up mental calculations involving multiplication and sort them into easy, medium or hard categories, then summarise what makes them fit into each category.

- Children collect examples of when they may need to multiply mentally in everyday life.

- Children collect ideas of when factor pairs are useful in other parts of mathematics.

Answers

Step 1

a	60	e	180
b	360	f	120
c	140	g	225
d	540	h	540

Step 2

	Can calculate the answer using 3×3	Cannot calculate the answer using 3×3
Can calculate the answer using 4×5	b	d, f
Cannot calculate the answer using 4×5	e, g	a, c, h

Step 3

a 540 minutes

b 600 months

c 54 000 metres (or 54 km)

d 200 cm (or 2 metres)

e 360 petals

Step 4

a $360 = 2 \times 180, 3 \times 120, 4 \times 90, 5 \times 72, 6 \times 60, 8 \times 45, 9 \times 40, 10 \times 36, 12 \times 30, 15 \times 24, 18 \times 20$.
There are 11 ways if the order does not matter.

$2 \times 2 \times 90, 2 \times 3 \times 60, 2 \times 4 \times 45, 2 \times 5 \times 36, 2 \times 6 \times 30, 2 \times 9 \times 20, 2 \times 10 \times 18, 2 \times 12 \times 15, 3 \times 3 \times 40, 3 \times 4 \times 30, 3 \times 5 \times 24, 3 \times 6 \times 20, 3 \times 8 \times 15, 3 \times 10 \times 12, 4 \times 5 \times 18, 4 \times 6 \times 15, 4 \times 9 \times 10, 5 \times 6 \times 12, 5 \times 8 \times 9, 6 \times 6 \times 10$.
There are 20 ways if the order does not matter.

b

$3 \times 6 \times 8$	3×48	18×8
$3 \times 8 \times 6$	3×48	24×6
$6 \times 3 \times 8$	6×24	18×8
$6 \times 8 \times 3$	6×24	48×3
$8 \times 3 \times 6$	8×18	24×6
$8 \times 6 \times 3$	8×18	48×3

Individual answers.

- **Multiply 2-digit and 3-digit numbers by a single-digit number using formal written layout.**
- **Solve problems involving multiplying and adding, including using the distributive law to multiply 2-digit numbers by single-digit numbers.**

Homework 13 and 14   Practice Book pp 27–30

Representations and resources
Number rods, place-value counters.

Mathematical vocabulary
Partition, digit, number sentence, multiplication, addition

Warming up
Practise identifying tens and ones in numbers using questioning: *How many tens are there in 97? How many ones?*), *How many tens are there in 256?*, etc. Following on from this, give children quick fire calculations involving multiplying by ten and multiples of ten. Use a variety of vocabulary, e.g. *Work out 10 × 23. What is the product of 30 × 6?*

Background knowledge
Arrays are a crucial model to use when multiplying 2-digit numbers by single digits and they are the first step in developing the formal written method. You begin by presenting the calculation as an array. You then draw the array as a grid. In Unit 8 you will use arrays to develop the short written method. Represent the arrays using concrete manipulatives (e.g. number rods and place-value counters) and sketches (e.g. grids). The rectangular shape is fundamental in reinforcing children's understanding of the nature of multiplication. Continue to use the bar model to represent word problems. Drawing the diagram focuses their attention on the structure of the problem and they are able to make sense of it and solve it from there. The order in which operations should be carried out is clear from a bar model and avoids 'rules' such as BIDMAS, which are better introduced as a memory aid once children have grasped the underlying concept.

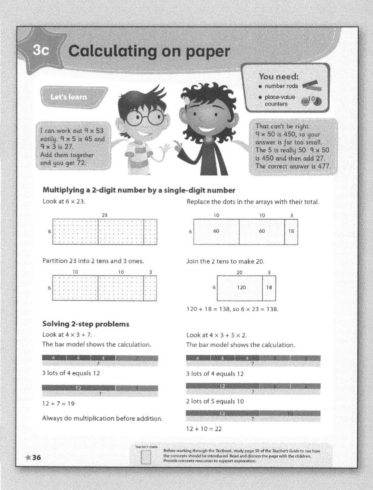

Let's learn: Modelling and teaching
Multiplying a 2-digit number by a single-digit number

- At this stage, children are likely to use a combination of the formal written method and mental calculation strategies. They will often work out the calculation mentally by jotting down interim calculations and diagrams. Look at the first diagram in the Textbook. Ask: *How could you represent this using counters?* Model the diagram using counters as a class. Ask: *How could you represent the diagram using place-value counters?* Prompt, if necessary, for the idea of a tens counter replacing ten separate counters.

- Ask children how they know that the first diagram in the Textbook shows 6 × 23. They may say that there are six rows, each with 23 dots, or that there are 23 columns, each with six dots. Look at the second diagram. Ask: *How does this relate to our model using place-value counters?* Look at the third diagram. Ask: *How does this diagram make the*

calculation easier? (Establish that splitting into tens is much easier for calculation.) Look at the final diagram. Ask: *Why is it written in this way?* (It is more efficient as there is less writing required.)

Solving 2-step problems

- Ask children to represent the bar model shown in the Textbook using number rods. Ask: *How do you know that these models show the calculation 4 × 3 + 7?* Guide children by asking questions such as: *Which part shows 4 × 3? Where is the 'add 7'?* During the discussion, sketch the bar model on the whiteboard and continue to make the connection between the visual and concrete representation.

- Ask children to create their own bar model for 3 × 5 + 8 using number rods and sketches.

Let's practise: Digging deeper

Step 1

Give children time to recall their thinking during the Let's learn section. Ask them how they could start on these questions, allowing them to discuss their responses in pairs. Ask questions such as: *How could we split up 32 to make it easier to work with?* Children should draw arrays to support their calculations. If they use an array of dots, you could prompt a more efficient strategy by commenting on how much there is to write.

Step 2

Children should draw a bar model for each calculation. The process of thinking about the diagram is helpful in prompting understanding. Encourage children to fully explain at least one of their calculations and diagrams in order to deepen understanding.

Step 3

Sorting out the information in a word problem can present challenges and, again, drawing a diagram can help. It is helpful for children to fully explain at least some examples. The money contexts are likely to be familiar to children and it is helpful to connect the same structure with the other contexts such as weight and length.

Step 4

The first task develops the idea of partitioning and that there is more than one way to partition a number. Use discussion to draw out the idea that it is simply a number bond for the larger number. Encourage children to reason about $10 + 10 + 10 + 4$ or $30 + 4$ are helpful partitions of 34 if you need to multiply 34 by another number. This reinforces earlier work on multiplying by ten and 100 and multiples of ten and 100. Children can then make up their own calculation. Encourage them to discuss in pairs. Ask questions such as: *Is this a hard or easy calculation? Why?*

The second task gives practice for multiplying and adding whilst focusing on a problem. Encourage children to notice any patterns that emerge. Children can make any length of line apart from one, two, four and seven. This becomes clear quickly, as long as children realise that once they have three, five, six, nine and 12 they can make any other number by adding a multiple of five.

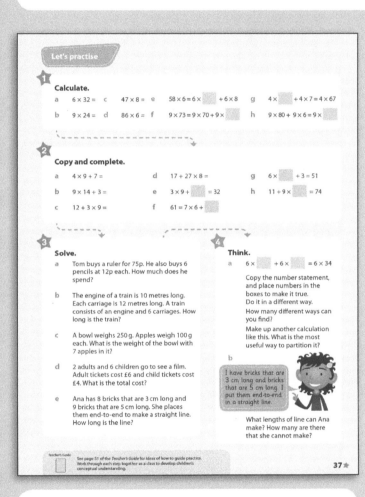

Ensuring progress

Supporting understanding

Work with children in a focus group using place-value counters to model calculations for both types of question. Ask children to explain what they need to do.

Broadening understanding

Children could make up their own examples of questions requiring these techniques. In each case they should draw a bar model and explain the relationship between the problem and the diagram.

✓ Concept mastered

Children can use the distributive law to multiply 2-digit numbers by single-digit numbers and solve problems involving multiplying and adding.

Follow-up ideas

- Draw a poster or make a presentation to show how to multiply a 2-digit number by a single-digit number.

- Use programming software to animate how you multiply a 2-digit number by a single-digit number.

- Collect ideas of contexts where you might need to multiply and add and make a collage of them.

Answers

Step 1			
a	192	e	50
b	216	f	3
c	376	g	60
d	516	h	86

Step 2			
a	43	e	5
b	129	f	19
c	39	g	8
d	233	h	7

Step 3	
a	£1.47 or 147p
b	82 m
c	950 g
d	£36
e	69 cm

Step 4	
a	Any pair of numbers that add up to 34.
b	Individual answers.

Three in a line

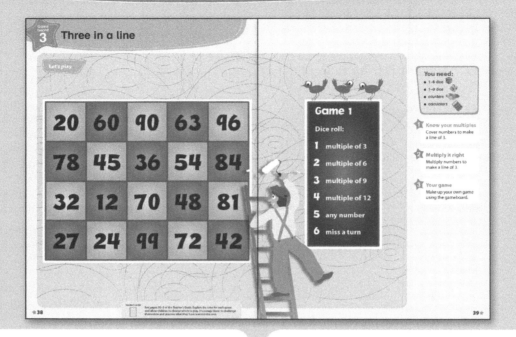

Game 1: Know your multiples

Players roll the dice and use the key to cover multiples of three, six, nine and 12. The aim is to get three counters in a line, with no gaps.

Maths focus

- Identify multiples of three, six, nine and 12

Resources

Pile of counters per player (1 colour per player), 1–6 dice (1).

How to play

This game is played in pairs. Players take it in turns to roll the dice. They look at the key to see whether they need to cover a multiple of three, six, nine or 12 with a counter. If the dice shows five, the player may cover any number with a counter. If the dice shows six, the player misses that turn. The aim of the game is to make a line of three counters. The line may be horizontal, vertical or diagonal, but there should be no gaps in the line.

Making it easier

Use a multiplication table square to aid the identification of multiples of a given number.

Making it harder

Allow straight lines that are oblique, so that each counter is a 'knight's move' from the previous one. This is two along and one up. Encourage children to think strategically, trying to prevent their opponent from making a line of three as well as aiming to make a line of three themselves.

Game 2: Multiply it right

Players roll the dice and multiply a number of their choice from the gameboard. If they get it right, they can cover that number with a counter. The aim is to get three counters in a line, with no gaps.

Maths focus

- Multiply a 2-digit number by a single-digit number

Resources

Pile of counters per player (1 colour per player), 1–9 dice (1), calculators.

How to play

This game is played in pairs. Players take it in turns to roll the dice. They then choose a number on the gameboard and multiply it by the dice number. They check their answer using a calculator – if they are correct, they can cover the number on the gameboard with a counter. The aim of the game is to get three counters in any horizontal, vertical or diagonal line; there should be no gaps in the line.

Making it easier

Let children use a multiplication square to help them.

Making it harder

Allow straight lines that are oblique, so that each counter is a 'knight's move' from the previous one. This is two along and one up. Encourage children to think strategically, trying to prevent their opponent from making a line of three as well as aiming to make a line of three themselves.

Game 3: Your game

Children should invent their own game, designing rules that use the concepts covered in the unit. Challenge children to make their game easier or harder.

Three in a line

Choose a game to play.

Game 1: Know your multiples

You need:
- pile of counters per player (1 colour per player)
- 1–6 dice

How to play
- Take turns to roll the dice.
- Look at the key to see whether you need to cover a multiple of 3, 6, 9 or 12 with your counter.
  - If you roll a 5, you can cover any number with your counter.
  - If you roll a 6, miss that turn.
- The winner is the first player to get 3 counters in a line. The line can be horizontal, vertical or diagonal, but there must be no gaps.

Game 2: Multiply it right

You need:
- pile of counters per player (1 colour per player)
- 1–9 dice
- calculator

How to play
- Take turns to roll the dice.
  - Choose a number on the gameboard and multiply it by the dice number.
  - Check your answer with a calculator. If you are correct, you can cover the number with a counter.
- The winner is the first player to get 3 counters in a line. The line can be horizontal, vertical or diagonal, but there must be no gaps.

Game 3: Your game

- Make up your own game using the gameboard.
- How can you make your game easier or harder?
- What are the rules for your game? Explain them to someone.

Please help your child by reading the instructions and playing the game together.

Assessment task 1

Running the task

In this task, children act as the teacher. Prompt children to give helpful feedback that will move Ana on in her learning by asking questions such as: *Do you think that will help Ana get it right next time? Would you find that helpful if it was written on your work?* Writing feedback such as this helps deepen learning and shows the teacher where misconceptions may be a barrier to progress.

Children will need to complete the questions in order to identify the error and give constructive feedback. Remind them that they can use place-value counters, coloured rods and/or the bar model to find the correct answers. Some children may benefit from revisiting the activities from the Let's learn section of each concept.

Ask children to explain the error using precise mathematical vocabulary before they write their feedback, e.g.:

In part a, Ana has made the ones digit six each time, instead of using six as the jump.

In part b, the error is using the associative law with subtraction. This law does not apply to subtraction or a mixture of addition and subtraction.

In part c, Ana has not multiplied the ones digit by 9.

In part d, Ana has treated the tens digit as a single digit. She hasn't spotted that it means 2 tens.

In part e, the error is in multiplying by 3 twice.

In part f, Ana has made a mistake by doing the addition before the multiplication. This may be because she has worked from left to right.

In part g, the error is in doing the subtraction before the multiplications.

Evidencing mastery

Identification of the correct answer and what the mistake was, including feedback, for each one suggests mastery.

Appropriate feedback that will help Ana understand what she did wrong and so get it right next time is further, more convincing, evidence.

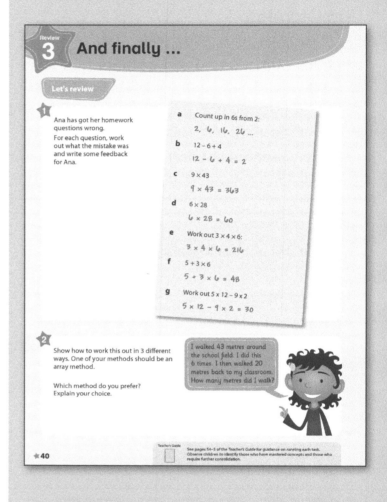

Assessment task 2

Running the task

Recap multiplication facts for six, nine and 12 by suggesting a digit and asking for facts from the six, nine and 12 multiplication tables that involve that digit, e.g. if you give 4 you could expect children to say $4 \times 6 = 24$, $6 \times 7 = 42$, $6 \times 9 = 54$, etc.

Allow children to use resources such as place-value counters and coloured rods to support solving the problem and calculating the answer. Ask: *Can you use the rods to help decide which operations to use?*

To calculate the answer children need to multiply 43 and 6. The array method is the most efficient method for this. To prompt children to use the array method, you could ask: *Can you use the place-value counters to help you work this out?* More informal methods may also be supported by the place-value counters.

Children might choose to use a mental calculation strategy. $43 \times 6 = 258$ may be calculated mentally by $40 \times 6 = 240$; adding $3 \times 6 = 18$ to make 258; then adding 20 to get a final answer of 278 metres.

For a third method prompt: *Can you think of a more unusual way of working this out?*

Evidencing mastery

Being able to offer a third method suggests mastery of calculation and correct application of the more formal method and a mental method suggest children have grasped the ideas in the unit. The explanation of which method they prefer may also contain thoughts that suggest mastery of the topic.

Assessment task 3

Running the task

Children should be familiar with a multiplication grid, but you may wish to start by showing how one is generated. Explain that the numbers at the top of the columns and at the start of the rows do not need to be in order. Children may have already deduced this from the given numbers. Children need to look at two of the given numbers in order to be certain which numbers generated a given number and which way round they go. If they start with ten, that is generated by 2×5. Five cannot go at the start of the row because it is not a factor of 18. If they place five there, you could question their reasoning or wait until they have finished, so they have the chance to correct themselves. Finally, ask children if they have checked all of their answers. Encourage children to record their decisions and justify where they have put the numbers.

Evidencing mastery

The correct answer is shown below.

×	6	5	8	9
12	72	60	96	108
3	18	15	24	27
2	12	10	16	18
4	24	20	32	36

Children may show mastery by completing this correctly unaided. It requires significant reasoning and it is essential for children to check what they have done. Those who make mistakes are likely not to have been thinking about all of the possibilities, so mastery is yet to come.

Concepts mastered

- ☑ Children can count in steps of six and nine. They can recall and use multiplication table facts for six, nine and 12.

- ☑ Children can use factor pairs and commutativity to do mental calculations involving multiplication.

- ☑ Children can use the distributive law to multiply 2-digit numbers by a single-digit and solve problems involving multiplying and adding.

Did you know?

You could discuss that the number 12 is significant in many cultures. The reasons for this are unclear, but it could be from the length of the lunar month, which gives 12 months, approximately, in a year. Another possible reason is that it has many factors, which allows it to be split into a variety of fractions.

12 links with the measures of inches and hours and these link with science.

The size of a jury varies around the world; in the UK there are 12 jurors.

Links with the world's religions are particularly vast, with the 12 tribes of Israel and many other references to 12 in The Bible. Greek and Roman mythology also feature 12 in many stories. Astrology, with the 12 signs of the Zodiac, links science and religion. Children could spend time researching where 12 is significant in different cultures.

Mathematical focus

★ Geometry: properties of shape

Prior learning

Children should already be able to:

- recognise that angles are a property of shape or a description of a turn

- identify right angles, recognise that two right angles make half a turn, three make three-quarters of a turn and four a complete turn

- identify whether angles are greater than or less than a right angle.

Key new learning

- Identify acute and obtuse angles and compare and order angles up to two right angles by size.

- Compare and classify geometric shapes, including quadrilaterals and triangles, based on their properties and sizes.

- Identify lines of symmetry in 2-D shapes presented in different orientations.

Making connections

- Angles, shapes and symmetry are not only important in mathematics but also in art and design technology. Some artists are well known for their use of lines and angles. Children could investigate an artist, e.g. the later work of Pablo Picasso or cubism generally, looking at angles and shapes. Other artists they could explore are Piet Mondrian or Wassily Kandinsky.

- Children see angles can be linked to fractions. A quarter of a circle is 90°; a third of a circle is an obtuse angle of 120°, while a sixth or an eighth of a circle gives acute angles of 60° or 45° respectively. Children may experience angles in fractions in a practical sense if they cut up a cake or a pizza to share.

- Symmetry occurs in many aspects of everyday life. Many man-made artefacts have a line of symmetry, e.g. spoons and forks, furniture, lights, screens, windows. There are examples of symmetry in architecture at every scale, from the grandeur of buildings like The White House to simple cottages. Most mosques are symmetrical. Interior décor also often involves symmetry, e.g. floor tiling, rugs and wallpaper. Children could collect examples to make a classroom display. Symmetry is also evident in nature, e.g. in most living creatures.

Unit 4 — 2-D shapes, angles and symmetry

What shapes and angles can you see in this bicycle?

What angles can you see on these origami elephants?

42

💬 Talk about

Children may already have come across the terms for different triangles (equilateral, isosceles and scalene) and angle vocabulary (acute and obtuse) but in this unit the vocabulary is defined and learnt.

Take time to discuss the words and their derivations given in each concept spread. Break them down into syllables to aid children's memory and spelling of them. You could display the words alongside the appropriate diagrams. The ability to visualise shapes from spoken or written words is important so that children can solve word problems. You can help them to become more proficient through practice using the new vocabulary in context.

Engaging and exploring

Let children look at the pictures and the accompanying questions. Encourage them to think about and discuss the mathematics that they demonstrate. Use this is an opportunity to assess children's understanding of angles, shapes and symmetry. The understanding of angles develops gradually over a number of years. Year 4 children are learning to compare angles by size and beginning to appreciate that the standard unit for measuring angles is degrees and that there are 360° in a complete turn. After this opening, discuss the photos in your chosen order.

The first photo shows a bicycle and asks about the shapes and angles that can be seen. Through discussion, children should identify different triangles and quadrilaterals. Children may know that triangles are rigid shapes which is why they are useful for building strong shapes. Draw children's attention to the different angles in the photo. Ask them to describe what

they see, e.g. there are very small angles between the spokes and larger angles within the frame. Remind children that an angle is an amount of turn. Look at bikes, scooters or other toys in the playground. Alternatively, ask children to look at their bikes or scooters at home. Ask whether they see the same or different shapes compared to the photo. Challenge them to measure some of the angles in their bikes, scooters or toys using an angle tester.

The second photo shows two origami elephants. Origami animals are made by folding paper. Children may have seen origami birds, frogs or butterflies. Here, the baby origami elephant is identical to the adult one, simply smaller in size. Reinforce that the angles are the same. Ask them to look for angles of different sizes and see if they can identify any right angles. Ask them which is the smallest angle that they can see and which is the largest angle. Find simple origami animals on the Internet. Ask children to make the animals and discuss the angles they can see.

The photo of the spider's web should encourage children to think about angles and symmetry in nature. Ask: *What can you see? Are all the angles equal? Is the shape symmetrical?* Challenge children to draw their own web. Often nature is not perfectly symmetrical. Challenge children to explore the playground and find examples of symmetry in nature. Make a poster of their findings and discuss the symmetry and angles that they can see.

This charming photo of identical giant panda twins almost has a line of symmetry. Ask children to compare the two sides of the image. Give them a mirror to confirm the similarities and differences. Most animals, including humans, have a central line of symmetry. Children can use a mirror to explore the similarity of the left and right-hand sides of faces in magazines or photos. Draw out the idea that the mirror image is identical but reversed.

The final photo shows the front of Notre Dame Cathedral in Paris, a symmetrical building. Many cathedrals, mosques and other religious buildings are symmetrical. Encourage children to look for parts of the building in the photo that are the same on each side as well as the overall symmetry, e.g. the windows. Ask children to research photos of well-known buildings and identify which have a vertical line of symmetry.

I wonder how many different angles are in this web?

What do you notice in this photo?

Can you see the symmetry in this photo?

Teacher's Guide Look at the pictures with the children and discuss the questions.
See pages 56–7 of the Teacher's Guide for key ideas to draw out.

43

Checking understanding

Children can describe the different types of triangles, most quadrilaterals and other shapes, based on their properties. They identify acute and obtuse angles and can compare and order them. They can identify lines of symmetry in 2-D shapes.

Things to think about

- How will you organise groupings to recognise strengths in children who may find numeracy challenging but have strong spatial awareness?

- How will you check that the classroom and the outside school environment are shape-rich settings?

- How can you draw out reasoning? To achieve this ask children to describe and explain their thinking.

- How will you ensure that children understand and use appropriate vocabulary?

- Which problem-solving strategies will you use to deepen understanding? The unit lends itself to using Always, sometimes, never; Another, another, another; Convince me; Peculiar, obvious, general; Silly answers and What's the same? What's different?

- **Identify acute and obtuse angles and compare and order angles up to two right angles by size.**

Homework 15 and 16   Practice Book pp 31–4   Identifying angles

Mathematical vocabulary

Acute angle, obtuse angle, right angle, degree (°)

Warming up

Practise the nine times table, then the 90 times table. Look at the relationship with the nine times table. Discuss with children how this table relates to angles.

Ask children to stand and turn through 90°, 180°, 270° and 360°. *How many degrees are there in two complete turns?* The answer is 720° (4 × 90 × 2). *Three turns?* The answer is 1080° (4 × 90 × 3).

Representations and resources

Angle measures (e.g. two geostrips joined with a paper fastener), individual whiteboards and pens, rulers, cameras.

Background knowledge

Children can already identify right angles, and that two right angles make half a turn, three right angles make three-quarters of a turn and four right angles make a complete turn. They can say whether an angle is greater or less than a right angle.

In this concept you will build on this prior knowledge, introducing the terms 'acute' (angles less than 90°) and 'obtuse' (angles greater than 90° but less than 180°). Use this vocabulary and the terms 'smaller than' and 'greater than' to compare and order angles. Angles can be viewed statically, as a property of a shape, or dynamically, as an amount of turn.

Let's learn: Modelling and teaching

Right angles

- Begin by checking children understand that an angle is an amount of turn. Draw two angles, both about 45° but with obviously different length arms. *Are these angles the same size?* Show children the misconception cartoon in the Textbook. Can children explain Ana's mistake? Demonstrate that two angles are the same using an angle measure (e.g. two geostrips joined with a paper fastener).

- Children are beginning to learn that angles are measured in degrees (°). Show them how to write the symbol as a small superscript circle and discuss the square mark, a geometry symbol that indicates a right angle. Children know that a right angle is 90°. Give each child four pieces of A4 paper and tell them to mark one corner on each with the right angle symbol. Ask them to put to marked corners together. *What angle have you made?* Identify that they have made two 90° right angles or a straight line or half a turn. Ask what angle they would make if they put three marked corners together. (Three 90° right angles are equal to 270° or three-quarters of a turn.)

Acute and obtuse angles

- The Textbook gives the definition of acute and obtuse

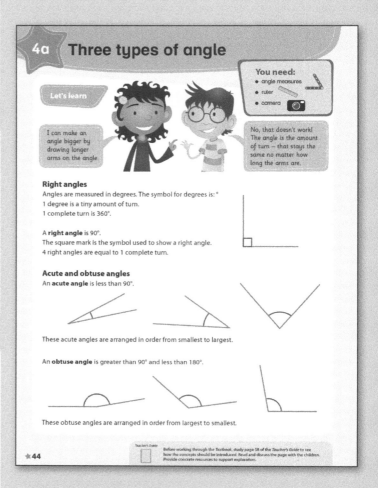

angles. Help children to remember these words by telling them that an acute angle is 'little and cute' and the larger **ob**tuse angle is '**ob**ese'.

- Give children a pair of geostrips joined by a split pin and ask them to open them to make different angles, e.g. an acute angle, a right angle, an obtuse angle, half a right angle. Reinforce that an angle is an amount of turn.

- Ask children to draw and cut out an acute and an obtuse angle. They should then pair up and work together to put the four angles in order of size. Ask them to show you where a right angle would fit in the order. They can compare their angles with the ones in the Textbook.

Let's practise: Digging deeper

Step 1

In this step, children first need to decide if an angle is a right angle, acute or obtuse. Most children will be able to do this visually but you can support children who find this challenging by giving them a right-angle tester. The next step is to order the angles by size and, again, most children will be able to do this by eye. Give an angle measure to those children who cannot do this so that they can physically compare the sizes. Encourage children to justify their order.

Step 2

Children have not yet learnt the names for the different types of triangles and quadrilaterals but they do not need to know the names in order to carry out the task. The idea is that they focus on describing the difference in the properties. Allow children to explore all properties but ensure that they focus particulary

on angles. Observe how confident children are in using the vocabulary of angles precisely.

Step 3

You could begin by asking children to make a right angle with their body. Try to ensure that all children are able to generate clear angle and line shapes individually and in pairs. They can then use a camera or tablet to photograph their angles and make a classroom display. Together, use the display to agree statements comparing the angles shown. This is a good opportunity to develop children's geometric reasoning.

Step 4

Children should draw a pentagon that fits Ana's description. If they need support, ask: *What pentagon shapes can you imagine? Would any of them fit the description? Do you think the pentagon will be symmetrical?* In the second part of the task, children can combine knowledge and imagination to draw interesting polygons. If they try to draw a triangle to fit the brief, they will discover that it is impossible.

Ensuring progress
Supporting understanding

Some children may continue to be distracted by the length of the arms of an angle, unequal arms or different orientations. If they find it challenging to decide whether an angle is acute, right or obtuse, explain that it can help to move the page around until one of the lines is horizontal.

Broadening understanding

Children who have no difficulty identifying acute, right and obtuse angles may enjoy estimating the approximate size of angles in degrees, e.g. to the nearest ten degrees. Help them to visualise half a right angle which is 45° (90° ÷ 2) and then they can think whether the angle is bigger or smaller than that. You may have children who ask you what an angle that is greater than 180° is called. Tell them that they are reflex angles and that they will learn more about them next year.

☑ **Concept mastered**

Children can identify acute and obtuse angles and compare and order them. They know that angles are measured in degrees, that a right angle is 90° and a complete turn is 360°.

Follow-up ideas

- Make an angle tester that can measure all sizes of angles. Cut two identical circles from card, preferably different colours. Mark and cut to the centre of each circle. Slide the circles together to interlock. Now the circles are interlocked, they can be turned to make different angles. Ask children to show you an angle that is less than a right angle, etc.

- Challenge children to draw a diagram to show how much pizza a family of three (four, five or six) would have if they shared a pizza equally. Ask them to tell you in each case whether the pizza slices are acute or obtuse angles.

Answers

Step 1

Acute angles: f, c, e, a

Obtuse angles: b, h, d, g

Step 2

a   2 sides the same length; one has 3 acute angles, the other has 2 acute angles and 1 obtuse angle.

b   Sides are the same length; one has 4 right angles, the other has 2 acute angles and 2 obtuse angles.

c   The triangle has two sides the same length as the sides of the square. Both shapes have a right angle. One shape is a triangle; the other is a square.

d   Sides are the same length. They both have 2 acute angles and 2 obtuse angles. The sizes of the angles are different.

Step 4

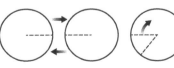

4b Triangles

- **Identify acute and obtuse angles and compare and order angles up to two right angles by size.**
- **Compare and classify geometric shapes, including quadrilaterals and triangles, based on their properties and sizes.**

Homework 17 and 18   Practice Book pp 35–6   2D Shapes   Properties of triangles

Mathematical vocabulary

Equilateral triangle, isosceles triangle, scalene triangle, polygon

Representations and resources

2-D shapes, right-angle tester, dotted paper, rulers, geoboard, rubber bands.

Warming up

Ask children to use mental methods to solve division problems such as 800 ÷ 4. The answer of 200 can be derived from 4 × 2 = 8 or 8 ÷ 4 = 2. Use examples from the six, nine and 12 times tables that children have been studying in the previous unit, e.g. 360 ÷ 6, 3600 ÷ 6.

Background knowledge

Angles are a property of shapes. This property can be used to recognise and classify the different types of triangles. Sharing the derivations of the words with children may help them to remember the challenging vocabulary. 'Isosceles' comes from the Greek and means 'equal legs'. 'Equilateral' is Latin for equal-sided. 'Scalene' means 'unequal'.

Let's learn: Modelling and teaching

Definition of a triangle

- Revisiting the definition of a triangle gives an opportunity to discuss the important terms it contains: 2-D, three and straight. '2-D' shapes have no thickness (although of course, the 2-D shapes that children handle in the classroom necessarily do). Give children a variety of 2-D triangles and talk through each part of the definition in detail. The very name 'triangle' includes the prefix for three. 'Straight' is important; it means that shapes with a curved edge, e.g. a quarter of a circle, are not triangles.

- Display some triangles and ask children to name the angles, and to look for angles that are the same size, or right angles. Explain that they are going to use the sizes of angles to classify triangles.

Types of triangles

- Draw an equilateral triangle on the board. Discuss that this triangle has three sides of equal length and three acute angles of 60°. Now ask if they can draw a different kind of triangle. Continue drawing and discussing triangles until all types have been identified. The equilateral triangle is a regular triangle. Isosceles triangles and scalene triangles may have a right angle or an obtuse angle. Use the misconception cartoon to highlight this.

- The table in the Textbook summarises the names for the different types of triangles and their properties.

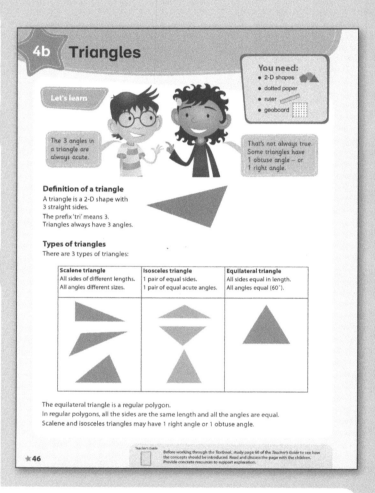

- Give groups of children a variety of 2-D triangles. Ask each group to write the table headings from the Textbook on a large piece of paper and to sort the shapes into the correct column. Ask each group to justify their sort. Compare children's responses to the table in the Textbook.

- Ask children to complete the statements 'All triangles have … ' and 'Some triangles have …'. Establish that all triangles have three sides and three angles. Some triangles have: all acute angles; one obtuse angle; one right angle; all sides equal; all angles equal; two sides equal; two angles equal; no sides equal or no angles equal.

Let's practise: Digging deeper

Step 1

Prior to the task, show children a 2-D triangle and ask them questions about it. *Does it have an obtuse angle? How many acute angles does it have?* Repeat with different triangles. Children who are less secure may appreciate using a right-angle tester. You could use the diagrams to ask children other questions about triangles.

Step 2

Make sure children read each statement carefully and discuss their ideas. They may like to test their ideas by drawing and testing different triangles.

Prompt children to use the correct vocabulary to justify their responses. Some right-angled triangles have two sides the same length – they are isosceles right-angled triangles; other isosceles triangles can have an obtuse angle. An equilateral triangle always has three equal angles. The final statement is never true. If you draw lines with two right angles from a base line they will be parallel and can never meet to form a triangle.

Step 3

In this task children are drawing triangles on a three by three dotted grid. For support, give children a geoboard and rubber bands to try out triangles on a three by three portion of the board. Encourage them to be systematic in the way that they look for the triangles. They can draw scalene right-angled triangles and isosceles triangles. Check that they do not repeat the same triangles in a different orientation. Children who complete the task quickly could investigate the more complex task of finding the different triangles that can be made on a four by four dotted grid.

Step 4

Make sure that children understand the task. Only one line is required to divide a square. Two lines are required for the pentagon. The hexagon can be divided in two different ways, each time using three lines to give four triangles, as illustrated. Approaching the task systematically, this would suggest that the heptagon will require four lines and give five triangles and this is indeed the case. Suggest that children construct a table to record the number of sides and the number of diagonals. Ask: *What do you notice?*

Ensuring progress

Supporting understanding

Give children the opportunity to handle and sort 2-D shapes into the different types of triangles. Display the types of triangles and their properties in the classroom.

Broadening understanding

In Step 4 challenge children to predict how many lines will be needed for a dodecagon (12-sided polygon) and how many triangles there will be. Ask them to explain how they know. Children who have a good understanding of angles may be able to explain why it is not possible to have two right angles in a triangle.

 Concept mastered

Children can recognise, compare and classify equilateral, isosceles and scalene triangles.

Follow-up ideas

- Use the Internet to find simple instructions to fold an equilateral triangle. Give children different-coloured paper and ask them to make equilateral triangle designs.

- Read *The Greedy Triangle* by Marilyn Burns (Scholastic) ISBN 978-0545042208. This story shows triangles and other polygons in many different forms and positions and places them in contexts that children recognise. Children could write their own triangle story.

- The number sequence 1, 3, 6, 10, 15 is the triangular number sequence. Let children play with the numbers in this sequence using concrete materials.

Answers

Step 1
a g, p **c** 2, 6

Step 2
a sometimes

b sometimes

c always

d never

Step 3
There are many possible triangles. These include 3 right-angled and 2 isosceles triangles.

Step 4
The number of triangles is equal to the number of sides minus 2.

Let's practise

1 Answer these.

a List the obtuse angles.

b Find 3 right angles.

c Identify the right-angled scalene triangles.

2 Decide.
Here are 4 cards. Decide if the statements are:
- always true   - sometimes true   - never true.
Explain your reasoning.

a A right-angled triangle has 2 sides the same length.

b An isosceles triangle has an obtuse angle.

c An equilateral triangle has 3 equal angles.

d Some triangles have 2 right angles.

3 Draw.
Look at this triangle. It has been drawn on a 3 × 3 dotted grid.

Use a 3 × 3 grid.
Draw and describe as many different triangles as you can within the 9 dots.

4 Think.
Here are 2 ways to divide a regular hexagon into triangles.

Draw regular polygons: square, pentagon, hexagon, heptagon and octagon. Divide each one into triangles.
Your lines must join 2 vertices and may not cross.
Describe the triangles. Can you spot any patterns? Explain what you discover.

See page 61 of the *Teacher's Guide* for ideas of how to guide practice. Work through each step together as a class to develop children's conceptual understanding.

47

4c Quadrilaterals

• Compare and classify geometric shapes, including quadrilaterals and triangles, based on their properties and sizes.

Homework 19 and 20   Practice Book pp 37–40   2D Shapes

Mathematical vocabulary

Parallelogram, quadrilateral, rectangle, rhombus, square

Representations and resources

Fruit and utensils for cutting (or pictures of fruit and scissors), camera, dotted paper, rulers, geoboard, rubber bands, 2-D shapes.

Warming up

Practise rounding numbers. Write a 4-digit number on the board. Ask children to round the number to the nearest ten, 100 and 1000. Repeat with different numbers. Turn the problem around by writing a multiple of 100 on the board and asking children what are the largest and smallest numbers that would give this number when rounded, e.g. *2300 has been rounded to the nearest 100*. The largest number that gives this is 2349 and the smallest number is 2250.

Repeat by writing a multiple of ten or 1000 and finding the largest and smallest numbers that round to the number.

Background knowledge

'Quadrilateral' means four-sided and just as the different types of triangles have specific names, the different quadrilaterals do too. In this concept two new ones are introduced, the parallelogram (which has two pairs of equal and parallel sides, and two pairs of equal angles) and rhombus (which has four equal sides and two pairs of equal angles). Parallelogram and rhombus are challenging words to spell. Point out to children that the first 'l' sound is a double 'l'. 'Rh' is not a common beginning in English, although it does occur in rhythm, rhino and rhubarb, etc. It is important to draw out the relationship between a square, rhombus, parallelogram and rectangle by focusing on the number of equal sides and angles.

There are other named quadrilaterals (kite and trapezium). If children mention them at this stage, tell them the names and explain that they will meet them in Unit 9.

Let's learn: Modelling and teaching

Definition of a quadrilateral

• Give children quadrilaterals drawn on paper. Ask them to write a definition for a quadrilateral and discuss their responses, picking out important words. **Four** is a vital word in the definitions; the word quadrilateral means four sides. Another important concept is **2-D**, or children may say flat. Remind them that 2-D stands for two dimensional and therefore 2-D shapes have no thickness. **Straight** is the final important word; the sides of a quadrilateral must be straight.

• Explain that some special quadrilaterals have particular properties.

Linking quadrilaterals

• Talk through the diagram in the Textbook with children. Ask them to tell you what you would have to write on the arrows to go around the diagram in the opposite direction.

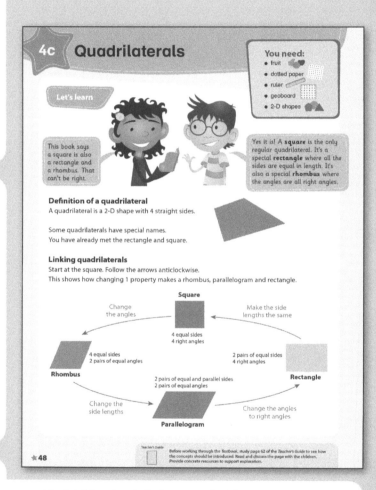

Model this using 2-D shapes and sticky notes.

• Highlight that a regular polygon has equal sides and equal angles. Ask children to identify the only regular quadrilateral. Ask why rhombuses, parallelograms and rectangles are not regular quadrilaterals. (While Rectangles have equal angles and rhombuses have equal sides, but only a square has both.)

• Show children a quadrilateral with no equal sides and no equal angles. This is an irregular quadrilateral and has no specific name. Although rectangles, parallelograms and rhombuses are irregular, they have particular properties and their own names.

• Write properties on cards, e.g. equal angles, opposite sides equal in length, and select them randomly, asking children to tell you which quadrilaterals fulfil the criterion.

Let's practise: Digging deeper

Step 1

Children should read each description carefully and then visualise the shape and draw it. They should then check again that each property fits the shape that they have drawn. Writing their own description challenges them to think clearly about properties.

Step 2

Prior to the task, show children different 2-D shapes and ask them to name them and describe what properties they used to identify each shape. Revisit Carroll diagrams and check that children understand that ~~'Quadrilateral'~~ means any shape that is not a quadrilateral. Only two polygons (square and rhombus) fit in the quadrilateral/all sides the same length section. Many different shapes can be drawn in the other sections. Use questioning to encourage children to justify their choices. Take the opportunity to reinforce the fact that a square is a special kind of rhombus.

Step 3

This task could be done with real fruit, pictures of fruit or drawings. If children use actual fruit make sure that a risk assessment is carried out, allergies considered and that they draw a plan before they begin to avoid waste. Fruits like apple, pear, mango and pineapple can be sliced and cut into different types of triangles or quadrilaterals. Add a little lemon juice to cut fruits to prevent discolouration. Take photos of the outcomes to share with other groups of children. You could extend the task by asking children to cost their design using supermarket data from the Internet.

Step 4

Children could try this investigation on a four by four section of a geoboard and use squared or dotted paper to record their findings. Encourage them to be systematic, e.g. finding 2×1, 3×1, 4×1, etc. Ask: *What size squares can be made? Are there more rectangles than squares? Can you explain why?* There are fewer parallelograms than they expect because one corner of the slanting shapes quickly 'falls off' the grid. You could ask children to explain why you cannot make a rhombus.

Let's practise

1 Draw.
Draw and name these shapes:

a My opposite sides are equal and parallel. I have no right angles.

b All my angles are right angles. My 4 sides are all the same length.

Write a similar description for another shape.

2 Classify.
Copy this Carroll diagram.
Draw 6 different shapes to fill it.
Put at least 1 shape in each section.

	All sides the same length	~~All sides the same length~~
Quadrilateral		
~~Quadrilateral~~		

3 Apply.
"I can cut different triangles from thin slices of apple."
"If I cut this banana diagonally, I can trim the slice to make a parallelogram."

4 Think.
Use a grid of 16 dots.

How many **different** squares, rectangles, rhombuses and parallelograms can you draw? Every corner of the quadrilateral must be on a dot.

Make a mathematical fruit salad. Include triangular and quadrilateral patterns and shapes.

See page 63 of the *Teacher's Guide* for ideas of how to guide practice. Work through each step together as a class to develop children's conceptual understanding.

49

Follow-up ideas

- Challenge children to design a poster of the different types of triangles and quadrilaterals, showing their properties.

- Ask four children to stand inside a long rope ring (about five metres) with the rope at waist level. Pick a quadrilateral and ask another child to instruct them how to move to make that shape. Repeat with different quadrilaterals.

- Look at cubist art, e.g. by Picasso, in which objects and people are broken up and reassembled in an abstract form often using plane shapes such as triangles and quadrilaterals. Give children the opportunity to draw their own cubist painting and challenge them to include as many different types of triangles and quadrilaterals as they can.

Ensuring progress

Supporting understanding

You could make a set of cards with shapes and a matching set of the names for children to play pairs, which will help to consolidate the vocabulary and properties. Give children additional opportunities to handle and sort 2-D shapes into the different types of triangles and quadrilaterals.

Broadening understanding

Children can take turns to describe the properties of a particular type of triangle or quadrilateral for the class to identify. Ask children to find examples of particular triangles and quadrilaterals in everyday life.

✓ Concept mastered

Children know the properties of a square, rectangle, parallelogram and rhombus and understand how the shapes are related.

Answers

Step 1

a parallelogram or rhombus   b square

Step 2

	All sides the same length	~~All sides the same length~~
Quadrilateral	square, rhombus	rectangle, parallelogram, irregular quadrilateral (kite, trapezium)
~~Quadrilateral~~	equilateral triangle, other regular polygons	isosceles or scalene triangles other irregular polygons

Step 4

Possible squares: 1×1, 2×2, 3×3

Possible rectangles: 1×2, 1×3, 2×3

4 different parallelograms

- Compare and classify geometric shapes, including quadrilaterals and triangles, based on their properties and sizes.
- Identify lines of symmetry in 2-D shapes presented in different orientations.

Homework 21 and 22   Practice Book pp 41–3   2D Shapes   What is symmetry?

Representations and resources

Construction materials, mirrors, rulers, 2-D regular shapes.

Mathematical vocabulary

Symmetry, line of symmetry, reflection, reflection symmetry, symmetrical, mirror line, diagonal

Warming up

Revise some mental multiplication strategies with children. Ask them to tell you how they can multiply by four mentally. They can double the number (× 2) and then double the answer (× 2 again). Practise this strategy by asking them to multiply numbers by four, e.g. 37, 66, 73 and 84. Ask how they can multiply by five and 20 mentally. For five, multiply by ten and then divide by two and for 20, multiply by ten and then multiply by two. Multiply the same numbers, 37, 66, 73 and 84 by five and 20. Discuss with children whether they could carry out the operations in any order.

Background knowledge

Children learnt about vertical symmetry in Year 2 and in this concept spread they investigate horizontal lines of symmetry and those in other directions. Reflection symmetry is also known as line symmetry or mirror symmetry because each half is the reflection of the other. Use symmetrical polygons in various orientations to help children identify lines of symmetry in all directions. To help children develop their awareness of symmetry you could encourage them to use construction materials to build symmetrical models, e.g. spacecraft, bridges or castles.

Let's learn: Modelling and teaching

Reflection symmetry

- Explain the definition of reflection symmetry and lines of symmetry. Then, role play the misconception cartoon. This focuses on lines of symmetry in rectangles. Ask children to cut out rectangles and squares and confirm for themselves that squares have four lines of symmetry while rectangles have only two: one horizontal and one vertical. Compare their shapes to the images of the rectangle in the Textbook.

- Explore the lines of symmetry in other quadrilaterals through cutting and folding paper shapes. Ask children what they notice about the lines of symmetry in these shapes. Children often think that parallelograms will also have two lines of symmetry whereas actually they have no lines of symmetry.

- Lines of symmetry are imaginary lines. Some children with good spatial awareness are able to 'see' them easily. Tell children that a mirror will always confirm a line of

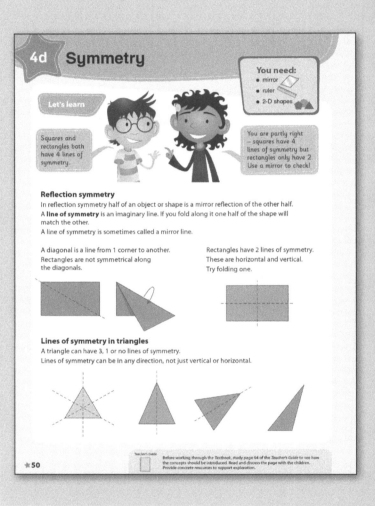

symmetry so if they are unsure they can check with a mirror until they have the confidence to 'see' them. Practise this using small mirrors and a variety of 2-D shapes, including squares, rectangles, parallelograms and rhombuses.

Lines of symmetry in triangles

- The Textbook has deliberately been designed with minimal text. The information is contained in the diagrams. Ask children to look at them and name the different types of triangles. Ask questions about them: *How many lines of symmetry does an equilateral triangle have? What type of triangle has no line of symmetry?*

- Children can cut out paper triangles and test symmetry by folding.

Let's practise: Digging deeper

Step 1

In this step, children analyse the shapes to determine whether or not each shape has symmetry and if it is symmetrical they look for all the lines of symmetry. Children should use a mirror. You could challenge children to draw another shape for each category.

Step 2

Children need to draw their own shapes in this step. Encourage them to check their diagrams with a mirror. The answers for the quadrilateral may involve types for which they have not yet learnt the names (trapezium and kite). They do not need to know the names but tell them if they ask.

Drawing pentagons is more challenging. There are a number that have one line of symmetry – think of an isosceles triangle with three sides drawn from the two equal sides. A regular pentagon has more than one line of symmetry – in fact, five.

Step 3

This practical task involves children looking for symmetrical and asymmetrical shapes in the classroom. Give children time to find as many examples as they can to complete the table. If there are sections where they cannot find examples, challenge them to think of shapes that would fit into these sections. Ask children to justify their choices referring to the shape of the objects and their properties.

Step 4

In this task children are looking for all the lines of symmetry in regular polygons. Allow them to use mirrors as a support. Use questions to draw out patterns and reasoning: *How many lines of symmetry does a square have? How many sides does a square have? How many lines of symmetry does a pentagon have? How many sides does a pentagon have? Do you think there might be a pattern? Have you noticed that sometimes the lines of symmetry go from the middle of a side to the middle of a side and sometimes they go from the middle of a side to the middle of an angle? Is there a pattern to this?*

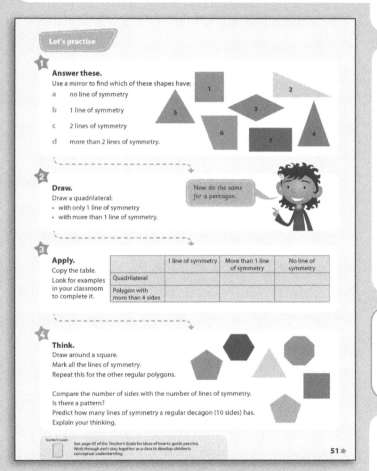

Ensuring progress

Supporting understanding

Some children find the vocabulary of shape intimidating. Work with them in a focus group to help them to grow in confidence in handling shapes and consolidate their knowledge. Remind children that lines of symmetry can be in any direction and that they can turn the page to check, and if necessary check with a mirror.

Broadening understanding

In Step 4 ask children how many lines of symmetry a polygon with n sides has, and how many a circle has. A polygon with n sides has n lines of symmetry. In a circle every line passing through the diameter is a line of symmetry and so there is an infinite number of lines of symmetry in a circle.

✓ Concept mastered

Children can identify lines of symmetry in 2-D shapes and know that lines can be in different orientations.

Answers

Step 1		
a	2, 6	c	3, 7
b	4	d	1, 5

Step 4

The number of lines of symmetry is equal to the number of sides in the polygon.

A regular decagon has 10 lines of symmetry.

Follow-up ideas

- Investigate the symmetry of upper-case letters.
- Collect wallpaper sample books and challenge children to draw lines of symmetry on the patterns.
- Give small groups a long loop of string and ask them each to hold it and stretch it out so that it has one line of symmetry. Challenge them to change the shape so that it has no lines of symmetry or two lines of symmetry. Ask them what shape they need to make for the string loop to have four lines of symmetry.
- Investigate symmetry in flags of different countries. Look for horizontal and vertical lines of symmetry, or both, or more. There are flags that fall into every category. Design a symmetrical flag. The Union Flag is not exactly symmetrical, ask children to explain why and to find out about the flag and the significance of flying it upside-down.

What's my property?

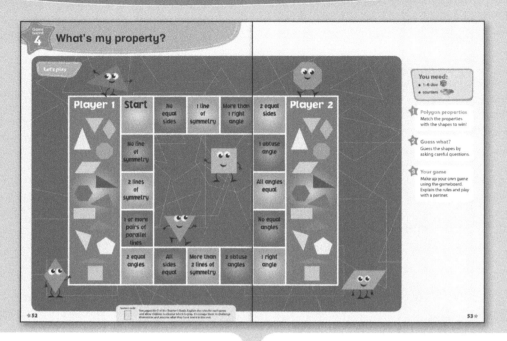

Game 1: Polygon properties

In this game of chance and skill a dice roll determines the property, then players decide where to place the counter from the possible choices.

Maths focus

- Identify different types of triangles, some quadrilaterals (rectangle, square, rhombus, parallelogram) and other geometric shapes based on their properties and sizes

Resources

15 counters per player (1 colour per player), 1–6 dice (1).

How to play

This game is for two players. Each player puts a counter on the Start square and chooses one of the sets of shapes. They take turns to roll the dice and move clockwise around the board. The property on each square they land on applies to more than one of the shapes so the player chooses which of the shapes to cover with a counter, e.g. 'all angles equal' applies to the equilateral triangle, square, pentagon, hexagon and octagon. The winner is the first player to cover all their shapes (or the player with the most shapes covered when play stops).

Making it easier

Give children a 'crib-sheet' with a list of the shapes and their properties for reference.

Making it harder

Children must correctly name the shape before they can cover it with a counter.

Game 2: Guess what?

In this game, players try to identify shapes though thoughtful questioning.

Maths focus

- Identify different types of triangles, some quadrilaterals (rectangle, square, rhombus, parallelogram) and other geometric shapes based on their properties and sizes

Resources

14 counters per player (one colour per player).

How to play

This game, for two players, is like 'Guess who' for shapes. One player chooses a shape from the shapes on the sides of the gameboard and makes a note of their choice without letting the other player see. The player guessing needs to identify the shape by asking yes/no questions; they use their counters to cover the shapes that are eliminated. So, asking the question 'Is it a triangle?' and receiving the answer 'Yes', allows them to cover up every shape that is not a triangle. Players score five points for each question asked or each incorrect guess. The winner is the person with the lower score after five rounds or within a given time limit.

Making it easier

Play the game with a smaller number of shapes.

Making it harder

Play without using counters so that players have to remember what shapes have been eliminated by their questions.

Game 3: Your game

Children should invent their own game designing rules that use the concepts covered in the unit. Challenge children to make their game easier or harder.

What's my property?

Choose a game to play.

Game 1: Polygon properties

You need:

- 15 counters per player (1 colour per player)
- 1–6 dice

How to play

- Both players place a counter on the Start square.
- Take turns to roll the dice and move clockwise around the board.
- Look at the description on the space you land on. Decide which shapes it applies to and choose 1 to cover with a counter.
- The winner is the first player to cover all their shapes.

Game 2: Guess what?

You need:

- 14 counters per player (1 colour per player)

How to play

- One player chooses a shape and makes a secret note of their choice.
- The player guessing asks a 'Yes/No' question to try to identify the shape, e.g. if you ask 'Is it a quadrilateral?' and the answer is 'No', then you can cover all the quadrilaterals with counters.
- Keep asking 'Yes/No' questions until you can guess the shape correctly.
- Score 5 points for each question or each incorrect guess.
- Swap roles and play again.
- The winner is the player with the lower score after 5 rounds or your own time limit.

Game 3: Your game

- Invent your own game using the gameboard.
- Do you need a dice to play?
- What are the rules for your game? Explain them to someone.

Please help your child by reading the instructions and playing the game together.

Assessment task 1

Resources

A4 thin card, 2 geo-strips fastened with a paper fastener.

Running the task

Before children begin the task, spend time recapping the different types of angles and their sizes. You could use a geo-strip angle tester, or an individual whiteboard, and ask them to show you, or draw, an acute angle and an obtuse angle. Next ask them to make a right angle and think about what size half a right angle would be and then to make it with the geo-strips, or draw it.

Let children make their angle testers. 135° is 90° plus 45° so children can combine these angles to make the obtuse angle. They can work on the task with a partner. Try to ensure that there are angles of different sizes in the classroom environment for children to 'find'. There may be floor patterns or tables with different angles. Right angles are everywhere so children will have no problem locating them. Discuss with children why right angles are so profuse. They produce structures that are perpendicular to horizontal surfaces so they make strong shapes. Children will spot them in doors, windows, tables, books and paper.

Watch children using their angle testers and encourage them to describe the angles numerically, e.g. as less than 45° as well as acute.

Evidencing mastery

Listen for children describing angles as acute or obtuse with clear understanding of the type of angle. If children are able to handle using the angle testers competently and complete the table with examples, they are clearly evidencing mastery in this area of mathematics.

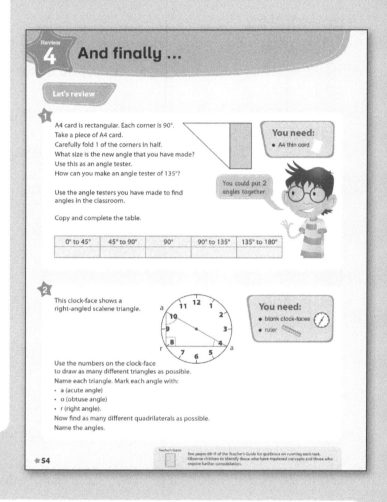

Assessment task 2

Resources

Printed clock-faces, rulers.

Running the task

You can use printed clock-faces or 12-point circles for children to record their findings. Discuss the example on the clock-face in the Textbook and check that children understand the task. Support children who draw the same shape in different orientations. Suggest that they turn the paper around or count the points in between the corners of the triangles. Children may explore the different triangles and then use fresh clock-faces to record their work more coherently. It is possible to draw all three types of triangles.

Children need to use the same strategies to check that their shapes are different when drawing quadrilaterals. They have not yet been taught the names for a kite or trapezium but can still draw them and identify the types of angles. If they ask the names for these shapes, you can tell them and explain that they will meet them in Unit 9.

Evidencing mastery

Look for children who are systematic in their approach and confidently recognise any duplicate shapes. Examples of equilateral, isosceles, scalene and right-angled triangles can be drawn. Listen for children discussing the types of triangles and identifying angles. Those showing mastery will be able to mark up the angles and name the triangles accurately. A range of quadrilaterals, e.g. square, rectangles, kites, trapeziums and irregular quadrilaterals can be drawn. Support children who are less secure by providing examples of different triangles and quadrilaterals for reference, however, note that if they need this support then they have not yet mastered this area of mathematics.

Assessment task 3

Resources

Mirrors.

Running the task

Play a game to revise identifying lines of symmetry. From a selection of triangles and quadrilaterals, pick one and ask children to stand up if it has one or more lines of symmetry. Choose a child to show the line of symmetry and ask another to name the shape. Repeat with other shapes. Read the task to check understanding. Children can work through the task independently or with a partner. You could ask children to describe the shapes and tell you the names. Support children who find the task challenging by focusing on one shape and working through each heading logically to decide where the shape fits. When you have helped in this way with a few shapes, let children continue independently.

Evidencing mastery

The first part of the task requires children to analyse the shapes according to properties. Here is the completed table for reference.

	No right angles	1 or more right angles
At least 1 line of symmetry	B, G, H	D, I, J
No line of symmetry	C, F	A, E

The second part of the task is more open-ended and asks children to think of another way to sort the shapes. Look for children who are able to design another Carroll diagram using titles such as the number of sides or the type of angles. Children who complete both parts of the task show clear evidence of mastery of this area of mathematics. Less-secure children may need support constructing their own table.

Concepts mastered

☑ Children can identify acute and obtuse angles and compare and order them. They know that angles are measured in degrees, that a right angle is 90° and a complete turn is 360°.

☑ Children can recognise, compare and classify equilateral, isosceles and scalene triangles.

☑ Children know the properties of a square, rectangle, parallelogram and rhombus and understand how the shapes are related.

☑ Children can identify lines of symmetry in 2-D shapes and know that lines can be in different orientations.

Did you know?

Symmetry comes from a Greek word meaning 'agreement in dimensions' and in everyday life the word refers to a sense of beautiful proportion and balance. Architects have long used symmetry in design and children could investigate many more buildings on the Internet, both much older (e.g. Ancient Greek) and newer. The Taj Mahal in India is a white marble mausoleum built for a Mughal emperor to house the tomb of his wife. More than three million people visit the Taj Mahal every year. The photo shows vertical symmetry and horizontal symmetry reflected in the Yamuna River. If you look at the plan from above it has four-fold symmetry. The marble is covered with beautiful intricate symmetrical designs.

The Petronas Towers in Kuala Lumpur are 452 metres high. From their opening in 1996 until 2004 they were the tallest building in the world and they are still the tallest twin buildings. The towers have a connecting 'skybridge' on the 41st and 42nd floors. The bridge is not attached but is designed to slide in and out of the towers so that it does not snap when the towers sway in the wind.

Different numbers

Mathematical focus

★ **Number: number and place value**

★ **Measurement: money, temperature, time, mass, volume/capacity**

★ **Statistics: interpret and present data**

Prior learning

Children should already be able to:

- count in multiples of 3, 4, 6, 8, 9, 50 and 100
- read and write numbers up to 1000 in numerals and words
- recognise the place value of each digit in a 3-digit number
- compare and order numbers up to 1000
- identify and represent numbers to 500 using different representations
- tell the time to the nearest minute and know that there are 60 minutes in an hour.

Key new learning

- Count in multiples of 6, 7, 9, 25 and 1000.
- Count backwards through zero to include negative numbers.
- Recognise the place value of each digit in a 4-digit number (thousands, hundreds, tens and ones).
- Order and compare numbers beyond 1000.
- Identify, represent and estimate numbers using different representations.
- Round any number to the nearest 10, 100 or 1000.
- Solve number and practical problems that involve all of the above and with increasingly large positive numbers.
- Read Roman numerals to 100 (I to C) and know that over time, the numeral system changed to include the concept of zero and place value.

Making connections

- Counting in steps underpins children's ability to recall multiplication and division facts; plenty of practice in saying the multiples in order will help embed the facts.
- Counting on and back through zero is covered in the context of temperature. Being able to read scales including negative numbers will help children read graph axes later on, and in other subjects such as science.
- Rounding numbers to the nearest 10, 100 and 1000 builds on and develops children's number sense and understanding of place value. It is useful for approximation and will support estimation.

Talk about

It is important to use precise mathematical vocabulary from the beginning. When talking about place value, including when rounding, ordering and comparing numbers, encourage children to describe the positional, multiplicative and additive properties of the numbers.

Discuss where negative numbers are seen in real life and ensure children can say these correctly out loud (e.g. minus six degrees Celsius). You could also discuss where they might see Roman numerals in real life these days.

Engaging and exploring

Ask children how many days there are in a week, two weeks, three weeks and so on. Use the picture of the calendar in the Textbook to link this to counting in steps of seven. Establish that the first three weeks in May are equivalent to 21 days. Make connections to the multiplication facts for the seven times table (e.g. $3 \times 7 = 21$) and also the corresponding division facts. Discuss the number of days in each month. You could teach children the rhyme '30 days has September, April, June and November, all the rest have 31 except February alone, which has 28 days clear and 29 in each leap year'. You could give children a copy of a diary page for a year and ask them to take their finger for a walk, e.g. start on 23rd February, count forward 14 days, back 24 hours, forward 3 weeks.

Ask children to tell you where in the world they would see penguins. Accept suggestions such as at a zoo or wildlife park, but establish that these penguins are in Antarctica. If children mention penguins that live in more temperate regions (e.g. the Galapagos penguin), explain that such penguins rely on currents bringing cold water from the Antarctic Ocean. Do children know where the Antarctic is? Use a globe to establish that it is the region around the Earth's South Pole and discuss the temperatures that would be found in Antarctica. Tell them that temperatures are usually below –20°C; the lowest ever temperature at ground level was recorded here at –89.2°C. Ask children why we call these temperatures 'sub-zero'. Ask children to imagine what that might feel like. You could also ask children to draw a number line from –20 to 20. They take their finger for a walk following your instructions, e.g. *Put your finger on five add three, take away 12*, and so on.

Look at the picture of the rugby match and ask whether children have ever been to a match (rugby or any other sport). Explore what 1000 is in terms of positional, multiplicative and additive place value. Ask children to draw a place-value grid with headings 1000, 100, 10 and 1. They place digit cards in each part and explain the elements of place value that they should have mastered in Unit 1. *Do you think there are over 1000 people watching the match?* Agree yes. You could tell them that many rugby stadiums can hold many thousands of spectators (the Allianz Park Stadium in London seats 10 000; the Twickenham Stadium, also in London, can take 82 000). Ask children where else they think more than 1000 things might be found, e.g. pebbles on a beach, cars in some multi-storey car parks.

You could take a vote of favourite sports, display the results as a frequency table and then ask children to make a pictogram or bar chart. They could choose a symbol to represent four people, or draw their scale with intervals of four; this will help them make sense of why it is useful to know their multiplication facts. Encourage them to answer questions about their representations.

Ask children to look at the picture of the clock and tell you what is different about it compared to the clocks that are usually used around the school. Write the Roman numerals for 1 to 12 (as seen on the clock), on the board and discuss how each is made. Compare IIII for four and IX for nine. Establish that IX means 'one before ten', or nine and explain that four was sometimes written IIII but more commonly as IV. Check children understand that, e.g. VI means 'one after five', or six. Can children list the Roman numerals for 13 to 20?

I wonder if there are over 1000 people watching the match?

Is there something wrong with the 4 on this clock?

Teacher's Guide Look at the pictures with the children and discuss the questions. See pages 70–1 of the Teacher's Guide for key ideas to draw out.

57

Things to think about

- How will you ask questions and give tasks that encourage reasoning when children are counting in sevens?

- What manipulatives and visual representations will you use to help conceptual understanding of place value with all children?

- How will you ensure children experience practical opportunities to link counting to time and money?

Checking understanding

You will know children have mastered these concepts when they can count fluently in steps of seven. They will be able to explain and demonstrate the properties of place value in 4-digit numbers, order and compare numbers beyond 1000 and round numbers to the nearest 10, 100 and 1000. They will understand how Roman numerals are made up and the importance of the development of zero as a place holder.

- **Count in multiples of seven.**
- **Count backwards through zero to include negative numbers.**
- **Solve number and practical problems that involve all of the above and with increasingly large positive numbers.**

Homework 23 and 24   Practice Book pp 44–6   Number Line

Representations and resources

Pendulum (three interlocking cubes on string), number line, coins or place-value counters, 1–6 dice.

Mathematical vocabulary

Multiple, zero, positive number, negative number

Warming up

Swing the pendulum from side to side. As it swings ask children to count in steps of six to 72 and back. Ask questions, e.g. *What are seven groups of six? How many sixes are there in 54?* Repeat for steps of nine and any other multiples children need to practise (e.g. three, four, five, eight).

Background knowledge

Children need to become fluent in counting in steps, and to link this counting to multiplication and division facts so that they can recall them instantly. The seven times table is perhaps the hardest to learn, so give children plenty of practice counting in sevens. They also need to be able to count backwards and forwards across zero. Negative numbers mirror positive numbers across zero. Some children may think that the negative numbers are getting larger as you move to the left along a number line. Using a vertical number line, and the context of rising and falling temperatures can help avoid or address this misconception.

Let's learn: Modelling and teaching

Counting in sevens

- Count in sevens from zero to the 12th multiple. Most children find counting in sevens quite difficult, so discuss strategies they can use to help them. Most children know their facts for the two and five times tables, so use these as a strategy for working out the sevens, e.g. $6 \times 2 = 12$ and $6 \times 5 = 30$ so $6 \times 7 = 42$. Work through examples, e.g. 9×7 and 12×7 in this way. Expect children to make jottings to help them keep track.

- Remind children of the relationship between counting in steps and multiplication facts; they know $5 \times 7 = 35$, so they also know that $7 \times 5 = 35$. Most children will use a range of strategies to help them count in sevens at first; with practice, they will be able to count fluently.

Temperature

- Remind children that negative numbers mirror positive numbers across zero. Draw a number line from –20 to 20 on the board and practise counting backwards and forwards, e.g. *Start on 7, count back 3, forward 2, back 10. Where do we finish?*

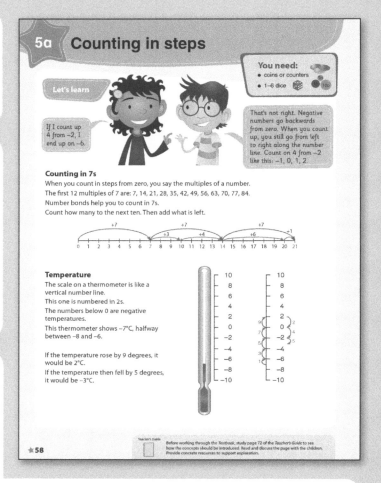

- Discuss when negative numbers can be found in the context of temperature. Ask: *Does the temperature outside ever fall below zero?* Look at the thermometer in the Textbook and ask children to tell you what temperature it shows. Discuss what happens to the liquid in the thermometer when the temperature rises and falls. Establish that if the temperature rises by nine degrees you need to count up to find the new temperature; if it then falls by five degrees, you need to count back down. Ask similar questions, e.g. *The temperature is 2°C. What will it be if gets six degrees colder? Four degrees warmer?* Record their answers using a number line.

Let's practise: Digging deeper

Step 1

This task asks children to write down the first 12 multiples of seven. They can do this by counting sevens from zero using any strategies they need to help them. They then write down different multiples of seven. They can use the lists they have written to help them, but they may also use other methods. If they know their four times table they can use the fact that $4 \times 7 = 28$ to write down the fourth multiple of seven.

Step 2

If necessary, rehearse counting forwards and backwards through zero before children begin the task. The first part asks them to work out what the temperatures listed would be if they fell by six degrees. The second part asks them to work out what the temperatures would be if they rose by five degrees.

Step 3

This tasks puts counting in sevens in a practical context. Before children begin, work though an example in which Tom earns 20p every weekend, relating counting in 20s to counting in twos. Make sure they understand that the multiples of 70 are the same as the multiples of seven, multiplied by ten. If children answer £8.40 to part d, ask: *Did Tom spend any of his savings?* You could discuss whether it is easier to count on in 70s from 290, or find the 12th multiple of 70 and subtract 60.

Step 4

This task gives children practice in counting on and back and links this to addition and subtraction. Before they begin, discuss when a subtraction can give a negative result. If you have five sweets, it is impossible to take away six; in contexts such as temperature, however, negative answers are possible. During the task, children roll two dice and count on and back from the first number to make two new numbers. They write the matching number statements. You might want to tell children to roll the two dice a particular number of times, e.g. ten. They could pool their answers with a partner's to help them reason about their results. They should realise that they can make any number between −5 and 12, although some are 'easier' to make than others because there are several different ways of making them.

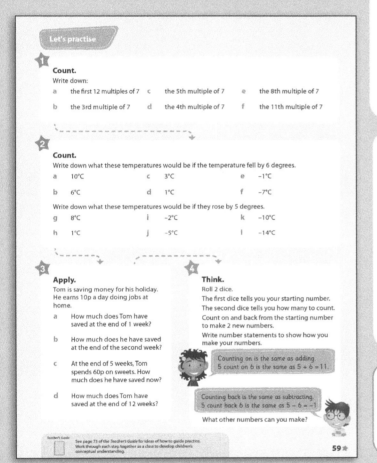

Ensuring progress

Supporting understanding

Some children will benefit from having a horizontal or vertical number line from −20 to 20 to support them in Step 2. For Step 3, they could use 10p coins or place-value counters to model the situation.

Broadening understanding

In Step 2 you could ask children to find the new temperatures if they fell and rose by a variety of degrees. You could extend Step 4 by asking children to repeat the task, so that the first dice gives a negative number. What number can they make now? (−12 to 5).

✓ Concept mastered

Children can count fluently in multiples of seven and count forwards and backwards through zero, including negative numbers.

Follow-up ideas

- Children could make up their own questions involving weeks for each other to solve (e.g. Ana goes swimming for one hour every day. How many hours does she swim in four weeks?)

- Children could make a game based on what they found out in Step 4. They draw a four by four grid and in each space write a number between −5 and 12 (or −12 and 12). They take turns to roll a pair of dice and count on or back from the first number to make a new number (deciding whether the starting number is positive or negative, if appropriate). If the number they make is on the grid, they cover it with a coloured counter. The aim is to get four counters in their colour in a row, horizontally, vertically or diagonally, before their partner.

Answers

Step 1

a   7, 14, 21, 28, 35, 42, 49, 56, 63, 70, 77, 84

b	21	e	56
c	35	f	77
d	28		

Step 2

a	4°C	e	−7°C
b	0°C	f	−13°C
c	−3°C	g	13°C
d	−5°C	h	6°C
i	3°C	k	−5°C
j	0°C	l	−9°C

Step 3

a   70p

b   140p or £1.40

c   290p or £2.90

d   780p or £7.80

Step 4

Numbers from −5 to 12 can be made.

Rounding, ordering and comparing

- Recognise the place value of each digit in a 4-digit number (thousands, hundreds, tens, and ones).
- Order and compare numbers beyond 1000.
- Identify, represent and estimate numbers using different representations.
- Round any number to the nearest 10, 100 or 1000.
- Solve number and practical problems that involve all of the above and with increasingly large positive numbers.

Homework 25 and 26   Practice Book pp 47–51   Comparing 4-digit numbers

Representations and resources

Clocks with movable hands, individual whiteboards and pens, place-value grids, digit cards, Base 10 apparatus, coins.

Mathematical vocabulary

Place value, positional, multiplicative, order, additive, greater than, less than, equal to, round

Warming up

Give each child a clock and ask them to show you different minutes past times, e.g. 23 minutes past eight, 48 minutes past three. Ask them to write the digital time for each on their whiteboard and then to tell you how many minutes to the next hour, e.g. 37 minutes to nine and 12 minutes to four. Ask them to find the difference between times that they find and to record their answers in hours and minutes.

Background knowledge

A conceptual understanding of place value underpins ordering, comparing and rounding numbers. It is important to continue to revise and refer to the positional, multiplicative and additive aspects of place value. Each part of a 4-digit number has a position and a value, e.g. in 3498, the 3 represents three lots of one thousand and hence its true value is 3000; repeating this for each digit gives the additive statement 3000 + 400 + 90 + 8 = 3498.

Let's learn: Modelling and teaching
Rounding

- Ask children to make a 4-digit number, using place-value grids and digit cards, and explain its positional, multiplicative and additive place value to a partner. They round their number to the nearest 10, 100 and 1000. This is useful when estimating answers.

- Discuss the number lines in the Textbook. Ask children to explain how to round 4628 to the nearest 10, 100 and 1000. Emphasise that one 4-digit number can be rounded in three different ways. Ask children to make up some 4-digit numbers and draw number lines. They position their number on their number lines and write it rounded to 10, 100 and 1000. Repeat several times. If a number is in the middle of the line, round up.

Ordering and comparing

- Ask children to look at the images of the Base 10 apparatus in the Textbook. Which is the greater number, and how do they know? Agree that 1346 is greater because it has

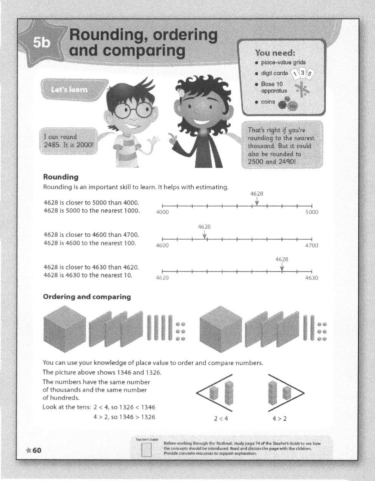

two more tens. Emphasise that place value is important for ordering and comparing numbers. We can look at each digit in each number in turn (starting from the left) and compare the first one that is different. Remind children what the symbols < and > mean. Ask them to make number statements using these.

- Ask children how they can make 1346 and 1326 equal. Agree that they could add 20 to 1326 or subtract 20 from 1346. Ask them to write the matching number statements (e.g. 1346 − 20 = 1326 and 1346 = 1326 + 20). Write five 4-digit numbers on the board where the hundreds differ. Ask children to order them from greatest to least, then choose pairs of numbers and compare them using the symbols < and >. Finally, they write number statements to show how to make them equal.

Let's practise: Digging deeper

Step 1

This task asks children to round numbers to the nearest 10, 100 and 1000. Before they begin, you might want to discuss what to do with numbers such as 1345; check children remember that, when rounding to the nearest ten, numbers with a ones digit of five or more are rounded up. They should draw an appropriate number line for each number to prove their thinking is correct. You may need to work with a group of children to ensure they draw the appropriate number lines.

Step 2

Before children begin the task, write pairs of numbers on the board for them to write on their whiteboards using the symbols < and >. For each, discuss how they know, with reference to place value.

Step 3

The first part of the task is to make the amounts using the fewest coins. Rehearse this first by writing amounts of money on the board and asking children to discuss with a partner the coins to use. The task then asks children to choose pairs and work out what they could add to one and subtract from the other to make them equal. Ask children what they notice. Draw out the idea that the amount being added and subtracted is the same.

Step 4

This task asks children to use the < and > symbols and four numbers to make the partially complete statement correct. There are several ways to do this: they need to find all of them. Encourage them to be systematic, using an ordered way of working, e.g. they could make the first number 366 and the second 324 and then 342. They could then make the first number 362 and the second 364 and then 346, and so on.

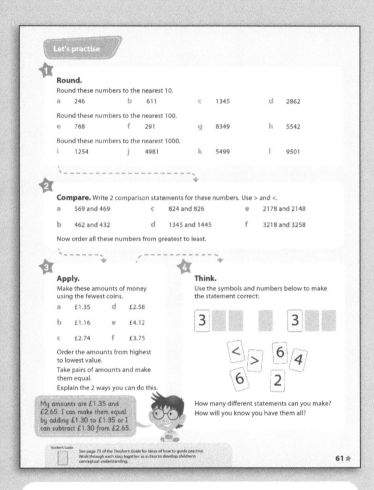

Let's practise

1 Round.

Round these numbers to the nearest 10.

a 246   b 611   c 1345   d 2862

Round these numbers to the nearest 100.

e 768   f 291   g 8349   h 5542

Round these numbers to the nearest 1000.

i 1254   j 4981   k 5499   l 9501

2 Compare. Write 2 comparison statements for these numbers. Use > and <.

a 569 and 469   c 824 and 826   e 2178 and 2148

b 462 and 432   d 1345 and 1445   f 3218 and 3258

Now order all these numbers from greatest to least.

3 Apply.

Make these amounts of money using the fewest coins.

a £1.35   d £2.58

b £1.16   e £4.12

c £2.74   f £3.75

Order the amounts from highest to lowest value.

Take pairs of amounts and make them equal.

Explain the 2 ways you can do this.

My amounts are £1.35 and £2.65. I can make them equal by adding £1.30 to £1.35 or I can subtract £1.30 from £2.65.

4 Think.

Use the symbols and numbers below to make the statement correct:

3 ▢▢ ▢ 3 ▢▢

< > 6 4

6 2

How many different statements can you make? How will you know you have them all?

See page 75 of the Teacher's Guide for ideas of how to guide practice. Work through each step together as a class to develop children's conceptual understanding.

61

Ensuring progress

Supporting understanding

If at any time (e.g. for Step 1) children would benefit from using manipulatives, such as Base 10 apparatus, make these available. If they forget which way round the < and > symbols need to be arranged, point them back to the model in the Textbook and ask them to draw these in their books as a reminder.

Broadening understanding

You could extend the task in Step 1 so that once children have compared the numbers, they work out what needs adding and subtracting to make them equal. In Step 3, you could ask children to make higher amounts of money, for example £6.87, £8.16, to compare and make equal.

 Concept mastered

Children can explain and demonstrate how to round numbers to the nearest 10, 100 and 1000. They can explain and demonstrate using their own examples how to order and compare numbers beyond 1000 using the < and > symbols.

Follow-up ideas

- Children collect items and measure their masses on scales. They order these from lightest to heaviest, pick pairs to compare using the < and > symbols and then work out what to add and subtract to make them equal.

- Children fill bottles with different volumes of water, then measure these and record in millilitres and litres and millilitres. They round these amounts to the nearest 10 ml, 100 ml and litre.

- Children use digit cards to make 4-digit numbers. They make six then round them to the nearest 10, 100 and 1000. They then order them from least to greatest. They take pairs of amounts to compare using < and > and work out what to add and subtract to make the pairs equal.

Answers

Step 1

a	250	g	8300
b	610	h	5500
c	1350	i	1000
d	2860	j	5000
e	800	k	5000
f	300	l	10000

Step 2

a 569 > 469, 469 < 569

b 462 > 432, 432 < 462

c 824 < 826, 826 > 824

d 1345 < 1445, 1445 > 1345

e 2178 > 2148, 2148 < 2178

f 3218 < 3258, 3258 > 3218

Greatest to least: 3258, 3218, 2178, 2148, 1445, 1345, 826, 824, 569, 469, 462, 432

Step 3

a £1, 20p, 10p, 5p

b £1, 10p, 5p, 1p

c £2, 50p, 20p, 2p, 2p

d £2, 50p, 5p, 2p, 1p

e £2, £2, 10p, 2p

f £2, £1, 50p, 20p, 5p

Highest to lowest: £4.12, £3.75, £2.74, £2.58, £1.35, £1.16

Step 4

366 > 324, 366 > 342, 362 < 364, 362 > 346, 326 < 364, 326 < 346

These statements can then be rearranged to give another six.

• **Read Roman numerals to 100 (I to C) and know that over time, the numeral system changed to include the concept of zero and place value.**

Homework 27 and 28   Practice Book pp 52–3

Mathematical vocabulary

Place value, positional, multiplicative, order, additive, Roman numerals

Representations and resources

Pendulum (three interlocking cubes on string), Base 10 apparatus, paper plates, card, scissors, paper fasteners, blank clock faces, number lines.

Warming up

Rehearse counting in steps of different sizes. Focus on six, seven and nine. Swing the pendulum from side to side and ask children to count in steps of one of these from zero to the 12th multiple and then back to zero. At times stop and ask children to say the multiplication statement and its commutative statement, e.g. nine multiplied by six equals 54, six multiplied by nine equals 54. Include division statements.

Background knowledge

The guidance from the National Curriculum suggests that Roman numerals should be put in their historical context so children understand that there have been different ways to write whole numbers and that the important concepts of zero and place value were introduced over a period of time. Roman numerals were invented as the Romans needed a system to easily price different goods and services. They began as notches on tally sticks; over time, some changed to other symbols, e.g. V (representing a hand) means five; IV means one before five, or four. Roman numbers were widely used throughout the Roman Empire in everyday life. Following the fall of the Roman Empire, numerals continued to be used throughout Europe up until the 1600s.

Let's learn: Modelling and teaching
Roman numerals to 100

• Introduce Roman numerals using the Background knowledge section, then discuss the cartoon. Agree that five tens is 50 and that XXXXX is a possible way of writing 50 in Roman numerals. Discuss why the Romans might have used other symbols for higher numbers. Ask children to look at the table in the Textbook and talk about the different symbols and what they represent. Point out that there was no symbol for zero.

• Discuss how to read and write Roman numerals, using the examples in the Textbook. Give children Base 10 apparatus and ask them to make different 2-digit numbers and write them using the equivalent Roman numerals. Then give children some numbers between one and 100 to convert to Roman numerals, and vice versa. Stress that, e.g. XL means '10 before 50' and LXX means '20 after 50'. Discuss the fact that, for multiples of ten, we just use the Roman numeral for ten the appropriate number of times, e.g. 30 is XXX. Explain that the Romans did not use zero as a place

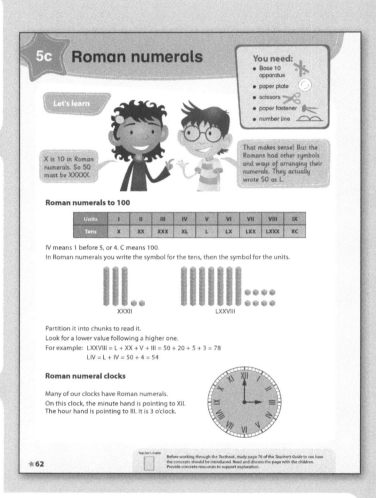

holder, and that place holders were developed in other number systems such as the one we use today.

Roman numeral clocks

• Ask children to tell you where they have seen clocks with Roman numerals. A famous one is the clock on the tower of the Houses of Parliament that houses the bell called Big Ben. If possible show them a picture of it.

• Ask children to look at the clock in the Textbook. Can they tell you what the Roman numerals are in our number system? You could give them paper plates, card, scissors and paper fasteners and ask them to make their own Roman clock. Ask them to show you times such as 10 o'clock, 35 minutes past 1. They could also write the times in different ways and find time intervals.

Let's practise: Digging deeper
Step 1

Before children begin the task, ask them to write Roman numerals for one, five, ten, 50 and 100 from memory. Challenge them to complete the task without using the table in the Textbook, but allow them to look if they need to. Children then make up some numbers of their own to write as Roman numbers, again without reference to the Textbook, if possible.

Step 2

This task asks children to convert Roman numerals to our numbers. Remind them to partition each number into separate chunks. Each chunk can then be converted separately, and then recombined to give the whole number. Children then use the table in the Textbook to make up their own Roman numerals to convert to our numbers. Encourage children to work in pairs, each challenging the other to write the correct number.

Step 3

Children need to draw Roman numeral clock faces for this task. Some children may benefit from being given pre-drawn clocks. They draw the times given and then write these in two other ways: these should be digital and minutes to the next hour. They then choose two clocks and find the difference in time between them. Encourage children to use a number line and to count on from the earlier time to the later one.

Step 4

This task asks children to find the Roman number between 1 and 100 that uses the most letters. They are likely to need the table in their Textbooks to do this. Encourage them to explain to a partner how they found the longest. The second part of the question asks them to find the smallest and largest Roman number using all the symbols I, V, X and L just once. Again, let them use the table in their Textbooks to help them.

Let's practise

1 Write.
Write these numbers using Roman numerals.

| a | 32 | c | 59 | e | 94 | g | 13 |
| b | 18 | d | 75 | f | 46 | h | 41 |

Write down some numbers of your own. Show them in Roman numerals.

2 Write.
Write these Roman numerals as the numbers we use today.

| a | XIV | c | XLII | e | LXXVI | g | XXIV |
| b | XXVII | d | LXII | f | XCIX | h | XCV |

Use the table in the Textbook to make up some more Roman numbers. Then write them in our numbers.

3 Draw.
Draw 6 clock faces that look like this.

Draw these times on them.
Write the times in 2 other ways by each clock.

a	10 minutes past 9	d	52 minutes past 8
b	40 minutes past 4	e	37 minutes past 11
c	23 minutes past 6	f	18 minutes past 2

Choose pairs of times that you have drawn. Find the time differences between them.

4 Think.

a Find the Roman number between 1 and 100 that uses the most letters. Write it down in Roman numerals and in our numbers.

b Use the Roman numerals I, V, X and L. Find the smallest Roman number you can make using each numeral once.

Now find the biggest!

Teacher's Guide: See page 77 of the Teacher's Guide for ideas on how to guide practice. Work through each step together as a class to develop children's conceptual understanding.

63

Follow-up ideas

- Ask children to find out where Roman numerals are still used today. They could research this on the Internet.

- Ask children to make Roman numerals to give to a partner to convert to our numbers. They could then write our numbers for a partner to convert to Roman numerals.

- Children make a pairs game. They write on separate cards our numbers and the Roman equivalent. When they have a set of about 20, they place them face down on the table. They take it in turns to pick two. If they have a match they keep the pair, if not they return them face down and keep trying.

Ensuring progress
Supporting understanding

In Step 1, provide Base 10 apparatus so that children can make the numbers first. They can use the apparatus to identify the number of tens and match this with the correct Roman numeral. They can then do the same for the ones, before combining the symbols to make the Roman number.

Broadening understanding

If appropriate, introduce the symbols for 200 to 900 and challenge children to include 3-digit numbers with one (or more) in the hundreds position for the final parts of Steps 1 and 2. Discuss examples such as 106 (CVI), to further illustrate the fact that the Romans didn't use zero as a place holder. In Step 4, children could make the smallest and largest Roman number possible using I, V, X, L and C.

✓ Concept mastered

Children can read and write any number up to 100 in Roman numerals from memory and explain how they did this.

Answers

Step 1

a	XXXII	e	XCIV
b	XVIII	f	XLVI
c	LIX	g	XIII
d	LXXV	h	XLI

Step 2

a	14	e	76
b	27	f	99
c	42	g	24
d	62	h	95

Step 3

a 9:10, 50 minutes to 10

b 4:40, 20 minutes to 5

c 6:23, 37 minutes to 7

d 8:52, 8 minutes to 9

e 11:37, 23 minutes to 12

f 2:18, 42 minutes to 3

Step 4

LXXXVIII = 88

XLIV = 44

LXVI = 66

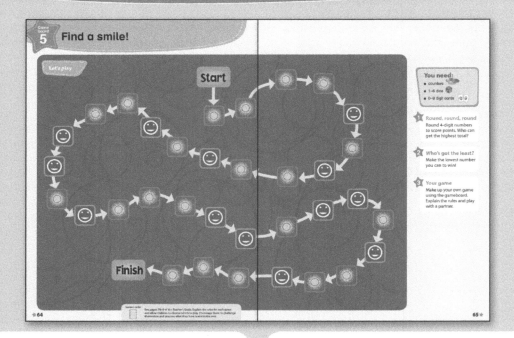

Game 1: Round, round, round

This game gives children practice in rounding numbers to 10, 100 and 1000. It can be played as a game of pure chance (children make their 4-digit numbers using the cards in the order they take them) or as a game of chance and strategy (children make the highest number they can with their four cards, leading to a higher score). If appropriate, you could not specify how they should make their numbers and see if they realise that the order in which they use the digit cards to make their number makes a difference.

Maths focus

- Round any number to the nearest 10, 100 or 1000

Resources

1 counter per player (1 colour per player), 1–6 dice (1), 0–9 digit cards (two sets).

How to play

This game should be played in pairs. Players shuffle the two sets of digit cards together and place them face down on the table. They place their counters on Start. They take it in turns to roll the dice and move their counter that number of spaces. If they land on a sun, they do nothing. If they land on a smiley face, they take four digit cards and make a 4-digit number. They round their number to the nearest 10, 100 and 1000 and tell their partner what these are. The number rounded to the nearest 1000 is their score. They return the digit cards to the pack, and play continues like this until both players land on Finish. The winner is the player with the higher total score.

Making it easier

Children could pick three digit cards and make a 3-digit number which they round to the nearest 10 and 100.

Making it harder

Children add the three rounded numbers each time to make their score. As play continues, they keep a running total for their scores.

Game 2: Who's got the least?

This game tests children's understanding of place value in 4-digit numbers and gives them practice in comparing numbers.

Maths focus

- Order and compare numbers beyond 1000

Resources

1 counter per player (1 colour per player), 1–6 dice (1), 0–9 digit cards (2 sets).

How to play

This game should be played in pairs. Players shuffle the two sets of digit cards together and place them face down on the table. They place their counters on Start. They take it in turns to roll the dice and move their counter that number of spaces. If they land on a sun they do nothing. If they land on a smiley face both players take four digit cards and make the lowest 4-digit number they can. They compare their numbers, finding out which is the greater and which is the least. The child that makes the lower number scores a point. Play continues until both players reach Finish. The winner is the player with the most points.

Making it easier

Children could pick three digit cards and make 3-digit numbers to compare.

Making it harder

When children compare their numbers, ask them to find the difference between them. The player who has the lowest number wins the difference in points.

Game 3: Your game

Children should invent their own game, designing rules that use the concepts covered in the unit. Challenge children to make their game easier or harder.

Unit 5 — Find a smile!

Choose a game to play.

Game 1: Round, round, round

You need:
- 1 counter per player (1 colour per player)
- 1–6 dice
- 0–9 digit cards (2 sets)

How to play
- Shuffle the digit cards and place them face down in a pile. Each player places a counter on Start.
- Take turns to roll the dice. Move your counter that number of spaces.
- If you land on a sun, do nothing.
- If you land on a smiley face, take 4 digit cards and make a 4-digit number.
  - ▶ Round your number to the nearest 10, 100 and 1000.
  - ▶ The number rounded to the nearest 1000 is your score. Write this down.
  - ▶ Return the digit cards to the pack.
- Continue until you both reach Finish. The winner is the player with the higher total score.

Game 2: Who's got the least?

You need:
- 1 counter per player (1 colour per player)
- 1–6 dice
- 0–9 digit cards (2 sets)

How to play
- Start the game in the same way as for Game 1.
- If you land on a sun, do nothing.
- If you land on a smiley face, both of you take 4 digit cards.
  - ▶ Make the lowest 4-digit number you can with the cards.
  - ▶ Compare your number with your partner's. The player who made the lower number scores a point.
  - ▶ Return the digit cards to the pack.
- Continue until you both reach Finish. The winner is the player with the most points.

Game 3: Your game

- Make up your own game using the gameboard.
- Can you think of something you could do if you land on a sun?
- What are the rules for your game? Explain them to someone.

Please help your child by reading the instructions and playing the game together.

Unit

Unit 5 — And finally ...

Assessment task 1

Running the task

Before children begin the task, recap what multiples are. Agree that they are numbers that occur when counting from zero in steps of different sizes. Together count in multiples of seven from zero to the 12th multiple and back again. Ask children to count from 14 backwards in steps of seven below zero. Ask them what they notice. Agree that the multiples they say below zero mirror the positive numbers on the other side of zero.

The task asks children to write down the first 12 multiples of seven. They then use this information and relate it to the days of the week. They need to use the facts that they have written to work out how many days there are in different numbers of weeks. Encourage them to use what they know, e.g. they know the tenth and fifth multiples of seven, so can work out 15 weeks by adding the two together, for 20 they double the tenth multiple and so on. You might wish to rehearse similar examples before children tackle the task independently. Encourage children to draw a number line to help them keep track of their thinking, as required. Ensure that they explain their strategies for finding these numbers of days either in writing or verbally to you, so that you can assess their understanding.

The second part of the task involves negative numbers. Children are asked to count back in sevens to numbers from a given number that will end at a number below zero. They then need to work out the starting number from a given number of multiples of seven.

Evidencing mastery

If children can fluently count in multiples of seven, and count forwards and backwards through zero, including negative numbers, they are evidencing mastery.

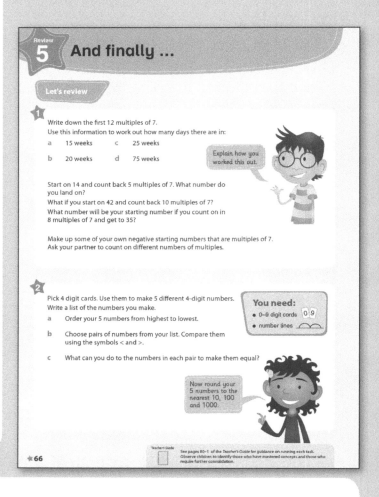

Assessment task 2

Resources

0–9 digit cards, Base 10 apparatus, number lines.

Running the task

Before children begin the task, remind them that an understanding of place value will help them become fluent in rounding, ordering and comparing numbers. You may also need to recap the positional, multiplicative and additive aspects of place value. Write some 4-digit numbers on the board that have the same digits in the thousands, hundreds and ones positions and different digits in the tens position (e.g. 4256, 4276, 4226). Ask children to explain how to order these from least to greatest. Write the symbols for 'is greater than' and 'is less than' on the board. Invite children to write a 4-digit number on each side and to explain how they know they are correct. Discuss how these can be made equal, emphasising that you can add the same number to the lower that you subtract from the higher.

The task asks children to pick four digit cards and use them to generate five different 4-digit numbers. Encourage them to write these down as they make them in a list. At least two

of the five numbers will have the same digit in one of the four positions, so children will need to look carefully at the thousands, hundreds and tens digits when ordering and comparing them. Observe children to check they work through the positions from left to right and ask questions to highlight and correct any errors, e.g. *How many hundreds are there in 2314? In 2413? Is 300 and something larger or smaller than 400?*

If children struggle, they might benefit from making the numbers using Base 10 apparatus, which will help them visualise which number is larger. You could also consider working with some children in an intervention group, focusing on 2- and then 3-digit numbers. The task also asks children to round their five numbers to the nearest 10, 100 and 1000; allow them to use number lines for this, and expect them to be able to explain their reasoning.

Evidencing mastery

If children can demonstrate how to round, order and compare numbers, and explain their thinking with reference to place value, they are evidencing mastery.

Concepts mastered

☑ Children can count fluently in multiples of seven and count forwards and backwards through zero, including negative numbers.

☑ Children can explain and demonstrate how to round numbers to the nearest 10, 100 and 1000. They can explain and demonstrate using their own examples how to order and compare numbers beyond 1000 using the < and > symbols.

☑ Children can read and write any number up to 100 in Roman numerals from memory and explain how they did this.

Assessment task 3

Running the task

Before children begin the task, remind them that the Romans partitioned their numbers into hundreds, tens and ones just like we do. Recap the letters they used to make numbers up to and including 100. You might like to call out different 2-digit numbers for them to write using Roman numerals and discuss how they work, especially the numerals for four, nine, 40 and 90. Similarly, you could draw some numbers using Roman numerals for them to convert to our numbers.

The task asks children to write different numbers as Roman numerals and then to convert Roman numbers to our numbers. Reasoning and memory are both important factors here. If children struggle, you could allow them to use the table in the Textbook (5c – Roman numerals) to help them, but bear in mind that these children have not yet mastered this requirement of the National Curriculum and will require further practice. Conversely, if children complete the task with ease, you could challenge them to make some numbers beyond 100, which exceeds the Year 4 requirement.

Evidencing mastery

Children who can remember without prompts and explain and demonstrate how to change our numbers to Roman numerals and vice versa are evidencing mastery.

Did you know?

Roman numerals appear to have started out as notches on tally sticks. Written accounts are contradictory, but it appears that Λ or V represented a hand and was used for five because we have five fingers. Similarly, X represented ten because if you link the fingers of two hands you get a shape that looks like an X, or because X is like two Vs, one upside down. Used as tally marks, the first Roman numerals would have produced numbers like this (for 22): IIIIΛIIIIXIIIIΛIIIIXII. This was unmanageable for larger numbers, and so the system we are familiar with today evolved, with, e.g. XX representing 20; other letters were introduced for specific numbers, such as L for 50.

We still use Roman numerals in many places. The medal in the Textbook shows 'XIII' indicating that the Winter Olympic Games, held in Lake Placid, New York, were the 13th since games began in 1924. Roman numerals are also used in almost all cases for the copyright date on films and television programs. They frequently appear on the preliminary pages of books, before the main page numbering; here the numerals are usually lower case letters (e.g. i, iv, xi). They are also often used for names, in particular kings and queens (e.g. Queen Elizabeth II) and Popes (e.g. Pope Francis I), but also when naming eldest sons where successive generations have the same first name.

Applying addition and subtraction

Mathematical focus

★ **Number: addition and subtraction**

★ **Measurement: distance, time, money**

★ **Statistics: interpret and present data, solve problems**

Prior learning

Children should already be able to:

- add and subtract numbers mentally using knowledge of place value and related facts

- recognise the place value of each digit in a 4-digit number (thousands, hundreds, tens, and ones)

- add and subtract numbers with up to 3 digits using the formal written method and becoming more confident with numbers with 4 digits

- find 10, 100 and 1000 more or less than a given number.

Key new learning

- Add and subtract numbers with up to four digits using the formal written methods of columnar addition and subtraction where appropriate.

- Estimate and use inverse operations to check answers to a calculation.

- Solve addition and subtraction two-step problems in contexts, deciding which operations and methods to use and why.

- Convert between different units of measure (e.g. kilometre to metre; hour to minute).

- Read, write and convert time between analogue and digital 12- and 24-hour clocks.

- Interpret and present discrete and continuous data using appropriate graphical methods, including bar charts and time graphs.

- Solve comparison, sum and difference problems using information presented in bar charts,pictograms, tables and other graphs.

- Estimate, compare and calculate using different measures, including money in pounds and pence.

Making connections

- Children use place value to help convert between different units of measure and use methods of calculation to add and subtract measurements.

- Finding sums and difference can be linked to to statistics, including presenting and interpreting data related to science investigations and geography work.

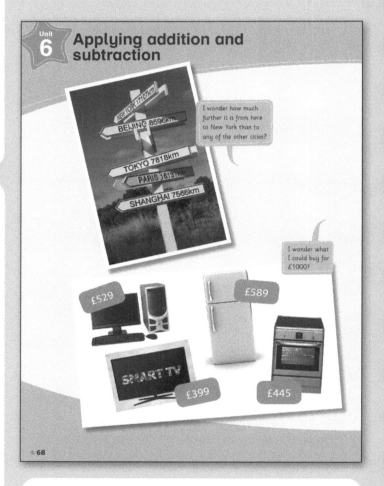

Talk about

It is important to use precise mathematical vocabulary from the beginning so children can talk confidently about the measures they are using and how the units of measurement relate to each other, e.g. kilo means 'thousand' so a kilometre is 1000 metres. In Year 4, children continue to secure the vocabulary related to time and convert between units to help them solve problems, e.g. from hours to minutes; minutes to seconds; years to months and weeks to days.

Engaging and exploring

Discuss why the road sign shows the distances in kilometres and not metres. Think about some lengths that should be measured in metres rather than kilometres. Look at the distances to the different cities shown on the sign post and discuss the possible position of the sign, e.g. how do we know that the sign is not in the United Kingdom or in Australia? Children may find it interesting to locate the different cities on a world map.

Consider the question and discuss the operation needed to find the answers. Children should recognise these as 'difference' calculations and model the concept using a bar representation. They can adopt a strategy of counting, e.g. from Paris 16131 km to Beijing 8596 km using bonds to 100 or 1000 to support the calculation or use a formal written method of subtraction. Explore differences between other cities or order them from the shortest to longest distance using knowledge of place value.

Discuss the prices of the items and the approximate prices to the nearest £100. Look at the question posed and the language used. Ask: *What operation will we need to use?* The question asks what can be bought for £1000 so addition will be useful here. The problem can be represented using the bar model. Ask: *How will the rounded prices help you with your calculations?* Establish that we can use the rounded prices to help us make an estimate.

Ask children to choose a calculation method of their choice for the additions, e.g. £529 + £445, but apply a mental method when making an estimate using the calculation £500 + £400, drawing on number bonds to 10 and relating this to 1000. The actual cost will be a little more than £900 because of rounding £445 and £529 down.

Talk about the different units of time and how these relate to each other. Perhaps discuss the length of some familiar television programmes or films, representing these in hours and then in minutes. Relate counting in steps of 60 minutes to counting in steps of six and using place value to help us. Perhaps pose some questions as children count, e.g. *60, 120; how many lots of 60 minutes is that? So how many lots of one hour is that?* Return to the original question and the recording time of five hours. Use the count to confirm that this is five steps of 60, or ten times more than five steps of six. Return to some of the familiar TV programmes you were discussing earlier and challenge children to find out the length of storage time left when one of the programmes is recorded. Look at the number line as a model for calculating time.

Ask children to talk about the time graph and some of the things they notice or know about it. They should refer to the scale and look at the changes in the height of the line as the time elapses. The scale goes up in steps of 500, but the graph shows unlabelled intervals of 250. They should apply knowledge of halves to find this. The time is given using the 12 hour notation, quickly ask children to convert the times to the 24 hour notation and explain their answers.

Discuss the change in height of the line and why this may have occurred. Discuss the number of visitors at the aquarium at different points in the afternoon, including times that are between labelled points, e.g. 2:30 p.m.

Return to how to solve the question. Again, children should recognise this as a 'difference' problem and apply an appropriate mental method, e.g. counting on. They should also notice that the point shown for 2 p.m. is 3 squares higher than at 1 p.m. which is equal to 1000 (2 squares) + 250 (1 square). Select a topic that children have studied in science (e.g. habitats or states of matter) and set them the task of recording their own data, creating a graph and interpreting it.

Things to think about

- How will you model and encourage the use of precise mathematical vocabulary when explaining thinking and reasoning? How will you share the language requirements with other adults before the start of a lesson or sequence of lessons?

- Can you make connections with measurement and statistics so that children recognise a purpose for applying methods of calculation? How will you ensure that children continue to develop mental methods even after a written method has been introduced?

- Can you encourage use of manipulatives and visual representations to help all children to continue to develop their conceptual understanding?

Checking understanding

You will know children have mastered these concepts when they can solve addition and subtraction problems in different contexts with more confidence, appropriately choosing and using number facts, understanding of place value and counting and mental and written methods. They can explain their decision making and justify their solutions.

- Add and subtract numbers with up to four digits using the formal written methods of columnar addition and subtraction where appropriate.
- Estimate and use inverse operations to check answers to a calculation.
- Solve addition and subtraction two-step problems in contexts, deciding which operations and methods to use and why.
- Convert between different units of measure (for example, kilometre to metre; hour to minute).
- Read, write and convert time between analogue and digital 12- and 24-hour clocks.
- Solve problems involving converting from hours to minutes; minutes to seconds; years to months; weeks to days.

Homework 29 and 30   Practice Book pp 54–8

Representations and resources

Base 10 apparatus, place-value counters, bar model, number rods, number line, analogue and digital clocks.

Mathematical vocabulary

Addition, subtraction, total, difference, distance, metre, kilometre, duration, hour, minute, analogue, digital

Warming up

Rehearse partitioning 3-digit and 4-digit numbers in different ways, e.g. 4682 = 4000 + 600 + 80 + 2 or 4000 + 500 + 70 + 12, etc. Give children several numbers and ask them to write as many equivalent statements as they can in 2 minutes. Partitioning in this way supports decomposition in subtraction and also converting metres to kilometres and metres.

Background knowledge

In Year 3 children use written methods when adding and subtracting 3- or 4-digit numbers that are not multiples of 10, 100 or 1000 and not single digits. However, mental strategies can still be an efficient choice, e.g. 4375 – 3998 is best solved using the 'difference' model or by rounding. Calculating durations in time can be connected to finding the difference. Number lines are useful to support this.

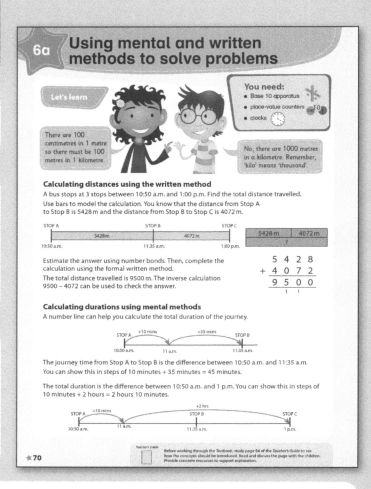

Let's learn: Modelling and teaching

Calculating distances using the written method

- Look at the bus journey representation in the Textbook. Ask children to explain why this is a useful representation. Elicit that the bars show how the parts relate to the whole journey. Discuss the different parts and labels. To find the total we must add the two distances. Both are given in metres.

- Ask children to use place value to describe each number. Can they now explain why a formal written method would be useful when finding the total distance? Stress that a mental method should be used to make an estimate.

- Model the formal written method using Base 10 apparatus or place-value counters. Focus on the use of number bonds. Use the inverse calculation to check the answer.

- Look and use the relationship between metres and kilometres. Use partitioning to show 9500 m as 9000 m + 500 m to establish that the distance is equivalent to 9 km 500 m or $9\frac{1}{2}$ km or 9.5 km.

Calculating durations using mental methods

- Model the first calculation on the number line with children showing the equivalent jumps on an analogue clock. Focus on using number bonds to count up to the next hour.

- Discuss why a formal method can not be used here (an hour would need to be exchanged and it has the value of 60 minutes and not 100 minutes).

- Ask children what is the same and what is different about the number line showing the total duration of the journey from Stop A to Stop C. Use the clocks to model.

Let's practise: Digging deeper

Step 1

Children should use rounding and mental methods to help make useful estimates. Encourage them to explain their choice to use a mental or written method. Listen for children who recognise when they can add or subtract a multiple or near multiple of a hundred. They should identify and apply the inverse calculation to check answers. Children also draw on conversion to help write 1275 m as 1 km 275 m.

Step 2

Focus on the different ways that the times are displayed. Children should use the number line to check whether times are in the morning or afternoon. You could extend the task by asking them to make up word problems for each calculation.

Step 3

Children should calculate the durations of different lessons, sessions, breaks, etc. They can record their findings in their own way but they should write times in hours and minutes and in minutes only. They can make up word problems to go with their findings and give to a partner to solve, e.g. 'The afternoon lessons start at 1:15 p.m. and we go home at 3:25 p.m. How long does our school afternoon last?'

Step 4

Children find pairs of distances that total 5 km 250 m.

Each pair of possible values must be given in metres so children will need to convert the total distance to 5250 m. Encourage them to find examples that can be solved using mental methods and those that require a written method. They could use Base 10 apparatus to support their investigation and explore patterns.

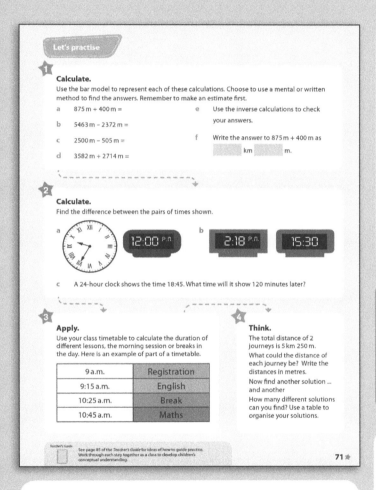

Ensuring progress

Supporting understanding

Work with children in a focus group. Use Base 10 apparatus to model written methods and mental calculations (adding and subtracting multiples of 100 or 1000). For Step 4, you could give them some pairs of possible solutions to check first and then use the manipulatives to help them make any corrections.

Broadening understanding

For Step 4, you can add a further criterion that children also need to suit. Once they have come up with a set of solutions, you could then reveal that the two distances have a difference of less than 1 km or are both multiples of 50 m, for instance. They must then check to see which of their original solutions are still possible and suggest some further examples.

✓ Concept mastered

Children can explain when it is better to use a mental or written method, but recognise that mental methods should be used for estimates and for calculating durations of time. They draw on the relationships between kilometres and metres and hours and minutes to convert measurements as required.

Follow-up ideas

- Explore simple bus and train timetables, discussing the use of 24-hour notation and why this is used. Children can make up different problems for others to solve that require calculation of intervals of time or use intervals, e.g. *Ali arrives at the library at 13:30 and stays for 1 hour 45 minutes. What time did he leave the library?*

- Explore distances between different locations in the local area using kilometres and metres. Convert between metres and kilometres so children become fluent when expressing measurements using either unit. Calculate some total distances as routes are planned around the area requiring them to add or subtract to find differences in distance to locations from a point, e.g. the school.

Answers

Step 1

a 1275 m

b 3091 m

c 1995 m

d 6296 m

e 1275 m – 400 m;
   3091 m + 2372 m;
   1995 m + 505 m;
   6296 m – 2714 m

f 1 km 275 m

Step 2

a 2 hours 25 minutes

b 1 hour 12 minutes

c 20:45

Step 3

Children's own investigations, e.g. *English starts at 9:15am and ends at 10:25am.* Children use the number line and/or a clock face to calculate the duration as 1 hour 10 minutes.

Step 4

Children's own set of solutions in a table, e.g.:

Distance 1	Distance 2	Total
5000 m	250 m	5250 m
4900 m	350 m	5250 m
3900 m	1350 m	5250 m
3925 m	1325 m	5250 m

- Solve addition and subtraction two-step problems in contexts, deciding which operations and methods to use and why.
- Interpret and present discrete and continuous data using appropriate graphical methods, including bar charts and time graphs.
- Solve comparison, sum and difference problems using information presented in bar charts, pictograms, tables and other graphs.

Homework 31 and 32   Practice Book pp 59–63

Representations and resources
Bar model, number rods, place-value grid, bar chart, squared paper, rulers.

Mathematical vocabulary
Addition, subtraction, sum, total, altogether, difference, scale, interval, more than, less than

Warming up
Challenge children to complete the diagram in as many ways as they can. This will allow for children to draw on their multiplication facts and place value, perhaps extending beyond 12 × 100. Reinforce the inverse relationship between multiplication and division.

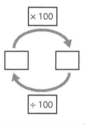

× 100

÷ 100

Background knowledge
A bar chart shows discrete data with values that are counted. It is a visual representation that can be used to find totals or compare data. Children have represented and interpreted data in bar charts and pictograms using a variety of simple scales. In Year 4 they use a greater range of scales. This relates to counting in steps of a constant size. Link bar charts to the bar model: both are used to find sum or differences, make comparisons and make sense of a particular problem or set of data.

Let's learn: Modelling and teaching
Sums and differences
- Use the misconception cartoon in the Textbook to explain the term 'sum'.

- Look at the bar models in the Textbook. Ask children to represent them using number rods. Discuss how each model relates to the calculation and how the unknown value is represented each time. Ask children to make up a story to go with each calculation, e.g. *Alfie has £1200 and Sally has £900. How much more money does Alfie have?*

- Explore the different mental methods suggested in the Textbook, looking carefully at related facts and place value. Explain that the strategy '10 and a bit' is also applied to the calculation 600 + 450 by relating it to the number bond 6 + 4 = 10. Use a place-value grid to show the related fact 60 + 40 = 100 and 600 + 400 +1000.

- Use a place-value grid to confirm that the answer to 1200 – 900 is one hundred times larger than the answer

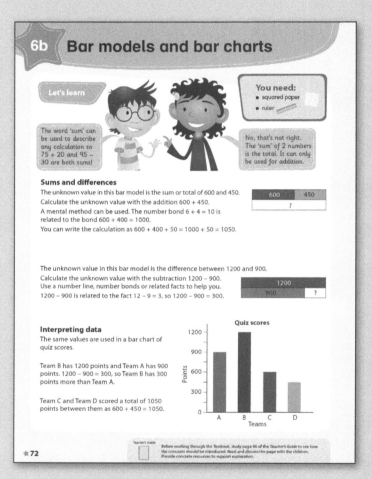

to the calculation 12 – 9. Elicit that the minuend and subtrahend are also one hundred times larger.

Interpreting data
- The bars now represent points score in a quiz and are shown in a bar chart. Ask children to model the bar chart using number rods. Encourage children to relate the previous calculation 1200 – 900 to finding the difference between the scores of Team B and Team A. Explore the scale on the bar chart and link this to counting in steps of three and place value.

- The total score for Team C and D is the same calculation 600 + 450 as explored previously. Ensure that children are secure that the bar 450 is positioned on the scale halfway between 300 and 600.

Let's practise: Digging deeper

Step 1

Encourage children to look for related facts or '10 and a bit'. Model d requires a two-step calculation. Children should decide whether to add 300 + 450 first and then subtract this from 1350 or perform two subtractions as 1350 – 450 – 300.

Step 2

Children use the bar chart to answer sum and difference questions. They should apply a mental method each time as all numbers involved are multiples of 50 and 100. For part d, they find the total number of points scored in the quiz. Encourage them to think about totals they already know.

Step 3

Children should use the value of the bars shown in Step 1 and the same scale as the 'Quiz' bar chart to draw a bar chart of their own. Check for good practice such as using a ruler to draw the axes and bars accurately and leaving an equal space between each bar. Children also make up two different questions about the chart for others to answer. Ask children: *Do you think the question is hard or easy? Why?*

Step 4

Children investigate sums and differences based on the bar chart from Step 3. Encourage them to consider mental methods and explain their choices.

Children can then choose two other characters, e.g. Oli and Tom and, again, find the total water used and find a range of differences. This task further supports solving problems with two-steps.

Ensuring progress

Supporting understanding

Work with children in a focus group to make bar charts using number rods or strips of paper. Use the same scale, i.e. labels of 300, or return to a scale with intervals of 50 but labelled every 100. Encourage children to write the values on the bars so that they do not always have to return to the scale to make comparisons.

Broadening understanding

Explore using different scales to draw the science investigation bar chart in Step 3. How would each value be represented if intervals of 200 are used? Children should also reason about unhelpful scales to use and why, e.g. scale with intervals of 10 because the bar chart would need to be too large or intervals of 500 where 450 would be trickier to show. Consider representing the same information in a pictogram.

Concept mastered

Children can explain how bar models relate to their addition and subtraction calculations.

They represent and interpret data represented on a bar chart and can answer and pose questions that involve finding sums and differences.

Let's practise

1 Calculate.
Work out the unknown value each time. Write the calculations that you use to help you.

a 900 | 750 | ?

c 1350 | 450 | ?

b 1500 | 1050 | ?

d 1350 | 300 | 450 | ?

2 Answer these.
Use the bar chart to answer these calculations.

a How many more points did Team A score than Team D?

b How many points did Team B and Team C score altogether?

c Which 2 teams scored a difference of 600 points?

d How many points were scored in the quiz in total?

3 Draw.

Mia	Tom	Oli	Eva	Ana
750 ml	1500 ml	1050 ml	300 ml	1350 ml

The table shows the amount of water used by each child for their science investigations.

a Draw a bar chart to show this information. Use the same scale as the Quiz score bar chart.

b Make up 2 questions to go with the bar chart. Swap your questions with a partner. Answer their questions.

4 Think.
Use the table and bar chart from Step 3 to answer these.

a Mia and Eva calculated the amount of water they used together. They then compared their total amount of water with the amount used by another child. How many differences can you find?

b Now pick another 2 children and find the total water used. Compare the total with the amount used by another child. How many differences can you find this time?

Teacher's Guide See page 87 of the Teacher's Guide for ideas of how to guide practice. Work through each step together as a class to develop children's conceptual understanding.

73

Follow-up ideas

- Further explore the time graph in the unit opener and compare the scale used here with the one used in this spread. Make up some more difference problems and look at durations of time when there were more or fewer than a certain number of visitors at the aquarium, e.g. *For how many minutes were there 750 or more visitors at the aquarium?*

- Pose a question that children should answer by collecting data or presenting information, e.g. *Which lesson is the longest in the school day?* They should decide which data to collect or how they can find out the information and decide how it should be represented. Encourage children to explore different scales and make up questions about it.

Answers

Step 1

a $900 + 750 = 1650$

b $1500 - 1050 = 450$

c $1350 + 450 = 1800$

d $1350 - 300 - 450 = 600$ or $300 + 450 = 750$ and $1350 - 750 = 600$

Step 2

a 450

b 1800

c B and C

d 3150

Step 3

Bar chart with labels, title etc. and intervals of 150.

Data shown for each of children as given in the table

Mia	Tom	Oli	Eva	Ana
750 ml	1500 ml	1050 ml	300 ml	1350 ml

Step 4

a Mia + Eva is
750 ml + 300 ml = 1050 ml

Differences are
1500 ml – 1050 ml = 450 ml
when comparing with Tom

1050 ml – 1050 ml = 0 ml
when comparing with Oli

1350 ml – 1050 ml = 300 ml
when comparing with Ana

b Children's own investigation, e.g. total of Tom and Eva is
1500 ml + 300 ml = 1800 ml and then making comparisons with the water used by other children to find differences.

- **Add and subtract numbers with up to four digits using the formal written methods of columnar addition and subtraction where appropriate.**
- **Estimate and use inverse operations to check answers to a calculation.**
- **Solve addition and subtraction two-step problems in contexts, deciding which operations and methods to use and why.**
- **Estimate, compare and calculate using different measures, including money in pounds and pence.**

Homework 33 and 34   Practice Book
pp 64–5

Representations and resources

Place-value grids, Gattegno charts, Base 10 apparatus, weighing scales, bar model, number rods, sticky notes.

Mathematical vocabulary

Add, subtract, sum, total, difference, pound, pence, kilogram, gram, convert, equivalent

Warming up

Rehearse number bonds of 100 and 1000, focusing on the relationship between, e.g. 3 and 7, 30 and 70, 300 and 700. Begin by giving children random numbers from 0 to 10. Children respond with the bond to 10 and then multiply by 10 to give the bond to 100 and then by 10 again to give the bond to 1000. They should explain their decisions as they go.

Background knowledge

In Year 4, children are introduced to decimal numbers with up to two places and relate this to measurement such as money. Although money is shown in pound notation with two decimal places, children will mainly carry out calculations in pence until they have developed conceptual understanding of decimals in Unit 7. This is also true for working with mass in this unit. Use a place-value grid to model converting units of measurement and relate this to multiplying and dividing by 100 or 1000.

Let's learn: Modelling and teaching

Different measures

- Discuss what children know about money and mass, the units they have used and the relationship between them. Use the place-value grid in the Textbook to identify that when converting kilograms to grams, the digit 1 is multiplied by 1000. Rehearse multiplying other single-digit numbers by 1000 using place-value grids and Gattegno charts.

- Discuss the mistake that Ana has made. Link this to the conversions you have been doing from kilograms to grams. Discuss the other calculation errors that are shown in the Textbook, including those in pounds and pence. Look at converting one of the values in each calculation so that the units of measurement are the same.

Word problems

- Introduce the word problem in the Textbook. Ask children to guide you as you describe the problem using the bar model. Suggest that converting may help in this

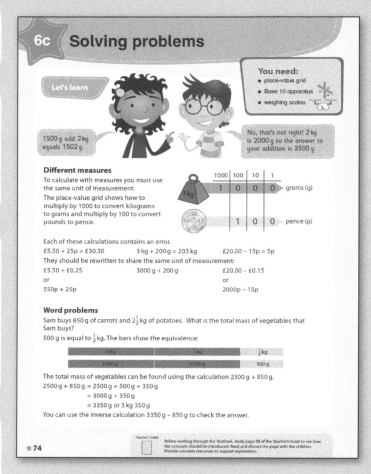

calculation. Ask children to identify which operation is needed to find the total mass of vegetables that Sam buys. How do they know?

- Use the bar model in the Textbook to explore the equivalence between $2\frac{1}{2}$ kg and 2500 g, noting that the bars are of equal length and have the same value. Relate $\frac{1}{2}$ kg to half of 1000 or the related fact, half of 10.

- Consider the calculation 2500 g + 850 g and agree that a mental method can be used as both numbers are multiples of 10 or 100. Discuss a useful estimate. Discuss mental strategies, e.g. using sequencing to become 2500 g + 800 g + 50 g or as 2500 g + 500 g + 350 g to help cross the thousands boundary. Check the answer against the estimate and by using the inverse subtraction.

Let's practise: Digging deeper

Step 1

Children should decide how to convert the values, but guide them towards converting to grams and pence so that calculations can be carried out using whole numbers. Ensure that children convert answers in pence back to pounds and pence. All numbers have been chosen so that a mental method is the most appropriate. Observe whether all children use a mental calculation strategy. If they use a written method, ask: *Why have you used this method? Can you think of a mental calculation strategy that might be more efficient?*

Step 2

Children solve the problems by converting all masses to grams and calculating using the written method. They should represent the problems using the bar model. They could then choose to represent the calculations using Base 10 apparatus to support their workings. They should also

use their knowledge of rounding and place value to make useful estimates. Children also write inverse calculations to check answers.

Step 3

Encourage children to weigh items that are heavier than 1 kg as well as some that are less than 1 kg. They should also use the language of mass to make comparisons (i.e. heavier and lighter). The children make up word problems using the masses recorded and represent them using bar models. They should solve each other's problems, carrying out the calculations in grams. They should decide whether to use a mental or written method and make an estimate first.

Step 4

This is a 'magic square' style problem. Encourage the children to calculate in pence. It would be useful to write the amounts on sticky notes so the values can be move around the grid as required. Children should draw on number bonds to 10 and 100 to help them make decisions.

Let's practise

1 Answer these.

Remember to think about the units and make an estimate first.

a   £10.50 + 235p =
c   £12.75 − £4.00 + 50p =
e   99p more than £4.99 =

b   5 kg − 750 g =
d   925 g less than 2½ kg =

Write an inverse calculation to check each of your answers.

2 Calculate.

Use a formal written method to solve these using grams.

a   The mass a plant pot filled with soil is 3 kg 450 g. Fred plants bulbs that weigh a total of 1362 g. What is the total mass now?

b   The mass of Mia's cat is 5 kg 929 g. Tom has a smaller cat. It has a mass of 2385 g. How much heavier is Mia's cat?

c   Write an inverse calculation to check each of your answers.

Remember to estimate each time and use Base 10 apparatus to represent your calculations.

3 Measure.

Weigh a set of different items in the classroom.

Record the masses of each in kilograms and in grams.

Choose 2 masses at a time and calculate their sum and their difference in grams.

Make up your own word problems using the masses for a friend to solve. Draw a bar model to represent your problem each time.

4 Think.

Place the different values of money in the grid so the total of each row is £30 and the total of each column is £20.

£12.45	£11.72	755p
828p	£10.73	927p

See page 89 of the Teacher's Guide for ideas of how to guide practice. Work through each step together as a class to develop children's conceptual understanding.

75 ★

Ensuring progress
Supporting understanding

You could work with a group of children as part of a problem solving team for Step 4, discussing starting points and modelling reasoning. You could simplify the task slightly so children only look at the columns. Use Base 10 apparatus to support calculations and the place-value grid to multiply the pounds value of each amount by 100, rather than representing the amount as a decimal.

Broadening understanding

Look at a range of other problems that require converting units of measurement. Include examples involving length and capacity so that children recognise that we apply the same approach when working with other areas of measurement. Children could make up their own word problems that do and do not require conversions for their friends to solve.

✓ Concept mastered

Children can explain the choices they make to use a mental or written method of addition and subtraction. They make useful estimates using knowledge of place value and rounding, and recognise how the inverse operation can be carried out to check the accuracy of an answer.

Follow-up ideas

- Use the results from the practical activity and represent the different masses using a bar chart. Masses should be plotted in grams and children should make decisions about an appropriate scale. Children could write and solve a range of one-step and two-step problems and calculations using the information shown.

- Use catalogues or the Internet to add and subtract amounts of money. Perhaps compare the total cost of buying three or four items from different supermarkets. Apply mental and written methods and aspects of multiplicative reasoning as several items of the same price or duplicate items are purchased.

Answers

Step 1

a   1285p or £12.85

b   4250 g or 4 kg 250 g

c   925p or £9.25

d   1575 g or 1 kg 575 g

e   598p or £5.98

Step 2

a   6165 g   b   2063 g

c   3544 g

d   6165 g − 2740 g;
2063 g + 1362 g;
3544 g + 2385 g

Step 3

Children's own investigation, e.g. weigh items and select two 1235 g and 436 g.

Find the total mass by adding 1235 g and 436 g. Find the difference by subtracting 436 g from 1235 g.

Step 4

Children complete the grid, e.g.:

£12.45	£9.27	£8.28
£7.55	£10.73	£11.72

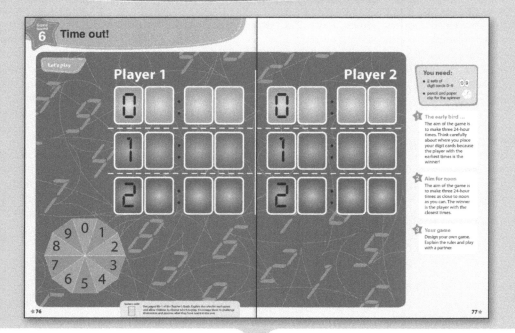

Game 1: The early bird ...

The aim is to make three 24-hour times.

Children should apply knowledge of the 24-hour clock notation and reason about the position of digits to achieve an earlier time than their partner.

Maths focus

- Time and calculating durations

Resources

0–9 digit cards (two sets), pencil and paperclip for the spinner.

How to play

Players take turns to spin the spinner and decide where the digit could be placed to start making three different times. Once a digit has been placed it cannot be moved. When the players' boards are filled, each pair of times is compared to find which is the earliest. A point is scored for the earliest time but no points are scored for times that are the same.

A bonus point is awarded for a time that is **more** than 3 hours earlier, e.g. Player 1 has 09:32 and Player 2 has 05:58. The difference can be calculated using a number line. Player 2 receives 2 points for this: one for having the earlier time and another for it being more than 3 hours earlier.

The winner of the game is the player with the most points.

Making it easier

Players can play in pairs to discuss where best to place the digit each time. The board could be adapted so the game involves the 12-hour clock and then children can focus more on calculating the interval between two times.

Making it harder

Play the game without the spinner. Two sets of 0–9 digit cards are shuffled together and laid face down in a pile. Players take turns to take a card from the pile and decide where to place it. There are only two cards of each digit in the pile and they don't know who will pick them!

Game 2: Aim for noon

The aim is to make three times as close to noon as you can. The winner is the player with the closest times.

Children apply knowledge of the 24-hour clock notation and reason about the position of digits to achieve times that are as close to noon as possible.

Maths focus

- Time and calculating durations

Resources

0–9 digit cards (two sets), pencil and paperclip for the spinner.

How to play

Players follow the same rules for Game 1, but this time they place digits to make different times that are as close to noon as possible. At the end of the game, each pair of times is compared and the closest time to noon scores a point. No points for times that are the same. The winner of the game is the player with the most points.

Making it easier

Adapt the game to use the 12-hour clock and then children can focus on calculating the interval between their time and noon. Players can also play in pairs to discuss strategies and work together to calculate the time interval.

Making it harder

Play the game without the spinner. Two sets of 0–9 digit cards are shuffled together and laid face down in a pile. Players take turns to take a card from the pile and decide where to place it. There are only two cards of each digit in the pile and they don't know who will pick them!

Game 3: Your game

Children should invent their own game designing rules that use the concepts covered in the unit. Challenge children to make their game easier or harder.

Time out!

Choose a game to play.

Game 1: The early bird …

You need:
- 2 sets of 0–9 digit cards
- pencil and paper clip for the spinner

How to play
- Place the pencil tip through the paperclip onto the centre of the spinner.
- Take it in turns to spin the spinner and think carefully about where to place the digit on your playing board.
- When all spaces are filled compare the times. A point is scored for earliest time but no points are scored for times that are the same.
- Get a bonus point if your time is **more** than 3 hours earlier than your partner's time.
- The winner of the game is the player with the most points.

Game 2: Aim for noon

You need:
- 2 sets of 0–9 digit cards
- pencil and paper clip for the spinner

How to play
- The aim of the game is to make three 24-hour times that are closer to noon than your partner's times.
- Place the pencil tip through the paperclip onto the centre of the spinner.
- Take it in turns to spin the spinner and think carefully about where to place the digit on your playing board.
- When all spaces are filled, work out which time in each pair is closest to noon to score a point. No points are scored for times that are the same.
- The winner of the game is the player with the most points.

Game 3: Your game

- You could use rules that are similar to 'Aim for noon' but make the game 'Aim for midnight'.
- You could change the rules of 'The early bird …' games so that players score points for the later time not the earlier time.
- You could mix the games so that a player tries to get the earliest time on the top row, the latest time on the bottom row and the time closed to noon on the middle row.

Please help your child by reading the instructions and playing the game together.

And finally …

Assessment task 1

Resources

Clock, Base 10 apparatus.

Running the task

You may wish to run this task with a small group of children or in pairs so that they can discuss the mathematics involved and reason about the most appropriate strategies. The task is set in a word problem context and requires children to calculate with distance and time. You may find it useful to hide the numbers in the problem to begin with so children can focus on what the problem is asking and which operations they will need to use. Once they have determined the steps they need to take, they can then carry out the calculations with the given measurements.

Base 10 apparatus should be made available so that children can represent the distance calculation and decide whether to use a mental or written method. They are likely to opt for a written method and should explain their choices. Look for those who use rounding and a mental method to make an estimate first and remind others to do this. Encourage children to identify their own checking calculation and use this to check the validity of their answer.

Ask children to explain why they will not use a written method to calculate a time interval. Look for children who can explain in some way that time does not have the same place value as our decimal number system. They could show each of the times on clocks and use these to represent the jumps on the number line as they count up from 09:35.

Evidencing mastery

Children use Base 10 apparatus to represent a calculation and can explain when a written or mental method is most appropriate. They fluently apply the method of rounding to help make estimates and recognise that a mental method should be used for this purpose.

They fluently count up to the next hour when calculating time intervals and then count on in hour steps as appropriate.

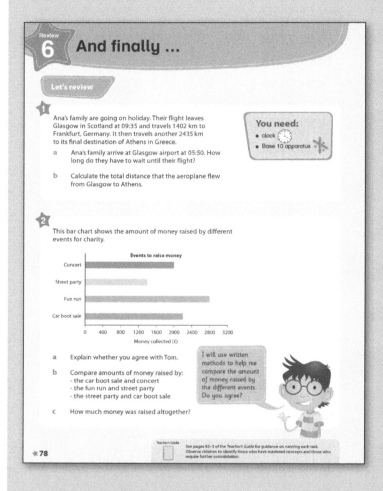

Assessment task 2

Running the task

You could begin by discussing some of the statistical representations that children have used recently and why information is shown in this way. Perhaps talk about the difference between discrete and continuous data and why the chart given shows discrete data. Ask children to discuss what they notice about the bar chart and what it shows. Consider the scale and ask them to describe the count it is related to. They should connect the count of 400 to the count of 4 but explain that all numbers in the count are 100 times larger using knowledge of place value to help them.

Children could work together to reason about Tom's statement and be prepared to explain their decision. Look for children who readily explain that all the values are multiples

of 100 so a mental method and related facts can be used.

Children should work through the comparisons, finding the values for each event and applying a mental method to find the difference. Let them explore finding different totals and encourage them to use strategies such as partitioning and '10 and a bit' to help them cross boundaries.

Evidencing mastery

Look for children who are beginning to fluently apply related facts and place value when calculating with numbers with up to two significant figures. Children should relate their calculating to the counting they have been doing in fours and in steps of 100. They draw on place value and number bonds to help them count on or back over boundaries.

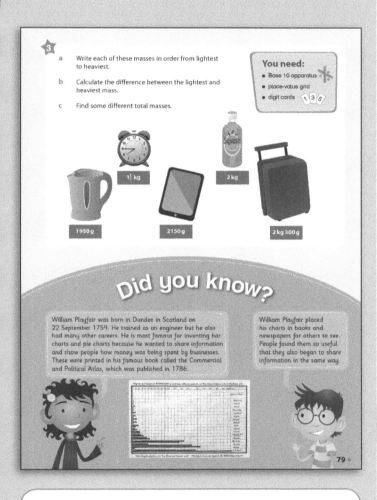

Assessment task 3

Resources

Base 10 apparatus, place-value grid, digit cards.

Running the task

This task requires children to draw on the relationship between units of measurement. You may find it useful to talk about the different measurements that they have been using recently and how they can use the place-value grid and digit cards to help show the relationships between them, e.g. between pounds and pence, metres and centimetres, kilometres and metres, etc. Return to measuring in kilograms and grams noting the same language 'kilo' being used and linking this to 1000.

Discuss what they will need to do to order the masses and guide them towards working in grams if they do not make this choice. Children can work together to convert the masses and make decisions about their order.

Ask children to represent calculations using Base 10 apparatus and explain whether a mental or written method should be applied. Again, look for those who make estimates first and use the inverse to check calculations.

Evidencing mastery

They are confident when multiplying single digits by 100 and 1000 and apply this when converting between units of measurement. Children who have mastered this concept also recognise when they should convert measurements so that calculations can be completed using the same unit of measurement. They can explain, e.g. that 2 kg + 1950 g is not equal to 1952 g as 2 kg is equivalent to 2000 g.

Did you know?

Children find out about the origin of some of the statistical representations they have been using and why they were invented. They may find it interesting to look at some of these early representations on the Internet and compare them with some of the computer generated charts we use today.

This William Playfair example has 34 bars: two for each of the companies it compared.

Look at the different ways that data is represented in science and in the media, and the range of information that it can represent.

Concepts mastered

☑ Children can explain when it is better to use a mental or written method, but recognise that mental methods should be used for estimates and for calculating durations of time. They draw on the relationships between kilometres and metres and hours and minutes to convert measurements as required.

☑ Children can explain how bar models relate to their addition and subtraction calculations. They represent and interpret data represented on a bar chart and can answer and pose questions that involve finding sums and differences.

☑ Children can explain the choices they make to use a mental or written method of addition and subtraction. They make useful estimates using knowledge of place value and rounding, and recognise how the inverse operation can be carried out to check the accuracy of an answer.

Fractions and decimals

Mathematical focus

★ **Number: fractions (including decimals)**

★ **Measurement: length, mass, money**

Prior learning

Children should already be able to:

- count up and down in tenths, recognise that tenths arise from dividing an object into ten equal parts and dividing single-digit numbers or quantities by ten

- recognise and show, using diagrams, equivalent fractions with small denominators

- add and subtract fractions with the same denominator within one whole

- compare and order unit fractions and fractions with the same denominator.

Key new learning

- Recognise and show, using diagrams, families of common equivalent fractions.

- Add and subtract fractions with the same denominator.

- Count up and down in hundredths; recognise that hundredths arise when dividing an object by 100 and dividing tenths by ten.

- Recognise and write decimal equivalents of any number of tenths or hundredths.

- Recognise and write decimal equivalents to a quarter, half and three quarters.

- Find the effect of dividing a single- or 2-digit number by ten and 100, identifying the value of the digits in the answer as ones, tenths and hundredths.

Making connections

- A solid understanding of equivalent fractions will help children later on in many areas of maths, including ratio and proportion.

- Decimal numbers are used in many other subjects as well as in everyday life. An obvious context is measurement. Children will see numbers with one decimal place when dealing with centimetres and millimetres; they will see numbers with two decimal places when dealing with metres and centimetres. Money provides a tangible opportunity for children to explore tenths and hundredths.

- An understanding of place value is important for all areas of mathematics. This unit builds on children's knowledge of the positional, multiplicative and additive aspects of place value, and the idea that our Base 10 number system increases and decreases by powers of ten.

Unit 7 Fractions and decimals

I wonder what fraction this slice of apple is of the whole apple?

If I eat $\frac{3}{18}$ of this chocolate bar, what fraction would be left?

★ 80

Talk about

Talk about the 'part, part, whole' nature of fractions. Remind children of the precise mathematical vocabulary that should be used by writing a fraction on the whiteboard. First draw the vinculum. This is the line that separates the numerator and the denominator. Write the denominator after the vinculum. This is the number of parts the whole amount is broken into. The numerator is the number of parts to be considered. Write this last.

Discuss the fact that a decimal is a fraction, it simply has a different appearance.

Engaging and exploring

Ask children to look at each picture and discuss the questions with a partner before discussing them as a class. Focus on each photo in turn.

Discuss the 'part, part, whole' of the apple. Expect children to tell you that the whole is the apple and the two parts are the small slice and the remaining part. Ask children to estimate the two fractions of the whole apple shown.

Cut a real apple into quarters and show one to children. Ask: *Does this match the slice in the photo?* Agree that the slice in the photo is smaller. Ask: *What could we do to make it the same?* Agree that you could cut your quarter in half. Do this and agree that the new parts are approximately the same size as the slice in the photo. Ask: *What fraction of the apple is the slice?* Agree one eighth. Establish that the other part of the apple in the photo must be seven eighths. Then write $\frac{1}{8} + \frac{7}{8}$ on the board and ask children what the sum would be. Agree

one whole, which is equivalent to eight eighths.

Explore other fractions in similar ways, e.g. using four smiley faces and one grumpy face drawn on the board. Ask: *What fraction are smiley? Grumpy? What is the sum if we add the two fractions together?*

Look at the picture of the chocolate bar and ask children to tell you what the whole is and what the parts are. Agree that the whole is the chocolate bar and the parts are the ten pieces. Ask: *What fraction would one piece be?* Agree one tenth. Discuss how you could answer the question in the Textbook. Review subtracting fractions with the same denominator ($1 - \frac{3}{10} = \frac{10}{10} - \frac{3}{10} = \frac{7}{10}$). Ask children make up some addition and subtraction statements using tenths within one whole, for example $\frac{4}{10} + \frac{6}{10} = \frac{10}{10} = 1$ and $\frac{9}{10} - \frac{1}{10} = \frac{8}{10}$.

Look at the photo of the children and establish that they are using a metre stick to measure. Discuss what they could be measuring. Ask: *How many centimetres are equivalent to a metre?* Agree 100 by looking at a metre stick. Can children tell you the significance of the blue and white segments of the stick in the photo? Agree that these are ten centimetre segments. Next ask children to estimate the width of one of the paving slabs in the photo by counting the number of segments that it is equivalent to. Establish that its width is approximately five segments which is 50 centimetres. Ask: *What is 50 centimetres as a fraction of a metre?* Agree half a metre. Can children tell you another way to describe this? Some may be able to tell you that it is 0.5 m. If possible, repeat the activity in the playground with paving stones on the ground, tiles or bricks in a wall.

Look together at the photo of the corn on the cobs. Find out if children know what this vegetable is, how it grows and what it tastes like. Establish that there are six in the picture. Discuss how many two and then three people would get if they shared them equally. *What about four?* Agree that each person would get one whole one; they could then cut the other two in half, so they would have a total of one and a half. *What about five people?* Agree that they would get one and the last would need to be cut into fifths so their total would be one and one fifth. You could then explore sharing other amounts between different numbers of people, e.g. five cakes between four.

Ask children to count the coins shown in the final photo and tell you their value. Agree there are 15 pound coins, so £15. Ask: *How many £2 coins could you make out of these? How many pennies? How many 50p coins?* Give children real or plastic coins to work with. Expect children to tell you how they know. Then explore the idea of one tenth, agreeing that the whole would be divided into ten. *If there were ten pound coins, what would one tenth be? What if there were 20? What is one tenth of these 15?* Agree that one tenth of £15 is £1.50. Ask children to tell you the value of different tenths, e.g. two tenths, three tenths and seven tenths. Do children know that five tenths is equivalent to half?

Things to think about

- What questions will you ask and what tasks will you use to encourage problem solving and reasoning, within the context of measures, when children are working with decimals?

- How will you use manipulatives and visual representations, particularly the bar model, to help develop conceptual understanding of fractions with all children?

- How will you use the bar model to solve problems that involve fractions and decimals?

- What problem solving strategies could you use, e.g.

  ▶ Odd one out

  ▶ What's the same? What's different?

Checking understanding

You will know children have mastered these concepts when they can explain and demonstrate what a fraction is and find families of common equivalent fractions. They will be able to add and subtract fractions with the same denominator. They will be able to count up and down in hundredths and write decimal equivalents of tenths and hundredths, and of a quarter, half and three quarters. They will understand the effect of dividing a number by ten and 100.

- Recognise and show, using diagrams, families of common equivalent fractions.
- Solve problems involving increasingly harder fractions to calculate quantities, and fractions to divide quantities, including non-unit fractions where the answer is a whole number.
- Add and subtract fractions with the same denominator.

Homework 35 and 36

Practice Book pp 66–70

Fraction Wall

Representations and resources

Strips of paper, rulers, scissors, interlocking cubes.

Mathematical vocabulary

Denominator, numerator, equivalent

Warming up

Recap finding fractions of amounts, reminding children that the whole is divided by the denominator to find the parts and then multiplied by the numerator to find the amount required. Ask children to find different fractions of one hour, e.g. $\frac{1}{12}, \frac{5}{12}, \frac{1}{2}, \frac{1}{5}, \frac{4}{5}, \frac{1}{4}, \frac{3}{4}, \frac{1}{3}$. Before you begin, ask children what they need to know in order to do this. Agree that they need to know that there are 60 minutes in an hour. You could then move on to finding fractions of a metre, e.g. $\frac{1}{10}, \frac{1}{4}, \frac{1}{2}, \frac{7}{10}, \frac{1}{5}, \frac{3}{5}$.

Background knowledge

Finding equivalent fractions is helpful for ordering and comparing fractions and also for adding and subtracting fractions with different denominators. For now, however, focus is on adding and subtracting fractions with the same denominator. It is important that children find out how to make equivalent fractions and are not just taught a rule. Encourage them to tell you what they notice about the numerators and denominators of the fractions they have converted to an equivalent. With plenty of practice they should be able to form the generalisation that the denominator and numerator are multiplied by the same number to give an equivalent fraction. In Year 4, children extend adding and subtracting fractions with the same denominators outside a whole.

7a Families of fractions

You need:
- strips of paper
- ruler
- scissors

Let's learn

$\frac{1}{2}$ can't be the same as $\frac{2}{4}$. They are different numbers.

They are the same! $\frac{1}{4}$ of 8 apples is 2. $\frac{2}{8}$ of 8 apples is also 2. They look different but the value is the same.

Equivalent fractions
These fraction models show that $\frac{1}{4}$, $\frac{2}{8}$ and $\frac{3}{12}$ are equivalent.
How many quarters, eighths and twelfths would be equivalent to $\frac{1}{2}$?

$\frac{1}{4}$ $\frac{1}{4} = \frac{2}{8}$ $\frac{1}{4} = \frac{3}{12}$

These fraction models show that $\frac{1}{3}$, $\frac{2}{6}$ and $\frac{3}{9}$ are equivalent.
How many thirds, sixths and ninths would be equivalent to 1 whole?

$\frac{1}{3}$ $\frac{1}{3} = \frac{2}{6}$ $\frac{1}{3} = \frac{3}{9}$

Adding and subtracting fractions
It is easy to add and subtract fractions with the same denominator. The denominators stays the same – just add or subtract the numerator.

Use diagrams or paper strips to explain why these fraction statements are true:

$\frac{5}{8} + \frac{7}{8} = \frac{12}{8} = 1\frac{4}{8} = 1\frac{1}{2}$ $2 - 1\frac{1}{3} = 1 - \frac{1}{3} = \frac{3}{3} - \frac{1}{3} = \frac{2}{3}$

$\frac{1}{4} + \frac{3}{4} = \frac{4}{4} = 1$ $2 - \frac{5}{6} = 1 + 1 - \frac{5}{6} = 1 + \frac{6}{6} - \frac{5}{6} = 1\frac{1}{6}$

Teacher's Guide: Before working through the Textbook, study page 96 of the Teacher's Guide to see how the concepts should be introduced. Read and discuss the page with the children. Provide concrete resources to support exploration.

★ 82

Let's learn: Modelling and teaching

Equivalent fractions

- Look at the models in the Textbook. Ask children to model the diagrams using paper strips and explain each one to a partner. Ask questions, e.g. *If one third is six, what is the whole? What is one sixth?* Ask children to look at one quarter and compare it with two eighths and three twelfths. They should tell you they have doubled the numerator and denominator of one quarter to get two eighths and multiplied by three to get three twelfths.

- What do they notice about one third, two sixths and three ninths? Can they come up with a generalisation so that they can find any equivalent fractions? They should be able to tell you that to find an equivalent fraction, you multiply (or divide) the denominator and numerator by the same

number. Ask them to use their rule to answer questions. Ask them if the generalisation applies to non-unit fractions such as two thirds. Try some out and agree that it does.

Adding and subtracting fractions

- Recap Year 3 work on adding and subtracting fractions with the same denominator within one whole.

- Carry out the following investigation to introduce adding fractions outside one whole. Give children strips of paper and ask them to fold them to make eighths, place them side by side and tell you the sum of five eighths and seven eighths. Agree twelve eighths, which is an improper fraction. They use their strips to work out what this would be as a mixed number. Repeat with thirds and sixths. Use the strips to look at subtracting fractions. *What is the difference between two and one and one third? Two and five sixths?*

Let's practise: Digging deeper

Step 1

The task asks children to find fractions equivalent to unit and then non-unit fractions. Before they begin the task recap this with them, ensuring that they understand the generalisation developed during the class session. At the end of the task they need to express this in their own words. Some children may benefit from folding paper strips in order to visualise the equivalences.

Step 2

Before children begin this task, rehearse adding and subtracting fractions and also mixed numbers and improper fractions. Call out pairs of fractions for them to add (with answers over one whole) and pairs of mixed numbers for them to subtract, all with the same denominator. Ensure that, for the addition questions, children change the answers from improper fractions to mixed numbers.

Children could go on to make up addition and subtraction statements for a partner to answer.

Step 3

Provide children with three strips of paper more than 30 cm in length, scissors and rulers. Children need to measure each strip so that it is 30 cm long, then divide one strip into fifths (each part 6 cm long), the second strip into tenths (each part 3 cm long) and the third into 15 equal parts (each part 2 cm long). They then cut each strip into its fraction parts and use these to find as many equivalent fractions as they can and list them. You could also ask them to write down what each fraction is in centimetres. You could rehearse this activity beforehand using halves, quarters and eighths.

Step 4

This task asks children to find some possible addition calculations that could have been made to give a sum of two and a half. To be successful they need to know the fractions that can be equivalent to half. They add numbers with the same denominator and therefore need to reason that, e.g. thirds and fifths cannot be options as neither can be equated with half. Encourage them to make up between five and eight possibilities.

Let's practise

1 **Write.**

Write down 3 equivalent fractions for each of these.

a $\frac{1}{2}$ c $\frac{1}{5}$ e $\frac{1}{10}$ g $\frac{2}{3}$

b $\frac{1}{3}$ d $\frac{1}{7}$ f $\frac{1}{12}$ h $\frac{5}{8}$

Explain how you found these.
What generalisation have you made?

2 **Calculate.**

Add these fractions.

a $\frac{4}{5} + \frac{3}{5}$ c $\frac{5}{8} + \frac{3}{8} + \frac{7}{8}$

b $\frac{2}{3} + \frac{2}{3}$ d $\frac{1}{4} + \frac{4}{4} + \frac{3}{4}$

Make sure you change the improper fractions to mixed numbers.

Subtract these fractions.

e $\frac{2}{3} - \frac{1}{3}$ g $\frac{4}{5} - \frac{2}{5}$ i $2 - \frac{3}{5}$ k $3 - 2\frac{1}{3}$

f $\frac{3}{4} - \frac{1}{4}$ h $\frac{5}{6} - \frac{3}{6}$ j $2 - 1\frac{1}{4}$ l $3 - 1\frac{1}{8}$

3 **Measure.**

Take 3 strips of paper. Measure them so that each is 30 cm long.
Use a ruler to divide your strips into 5ths, 10ths and 15ths.
Label each part with its fraction.
Cut each strip into its fraction parts.
Use the parts to find as many equivalent fractions as you can.
Make a list of them.

4 **Think.**

Ana added some fractions together. The sum was $2\frac{1}{2}$.
All her fractions had the same denominator.

Write down some of the possible fractions that I could have added.

Teacher's Guide See page 97 of the Teacher's Guide for ideas of how to guide practice. Work through each step together as a class to develop children's conceptual understanding.

83 ★

Ensuring progress

Supporting understanding

Give children interlocking cubes so they can recreate the models shown in the Textbook, and also use them to find other equivalent fractions, such as those for half and a fifth. Children do not need to master changing improper fractions to mixed numbers in Year 4, so if they find this difficult allow them to present their answers to Step 2 as improper fractions.

Broadening understanding

For the last part of Step 2, and in Step 4, encourage children to think of alternative ways of adding fractions and making two and a half with denominators that are not the same but are within the same family, e.g. halves, quarters and eighths and thirds and sixths.

✓ Concept mastered

Children can show and explain how to find equivalent fractions. They can add and subtract fractions with the same denominator.

Follow-up ideas

- Discuss how the generalisation for finding equivalent fractions of unit fractions can be reversed for finding equivalent fractions for , e.g. $\frac{8}{24}$, $\frac{12}{36}$. They should be able to tell you that they can divide the denominator and numerator by the same factor to find equivalent fractions for these.

- Challenge children, in pairs, to write down a unit or non-unit fraction and then find as many equivalent fractions as they can in two minutes.

- Children could draw a fraction wall with one whole, halves, quarters and eighths. Ask them to choose a value for the whole using a unit of measure (e.g. 1 m, 1 kg, £5) and find the values of each fraction in the measure they choose.

Answers

Step 1

Examples:

a $\frac{2}{4}, \frac{3}{6}, \frac{4}{8}$ e $\frac{2}{20}, \frac{3}{30}, \frac{4}{40}$

b $\frac{2}{6}, \frac{3}{9}, \frac{4}{12}$ f $\frac{2}{24}, \frac{3}{36}, \frac{4}{48}$

c $\frac{2}{10}, \frac{3}{15}, \frac{4}{20}$ g $\frac{4}{6}, \frac{6}{9}, \frac{8}{12}$

d $\frac{2}{16}, \frac{3}{24}, \frac{4}{32}$ h $\frac{10}{16}, \frac{15}{24}, \frac{20}{32}$

Step 2

a $\frac{7}{5} = 1\frac{2}{5}$ d $\frac{7}{4} = 1\frac{3}{4}$

b $\frac{4}{3} = 1\frac{1}{3}$ e $\frac{1}{3}$

c $\frac{15}{8} = 1\frac{7}{8}$ f $\frac{2}{4} = \frac{1}{2}$

g $\frac{2}{5}$ j $\frac{3}{4}$

h $\frac{2}{6} = \frac{1}{3}$ k $\frac{2}{3}$

i $1\frac{2}{5}$ l $1\frac{7}{8}$

Step 3

Examples: $\frac{1}{5} = \frac{2}{10}, \frac{2}{5} = \frac{4}{10}, \frac{3}{5} = \frac{6}{10},$
$\frac{4}{5} = \frac{8}{10}, \frac{1}{5} = \frac{3}{15}, \frac{2}{5} = \frac{6}{15}, \frac{3}{5} = \frac{9}{15}, \frac{4}{5} = \frac{12}{15}$

Step 4

Examples:

$2\frac{1}{4} + \frac{1}{4}$

$1\frac{2}{8} + 1\frac{2}{8}$

$\frac{1}{2} + \frac{1}{2} + \frac{1}{2} + \frac{1}{2} + \frac{1}{2}$

- **Count up and down in hundredths; recognise that hundredths arise when dividing an object by 100 and dividing tenths by ten.**
- **Recognise and write decimal equivalents of any number of tenths or hundredths.**
- **Recognise and write decimal equivalents to a quarter, half and three quarters.**
- **Find the effect of dividing a single- or 2-digit number by ten and 100, identifying the value of the digits in the answer as ones, tenths and hundredths.**

Homework 37 and 38

Practice Book pp 71–3

Fraction Wall

Representations and resources

Pendulum, Base 10 apparatus, place-value grids, digit cards, coins.

Mathematical vocabulary

Place value, Base 10, equivalent, decimal, fraction, tenths, hundredths

Warming up

Practise counting in tenths and hundredths. Swing the pendulum from side to side. As you do, children count from zero to one in tenths and back to zero. Repeat this but begin on different starting numbers, e.g. 3, 2.5, 6.1. Count in hundredths from zero to 0.1 and back to zero. Again, repeat from different starting numbers such as 0.4, 1, 3.5.

Background knowledge

A knowledge of the Base 10 aspect of place value is key to understanding tenths and hundredths. Our number system increases and decreases by powers of ten. Tenths appear when ones numbers are divided by ten and hundredths appear when tenths are divided by ten or ones are divided by 100. In Year 3, children began counting up and down in tenths and learnt that tenths arise from dividing an object into ten equal parts. The work covered in Year 4 is simply a progression from this.

Let's learn: Modelling and teaching

Decimals and fraction equivalences

- Explain that decimals are fractions: they are parts of a whole.

- Refer to the Base 10 illustrations in the Textbook. Ask children to tell you what each piece must represent to show 1.8. Agree that the stick represents one and the small cubes each represent one tenth. Ask children to use Base 10 equipment to prove this. They should be able to tell you that ten tenths are the same as the ones stick and place ten small cubes alongside the stick. Ask them to make different numbers, such as 1.4, 3.6, 12.9 using Base 10 apparatus and to write these as decimals and fractions. Repeat for hundredths.

- Ask children to look at the number lines in the Textbook and to list some decimal equivalents to tenths and hundredths.

- Discuss the equivalent decimals for half, quarter and three quarters. Refer to the number line showing tenths and discuss the position of quarter (halfway between two tenths and three tenths). Repeat for three quarters.

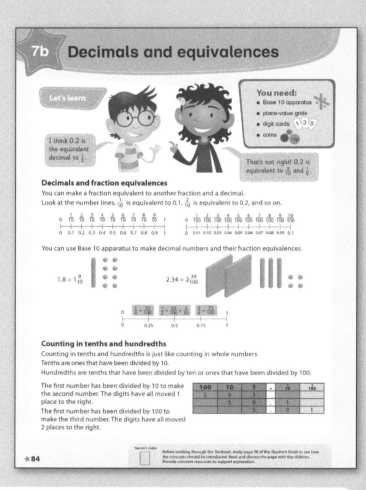

Counting in tenths and hundredths

- Agree that tenths arise when ones are divided by ten, and hundredths when tenths are divided by ten or ones are divided by 100. Look at the first number in the place-value grid in the Textbook and ask children to describe the positional, multiplicative and additive elements of place value. Ask them what has happened to the first number to make the second. Agree it has been divided by ten, so it is now ten times smaller and the digits have moved one place to the right. Discuss the third number. Establish that the first number has been divided by 100 or the second by ten.

- Give children time to explore this by making numbers on place-value grids with digit cards and divide them by ten and 100. They could record what they do using division statements.

Let's practise: Digging deeper

Step 1

Before beginning the task, ask children to explain to a partner how to convert tenths and hundredths to their decimal equivalents. They use the number lines in the Textbook for support if they need to. The fractions in the question are arranged in sets of unit fractions and non-unit fractions. Encourage children to see the pattern in these.

Step 2

Before children begin the task, rehearse converting decimals to fractions. Encourage them to simplify the fractions to their lowest terms. If necessary, revisit the generalisation that we find equivalent fractions by multiplying or dividing the denominator and numerator by the same number. Check children can apply this to simplify, e.g. $\frac{2}{10}$ to $\frac{1}{5}$, and $\frac{45}{100}$ to $\frac{9}{20}$.

Step 3

The first part of the task asks children to make the amounts using the fewest coins. You could rehearse this by writing amounts of money on the board and asking them to discuss with a partner the coins to use. When children describe the place value of the amounts, look for descriptions such as 'one whole and three tenths' for £1.30 and 'one tenth and three hundredths' for £0.13 or 13p.

Step 4

Encourage children to reason through part), e.g. the ones number must be six. For parts b and c, encourage them to list all the numbers that they can make in a systematic manner. Expect them to realise that they can make numbers with both one and two decimal places. They can then select the largest and smallest from their list.

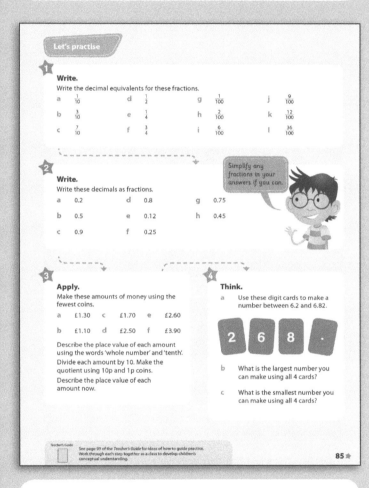

Ensuring progress

Supporting understanding

In Step 2, let children look through the Textbook to find representations that might help them simplify the fractions. Make place-value grids and digit cards available for Step 4 so that children can move digits around to help them create their numbers.

Broadening understanding

Extend Step 1 by reminding children that they know one fifth is equivalent to two tenths and asking them to convert two fifths, three fifths and four fifths to decimals. In Step 2 expect children to simplify or reduce the fractions to their lowest form without using representations.

 Concept mastered

Children can explain and demonstrate how to find decimal and fraction equivalents and can count forwards and backwards in tenths and hundredths. They understand the effect of dividing a single- or 2-digit number by ten or 100 and describe the value of the digits in the answer.

Follow-up ideas

- Ask children to measure different items around the classroom that are over a metre in length, and to record these measurements in three different ways (in centimetres, in metres and in centimetres and metres). They can then convert the decimal part of their metre measurement into a fraction.

- Challenge children to use three digit cards to create as many different numbers with one and two decimal places as they can. They record these on paper and then order them from lowest to highest.

- Give children shopping catalogues and ask them to select items. They write their choices down with their prices. They then convert the pence part of the amounts to fractions of a pound.

Answers

Step 1

a	0.1	g	0.01
b	0.3	h	0.02
c	0.7	i	0.06
d	0.5	j	0.09
e	0.25	k	0.12
f	0.75	l	0.36

Step 2

a	$\frac{2}{10} = \frac{1}{5}$	e	$\frac{12}{100} = \frac{3}{25}$
b	$\frac{5}{10} = \frac{1}{2}$	f	$\frac{25}{100} = \frac{1}{4}$
c	$\frac{9}{10}$	g	$\frac{75}{100} = \frac{3}{4}$
d	$\frac{8}{10} = \frac{4}{5}$	h	$\frac{45}{100} = \frac{9}{20}$

Step 3

a £1 + 20p + 10p; 1 whole and 3 tenths; 13p: 10p + 2p + 1p; 1 tenth and 3 hundredths.

b £1 + 10p; 1 whole and 1 tenth; 11p: 10p + 1p, 1 tenth and 1 hundredth.

c £1 + 50p + 20p; 1 whole and 7 tenths; 17p: 10p + 5p + 2p; 1 tenth and 7 hundredths.

d £2 + 50p; 2 wholes and 5 tenths; 25p: 20p + 5p; 2 tenths and 5 hundredths.

e £2 + 50p + 10p; 2 wholes and 6 tenths; 26p: 20p + 5p + 1p; 2 tenths and 6 hundredths.

f £2 + £1 + 50p + 20p + 20p; 3 wholes and 9 tenths; 39p: 20p + 10p + 5p + 2p + 2p; 3 tenths and 9 hundredths.

Step 4

a 6.28　b 86.2　c 2.68

You may need to discuss whether .268 and 862. are valid answers.

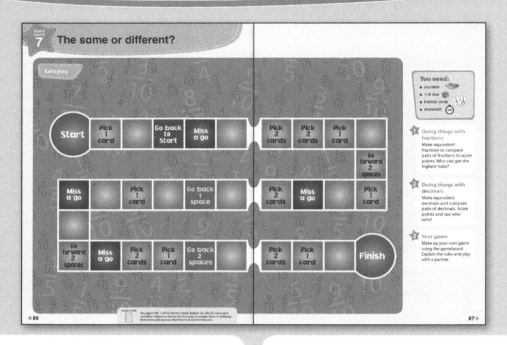

Game 1: Doing things with fractions

This game helps children rehearse and consolidate finding fraction equivalences and comparing fractions.

Maths focus

- Find equivalent fractions
- Compare fractions

Resources

1 counter per player (1 colour per player), 1–6 dice (1), fraction cards (unit fractions, tenths from $\frac{1}{10}$ to $\frac{9}{10}$, fifths from $\frac{1}{5}$ to $\frac{4}{5}$, $\frac{1}{4}$, $\frac{1}{2}$ and $\frac{3}{4}$), stopwatch (or minute timer).

How to play

This is a game for two players. Children shuffle the fraction cards and place them in a pile face down on the table. They put their counters on Start. They take it in turns to throw the dice and move their counter that number of spaces. If they land on a space, they do nothing. If they land on 'Pick 1 card' they take a fraction card from the pile. Their partner then times them for a minute as they make up as many equivalent fractions as they can. After a minute their partner checks to see if they agree with the equivalences made. The child who made the equivalent fractions counts how many they made and scores that number of points.

If they land on 'Pick 2 cards', they take two fraction cards and compare them, writing a number statement using the symbols > and <. If they are correct they score a point. Play continues like this until both players reach Finish. They find their final score. The winner is the child with the higher score.

Making it easier

Children could use the fraction cards for unit fractions, tenths, quarters and halves only.

Making it harder

Add extra fraction cards to include, e.g. thirds, sixths and eighths.

Game 2: Doing things with decimals

This game provides practice in finding fraction and decimal equivalences and comparing decimals.

Maths focus

- Find equivalences between fractions and decimals
- Compare decimals

Resources

1 counter per player (1 colour per player), 1–6 dice (1), fraction cards (unit fractions, tenths from $\frac{1}{10}$ to $\frac{9}{10}$, fifths from $\frac{1}{5}$ to $\frac{4}{5}$, $\frac{1}{4}$, $\frac{1}{2}$ and $\frac{3}{4}$).

How to play

For two players. Children shuffle the fraction cards and place them in a pile face down. They put their counters on Start. Taking turns they throw the dice and move their counter that number of spaces. If they land on 'Pick 1 card', they take a fraction card and work out the equivalent decimal. If their partner agrees, they score a point. If they land on 'Pick 2 cards', they take two cards and convert them to decimals. They then compare the two decimals, writing a number statement using the symbols > and <. If their partner agrees they score two points. Play continues until both players reach Finish. The winner is the player with the most points.

Making it easier

Use the fraction cards for tenths, quarters and halves only.

Making it harder

Children could pick three cards instead of two and make and record the six possible different comparison statements.

Game 3: Your game

Children should invent their own game designing rules that use the concepts covered in the unit. Challenge children to make their game easier or harder.

Unit 7 — The same or different?

Choose a game to play.

Game 1: Doing things with fractions

How to play

- Shuffle the cards and put them in a pile face down. Place your counters on Start.
- Take turns to roll the dice. Move your counter that number of spaces.
- If you land on 'Pick 1 card', take a fraction card.
  - ▶ Make up as many equivalent fractions as you can in 1 minute.
  - ▶ Your partner checks them and counts how many. Score that number of points.
- If you land on 'Pick 2 cards', take 2 fraction cards.
  - ▶ Compare them. Write a number statement using > and <.
  - ▶ Your partner checks it. If correct score 1 point.
- The winner is the player with the higher score when you both reach Finish.

You need:

- 1 counter per player (1 colour each)
- 1–6 dice
- fraction cards (unit fractions, tenths from $\frac{1}{10}$ to $\frac{9}{10}$, fifths from $\frac{1}{5}$ to $\frac{4}{5}$, $\frac{1}{4}$, $\frac{1}{2}$ and $\frac{3}{4}$)
- stopwatch

Game 2: Doing things with decimals

How to play

- Start in the same way as Game 1.
- If you land on 'Pick 1 card', take a fraction card.
  - ▶ Work out the equivalent decimal.
  - ▶ Your partner checks. If correct, score 1 point.
- If you land on 'Pick 2 cards', take 2 fraction cards.
  - ▶ Convert them to decimals. Compare them in a number statement using > and <.
  - ▶ Your partner checks it. If correct score 2 points.
- The winner is the player with the higher score when you both reach Finish.

You need:

- 1 counter per player (1 colour each)
- 1–6 dice
- fraction cards (unit fractions, tenths from $\frac{1}{10}$ to $\frac{9}{10}$, fifths from $\frac{1}{5}$ to $\frac{4}{5}$, $\frac{1}{4}$, $\frac{1}{2}$ and $\frac{3}{4}$)

Game 3: Your game

- Make up your own game using the gameboard.
- What are the rules for your game? Explain them to someone.

Please help your child by reading the instructions and playing the game together.

Assessment task 1

Running the task

Before children begin the task, write $\frac{1}{2}$, $\frac{2}{4}$ and $\frac{3}{6}$ on the board. Ask children to talk to a partner about what they notice about these fractions. *What are their similarities and differences?* Agree that they are the same value, but the appearance of each is different. Discuss how to convert half to two fourths. Agree that both the denominator and numerator are multiplied by two. Repeat for half and three sixths. Emphasise that the generalisation that they can make is that multiplying (or dividing) the denominator and numerator by the same multiplier will always give an equivalent fraction. Remind them that this generalisation works for both unit and non-unit fractions.

The first part of the task asks children to sort the fractions given into four groups of equivalent fractions; they should end up with four groups of four. If children put a fraction in the wrong group, highlight their error using questioning, e.g. *What do we multiply the numerator of this fraction by to get the numerator of this one? So what happens to the denominator?*

They then write down four equivalent fractions for four given fractions. The final part of the task asks children to make up their own fractions and find equivalences for these. Encourage them to make up some that can be reduced or simplified.

Children who struggle with this task may benefit from working with you in a small group, focusing on halves and quarters.

Evidencing mastery

If children can demonstrate and explain how to find equivalent fractions they are evidencing mastery. They understand and can apply the generalisation that to make an equivalent fraction you multiply the numerator and denominator by the same number. Those with a particularly strong grasp of the concept will also be confident in dividing to simplify fractions.

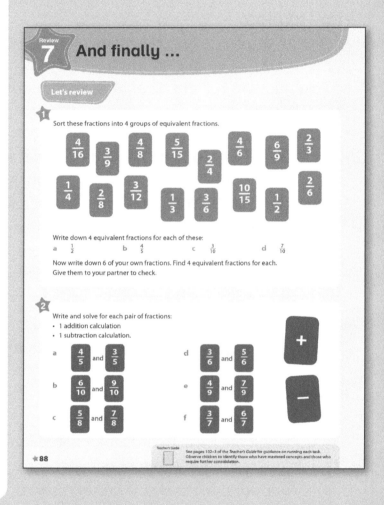

Assessment task 2

Resources

Fraction strips, counters, interlocking cubes.

Running the task

Rehearse adding and subtracting fractions with the same denominator. Write pairs of fractions on the board, e.g. $\frac{3}{4}$ and $\frac{2}{4}$. Ask children to add them and tell you want they can about the answer. Elicit that it is in an improper fraction. Ask: *What would it be as a mixed number?* Then ask them what subtraction calculation they can make with the two fractions. Establish that the one with the larger numerator needs to go first, to give a positive answer ($\frac{3}{4} - \frac{2}{4} = \frac{1}{4}$).

Once you have rehearsed this ask children to work through the task independently. As in your practice session, for the

addition encourage them to change the resultant improper fraction to a mixed number. This is an extra bonus which is not required for mastery at this level.

Look out for children who find this task difficult. Work with them on adding and subtracting fractions within one, using concrete resources, e.g. fraction strips, counters or interlocking cubes, until they are confident.

Evidencing mastery

If children can add and subtract fractions with the same denominator and explain how they achieved their results they are evidencing mastery of this aspect of mathematics. They should be able to recognise improper fractions; some will be able to convert these to mixed numbers.

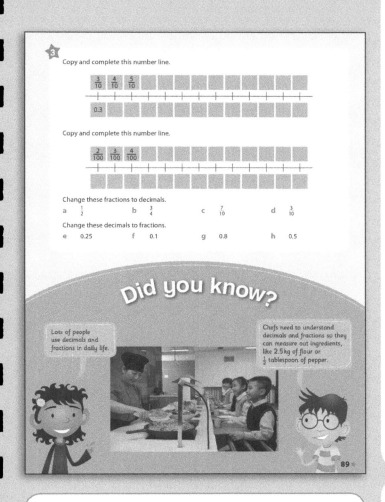

Concepts mastered

✓ Children can show and explain how to find equivalent fractions. They can add and subtract fractions with the same denominator.

✓ Children can explain and demonstrate how to find decimal and fraction equivalents and can count forwards and backwards in tenths and hundredths. They understand the effect of dividing a single- or 2-digit number by ten or 100 and describe the value of the digits in the answer.

Assessment task 3

Resources

Number lines, fractions strips.

Running the task

Prepare for the task by counting forwards and back in tenths and hundredths. First count together in fractional steps of tenths from zero to one and back to zero. Then ask volunteers to count in these steps using decimals. Repeat for hundredths. Ask children to tell you the equivalences for various tenths and hundredths, e.g. as four tenths, seven tenths, three hundredths, nine hundredths.

The first part of the task asks children to complete a number line, continuing a sequence in tenths past one whole. Children can write those over one whole as improper fractions or mixed numbers: both are correct and will show mastery. They also need to convert the sequence to decimals. They then do the same for hundredths.

Counting and continuing sequences of tenths and hundredths is an important skill; if any children are not secure in this, it is worth practising in small groups whenever you have the opportunity, and also with the whole class during future warm ups.

The final part of the task asks children to change a selection of fractions to decimals and then decimals to fractions. These are common equivalences which all children should be able to recall fluently. Those that cannot will benefit from additional practice using number lines and fraction strips.

Evidencing mastery

Children who have a firm grasp of these concepts will be able to count in tenths and hundredths fluently and accurately. They will be able to explain and demonstrate how to change fractions to decimals and vice versa, and have rapid recall of the decimal and fraction equivalences for quarter, half, three quarters and tenths.

Did you know?

Help children to really understand the relevance of fractions and decimals in real life. You could start with the example given in the Textbook: chefs and bakers need to understand decimals and fractions so they can measure out ingredients. If they are making food like pizzas, they need to know about fractions so they can cut them into equal pieces. What experience of cooking do children have? Can they remember any recipes or ingredients or whether they used decimals of fractions?

Money is another example of decimals in real life. The decimals separate the whole pounds and the pence, so we use decimals every time we go shopping.

Ask children what they want to be when they grow up, or what their parents/carers do. Do these jobs involve fractions and decimals? In many cases, the answer is yes, as many occupations involve measurement or calculation, e.g. architects and builders measure different parts of buildings, nurses and doctors calculate and measure medicine doses and football managers use decimals and fractions to analyse game statistics.

Methods for multiplying

Mathematical focus

★ Number: number and place value, multiplication and division

★ Measurement: money, time, mass, volume/capacity

Prior learning

Children should already be able to:

- count in multiples of 3, 4, 6 and 8
- recall multiplication table facts for 2, 3, 4, 5, 6, 8, 9 and 12
- multiply two simple numbers mentally
- use a method based on arrays to record more complex multiplication calculations
- solve simple problems involving multiplication or addition.

Key new learning

- Count in multiples of 7.
- Recall multiplication and division facts for the 7 and 11 times tables.
- Use place value, known and derived facts to multiply and divide mentally, including: multiplying by 0 and 1; dividing by 1; multiplying together three numbers.
- Multiply 2-digit numbers by a single-digit using a formal written layout.
- Solve problems involving multiplying and adding.
- Solve integer scaling problems.

Making connections

- The most common use of the multiplication facts for 7 at this stage is with days of the week. This links with the number of days in each month for working out how many weeks it is (or how many lots of 7 it is) until a given occasion.
- Scaling occurs when buying multiple items at the same price and this also involves using facts from the multiplication tables or a formal written method, depending on the size of the numbers involved. If there is more than one price involved multiplying and adding is required.
- Programming a spreadsheet may involve allowing for multiplying by 1 or zero and these may also come into a formal written method for multiplying.
- Converting between metric units involves multiplying and dividing by 10, 100 or 1000 and so involves both scaling and multiplying or dividing by one.
- Solving problems involving mass or capacity, as well as length, may involve multiplication using a formal written method or recall of facts from the multiplication table.

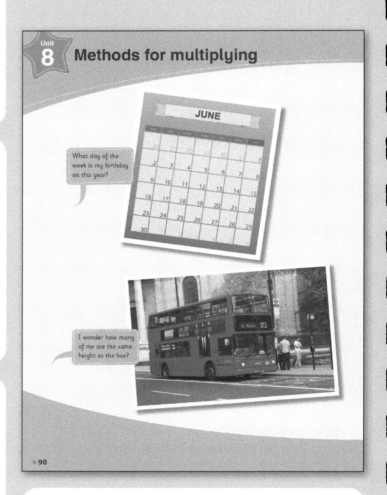

Talk about

Children will use the language of multiplying and dividing, using the terms factor and multiple where appropriate, as they explain their thinking (e.g. '3 is a factor of 12 and 12 is a multiple of 3'). They will apply it in the context of scaling; recognising multiplication as a relation. The alternative interpretation of multiplication as a relation through scaling is fundamental to later work on multipliers and scale factors, and it would be valuable to discuss how repeated addition does not quite work in a particular context.

Engaging and exploring

Using a calendar is an important aspect of adult life. It enables you to book holidays at the right time and organise appointments and visits. It also keeps track of when birthdays occur. Ask children questions about the calendar, e.g. *Who has a calendar on the wall at home? What sort of things are written on it?* Talk about what other uses there may be for a calendar and what alternatives people use to give them the same information. Ask children to count in steps of 7 from, say, the 2nd. *What happens?* They will hopefully notice that you stay on the same day of the week. Ask them why that is. Agree that there are seven days in a week. Ask questions such as: *How many days are there in two weeks? How many days are there between the 14th and the 21st?*

Comparing two lengths, to see how many times the height or width of one is of the other, is something we can do to get a sense of how tall or long something is. The height of a house, or a tree, is an example of this. Look at the photo and ask children to estimate their height compared to the man. Discuss how they can then work out how many times their height the bus is, e.g. they could measure using their finger or a small piece of paper, or visually divide up the front of the bus into (horizontal) quarters. *How accurate are our estimates?* You can apply a similar approach to estimate the size of dinosaurs, e.g. *How many times the height of a person was a Tyrannosaurus rex? How many times the height of a double-decker bus was a Diplodocus? How many Triceratops would fit along one side of the playground?* There is scope for an extended activity here as children assemble estimates of the sizes and record them in an appropriate way.

Items for sale in shops are stored and transported in pallets. Ask children why they think that might be. The number of individual items is the product of the number of pallets and the number of packs per pallet and the number of items in one pack. Work through the calculation step-by-step. First draw a 3 by 4 array to represent one pack. *What is 3 times 4?* Then count the packs on one pallet (6) and ask: *What is 6 times 12?* Finally, discuss how you could mentally work out 72 times 3 to find the total number of drinks. Children may find this challenging; tell them that they will be learning a written method that will help them multiply larger numbers like this.

One of the most common instances where you need to multiply and add is when shopping. Stationery is something children will be familiar with even if they have never bought or chosen their own. Gather a selection of stationery and write down the cost of the items. Ask questions such as: *How much do two pencils cost? How much do two pencils and a highlighter pen cost?* Guide the discussion to help children identify what information they need to answer the questions. You may wish to develop the activity into a role play, giving one child the role of the stationery shopkeeper and another child the role of customer.

Recipes are a rich source of mathematics but many people convert them without realising they are doing any mathematics. Making this 'hidden' mathematics visible is essential so that children realise the significance and importance of it in their, and their families', lives. Discuss ways of working out how many people the lasagne in the photograph will feed, e.g. you could estimate that you could cut it into six slices. *How many lasagnes like this would I need to feed 12 people? 3 people?* If appropriate, you could display a simple lasagne recipe (500 g mince, 1 jar tomato sauce, 1 jar white sauce, 100 g grated cheese, 12 sheets lasagne) and begin to discuss how to scale the ingredients up or down. You may wish to return to this discussion after concept 8d – Scaling.

How many drinks are there altogether?

I wonder how many of those I can afford?

How many people will that feed?

Teacher's Guide   Look at the pictures with the children and discuss the questions.
See pages 104–5 of the Teacher's Guide for key ideas to draw out.

91

Things to think about

- Will you encourage them to make conjectures about the ideas they meet in this unit and allow others to test those conjectures?

- How will you encourage children to work systematically and organise their work when exploring or solving?

- How will you expect them to record their thinking?

- What will you want to see in exercise books? Will you expect to see jottings to support calculation?

- Which concrete materials will you have available on all tables? Will you have place-value counters to support more formal written methods?

Checking understanding

You will know children have mastered these concepts when they can count forwards and backwards in steps of 7 from any number, recall the multiplication facts for 7 and 11 and apply them to solve problems. They can multiply and divide by 1, multiply by zero, and multiply three numbers together. They can use a formal written method to multiply a 2-digit number by a single digit, and solve problems involving multiplying and adding or scaling up or down using a whole number.

8a Multiplication table facts

- **Count in multiples of 7.**
- **Recall multiplication and division facts for the 7 and 11 times tables.**

 Homework 39 and 40   Practice Book pp 74–7   Number Line; 100 Squares

Mathematical vocabulary
Multiply, multiplication, multiples, factors, division

Representations and resources
Pendulum, number lines, bead strings, number rods, 100 squares.

Warming up
Using a pendulum, practise counting in steps of 2, 5, 6 and 8, starting from 0, then move on to counting in steps of 2, 5, 6 and 8 forwards and backwards from any number. Practise calendar facts, asking questions such as: *How many days in January? How many whole weeks is that? How long is it from the 5th of January to the 11th of February?*

Background knowledge
The 7 and 11 times tables are the last ones to learn. Children have all the other multiplication table facts available to them to use to spot patterns and exploit as necessary. Part of learning multiplication table facts is knowing and using their relationship with other facts. If a fact may be quickly deduced from another fact it aids recall. Being familiar with the multiplication table facts helps children recognise patterns in mathematics and other subjects where mathematics is used, as well as supporting fluency. This fluency builds confidence with mathematics – without it almost everything becomes very laborious and children become disengaged with the subject.

Let's learn: Modelling and teaching
Counting in 7s

- Begin by revising counting in 7s, as in 5a – Counting in steps. Recap strategies such as partitioning to bridge 10, or partitioning 7 into 5 + 2. Encourage children to use number lines to help them visualise the steps; alternatively, bead strings provide a concrete approach if required. Chant the steps with the children to help them become familiar with the multiples of 7.

- Look at the second number line in the Textbook and discuss how you could count in 7s from a number other than zero. Agree that you could use the same strategies as before. Use the example to show that you can also use the shift from the multiples of 7 to calculate each step. Model this for the children: 10 and 17 are both 3 more than multiples of 7 (7 and 14), so the next number in the count is 24 (3 more than 21). Ask: *What is the fourth step?* (31) Give children other starting numbers and ask them to count four steps of 7 in each case, using one of the above strategies to work out the numbers. Confirm their answers using a different strategy.

Multiplication facts for 7 and 11

- The model gives a clear picture of the multiplication table facts. Use number rods to reproduce the models in the

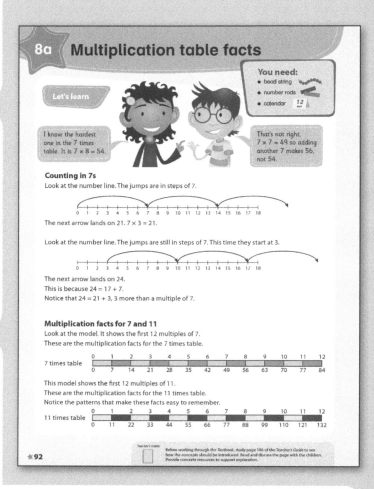

Textbook and place them against rods of length 10 to see the jumps clearly.

- Ask children to discuss ways of remembering the facts – this is much easier for 11 than for 7, although some children will find 11×11 and 12×11 challenging. Agree that, if they are unsure of a fact, they can count on or back from a known fact (e.g. $11 \times 11 = 110 + 11 = 121$). Spending the time discussing the facts to embed them is as useful as the strategies they may hear for remembering them. Call out the numbers from 1 to 12 in a random order, and ask children to multiply each one by 11, recording the answers in their exercise books and keeping track of their totals of correct answers; repeat for 7. This gives them ownership of the process. Ask: *Which do you find hard? Which do you find easy? Why?*

Let's practise: Digging deeper

Step 1

Children may be able to do this mentally, or select their own visual support such as a number line or 100 square. Although the numbers cross zero to become negative in part d, it is only as far as negative one so no extra support is necessary. The multiplication facts can be worked out from known facts as a first step towards memorising them.

Step 2

Children fill in missing terms in sequences that go up or down in steps of 11 or 7. For steps of 7, they could use the strategy of counting on in steps of 5 and then 2, or they could use other partitions of 7. For 11 the obvious partition is 10 and 1. Encourage a range of strategies by asking questions such as: *Can you do this in two stages? What might those be?* Three of the multiplication table facts are presented in a form using the division sign to encourage flexible recall of the facts.

Step 3

A calendar will be helpful for these questions: children can touch the dates on the calendar as they count on or back. In parts a and b, the count crosses into a new month; explore how this could be done without a calendar. Agree that, in part a, when you get to 27 October, you need to partition 7 into 4 (because there are 31 days in October) and 3, then continue counting in 7s from 3 November. Discuss different strategies for answering part e, such as counting on or finding the total number of days and dividing by 7.

Step 4

Children relate this multiplication table fact to other known facts to aid recall. Thinking about it in this way, as flexibly as possible, helps make connections with what is already known. Ask children which number facts they already know that might help. It is a good idea to reflect on which ways are more helpful. The question can be extended to other 'hard to remember' multiplication table facts.

Encourage children to think about the multiples of 7. They should realise that 35 days will take you to Tuesday as it is 5×7. They can then count on 5 more days to get to Sunday.

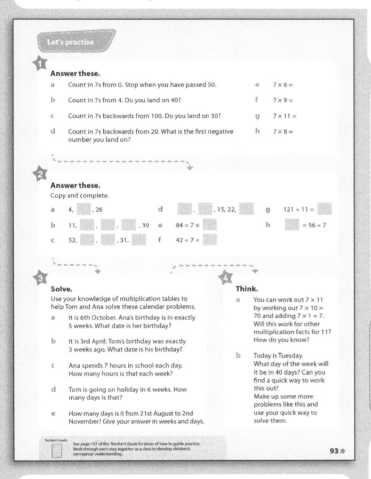

Ensuring progress

Supporting understanding

Working in a focus group, explore counting with bead strings. Ask questions such as: *Can you move the beads in a step of 10 then a step of 1? Can you move the beads in a step of 5 and 2? How can you do that in one step? What other partitions of 11 and 7 can you find? Can you show that on a number line? How about on a 100 square?*

Broadening understanding

Encourage children to construct problems and puzzles using the steps of 7 and multiplication facts involving 7 and 11, using Steps 3 and 4 as examples.

Concept mastered

Children can count forwards and backwards in steps of 7 from any number. They can recall the multiplication facts for 7 and 11 and apply them to solve problems.

Follow-up ideas

- In the run-up to Christmas or Easter or other event, count in 7s to work out how many weeks there are to go.

- Collect examples from their other lessons and life at home of using the multiplication facts for 7 and 11.

- Ask children to draw a 2 by 3 grid and write a 2-digit number in each space. Call out table facts (e.g. 7×8); if children have the answer on their grid they cross it out. The first to cross out all their numbers and call 'bingo' is the winner. Discuss whether there is anything children can do to increase their chance of winning (e.g. choose number that appear in several times tables, such as 36).

Answers

Step 1

a	7, 14, 21, 28, 35, 42, 49, 56		f	$42 \div 7 = 6$
b	no	f	63	g	$121 \div 11 = 11$
c	yes	g	77	h	$8 = 56 \div 7$
d	–1	h	56	
e	42			

Step 2

a   4, 15, 26

b   11, 18 , 25 , 32 , 39

c   52, 45 , 38 , 31, 24

d   1 , 8 , 15, 22, 29

e $84 = 7 \times 12$

Step 3

a   10th November

b   13th March

c   35 hours

d   42 days

e   73 days, 10 weeks and 3 days

Step 4

a   Answers will vary.

b   Sunday

- Use place value, known and derived facts to multiply and divide mentally, including: multiplying by 0 and 1; dividing by 1; multiplying together three numbers.

Homework 41 and 42   Practice Book pp 78–80

Mathematical vocabulary

Multiply, divide, identity, multiplicand, dividend, product

Representations and resources

Counters, number rods, 1–6 dice.

Warming up

Practise multiplication facts, including those that involve 1 as a multiplier or divisor, e.g. Work out 4×1, $9 \div 1$, etc. Then practise finding factor pairs of numbers: *What pairs of numbers multiply to make 40?* Children can include the products that involve 1. Following on from this, practise identifying multiples of given numbers, e.g. *Which of 34, 38, 42, 46 is a multiple of 6?*

Background knowledge

Zero and one are special numbers as they behave differently when used in calculations. One is called the 'identity' for multiplication (and division) as it does not change the value of the multiplicand or dividend. This actually makes it easy to use but many children make errors, often adding or subtracting instead. Zero, when used as a multiplier, makes any number zero. Dividing by zero cannot be done, which is why it is not included in the curriculum at this level.

Multiplication is a binary operation which means it can only be done to 2 numbers at a time. When there are 3 numbers in a product you have to use the associative law to multiply two of them and then multiply the product by the third number. This has been met before in Unit 3.

Let's learn: Modelling and teaching

Zero and one

- Write the calculation $\triangle \times \bullet = \triangle$ on the board. Ask children what they notice. Agree that the first number and the last number are the same. Tell children this can be any number, e.g. 5; write up $5 \times \bullet = 5$. Ask children to count out 5 counters. *How many lots of 5 counters do I need to make the statement true?* Agree 1. Repeat, substituting other numbers for the circle. Children could also test what happens when $\triangle$ is very large, or $\frac{1}{2}$, by writing down the statement and substituting different values for $\bullet$, to convince themselves that 1 is the only possible answer in all cases.

- To explore multiplying by zero, give children counters and ask them to count out, say, 4. Explain that you have 2 lots of 4. Ask: *How many do I have in total? 3 lots? 0 lots?* Repeat for other groups of counters, including 0 lots each time and asking children to write down their answers. Ask: *For how many lots is the answer always the same?* Agree 0. Write up the related number statements and agree that zero multiplied by any number is always zero.

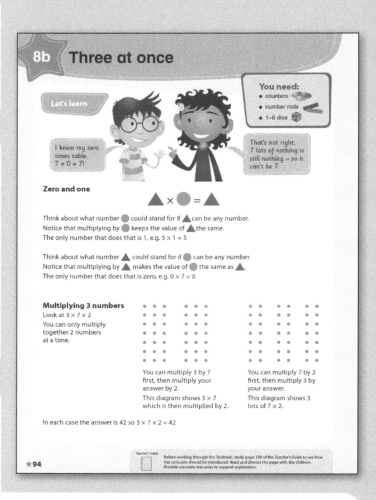

Multiplying 3 numbers

- Ask children to think about how they would work out $3 \times 7 \times 2$. Explain that multiplication can only be done to two numbers at a time. Have plenty of counters available. Remind them that drawing a picture or diagram can help and using concrete materials is also useful.

- Allow several minutes of thinking time and then ask for any ideas. If they are not forthcoming, show the 3 by 7 array in the Textbook and ask how it could help. Demonstrate multiplying by 2 to get 42. Then show how 7×2 could also be a starting point and that the answer will need to be multiplied by 3. Further support may be offered by starting with a group of 3 counters and building up to 7 lots of that and then 2 lots of 21 counters.

Let's practise: Digging deeper

Step 1

The calculations themselves are easy to work out. Some children may make errors through misinterpreting them. Ask children to phrase the calculation in their own words, e.g. What is seven lots of zero worth? Ask them to draw the appropriate array, or make it using counters. When three numbers are to be multiplied, ask children which two they will work out first. Encourage them to justify their choice so that they remain flexible in their approach.

Step 2

Ask children to phrase the questions in their own words, e.g. *What do I multiply eight by to get eight?* Or encourage them to start drawing the appropriate array to work out the missing numbers. It may not be necessary to complete the drawing as the important part is thinking through how to draw the diagram. That is usually enough to prompt the correct answer. Different

arrangements also develop understanding of the equals sign as indicating two things are 'worth the same'. Ask children to explain why their answer is correct and how they might explain to a fellow pupil who is struggling.

Step 3

Provide children with number rods to complete this task. By manipulating the rods, children will be able to practically explore multiplying three numbers. Prompt children as they complete the task by asking questions such as: *What is special about the size of the rods that makes them fit? What numbers could they represent? Is it easier to decide on the smallest number or the largest first before working out the rest?*

Step 4

The puzzle in part a allows children to exploit the properties of one and zero in order to use all four numbers to make each number from one to ten. To solve puzzles like this it can be helpful to make the target number without following all of the constraints and then see how you can include them by exploiting the properties of one and zero. Children should record their calculation, making it clear what order the steps should be done, perhaps using a number machine or annotations.

Part b allows children to see that they will only be able to generate some numbers this way. Primes above 5 will not be possible and children should be encouraged to explain why this is. The same applies for other numbers that do not appear.

Let's practise

1 **Calculate.**

a $7 \times 0 =$ c $0 \times 11 =$ e $2 \times 3 \times 5 =$ g $6 \times 4 \times 2 =$

b $3 \times 1 =$ d $1 \times 8 =$ f $10 \times 2 \times 5 =$ h $7 \times 1 \times 8 =$

2 **Answer these.**
Copy and complete.

a $8 \times \boxed{} = 8$ d $0 = \boxed{} \div 12$ g $48 \div 6 = 2 \times 2 \times \boxed{}$

b $0 = 11 \times \boxed{}$ e $2 \times \boxed{} \times 7 = 42$ h $8 \times \boxed{} \times \boxed{} = 40$

c $5 + \boxed{} = 5$ f $28 = 2 \times 2 \times \boxed{}$

3 **Solve.**

Solve these problems using number rods.

a The bar model represents the product of 3 single-digit numbers. Write down 4 possible products that it could represent.

b If each of the white bars represents 2, what do the other bars represent?

c If each of the red bars represents 6, what do the other bars represent?

d If the brown bar represents 8, what do the other bars represent?

Can you make another arrangement of rods with 3 layers so that each layer has the same size of rod? And another?

4 **Think.**

a Use the digits 0, 1, 2 and 3 once each to make each of the numbers from 1 to 10. You may use any of the operations $+$, $-$, $\times$ and $\div$ and you may place the digits next to each other to form 2-digit numbers, e.g. $1 = 1 + 2 \times 3 \times 0$.

b Throw 3 normal dice 10 times. Each time, multiply together the 3 numbers that are thrown and record the result. What do you notice about the products?

Teacher's Guide See page 109 of the *Teacher's Guide* for ideas of how to guide practice. Work through each step together as a class to develop children's conceptual understanding.

95 ★

Follow-up ideas

- Ask children to think about when they might multiply or divide by one and to make a poster of the ideas.

- Ask children to think about when they might multiply by zero. Are there any occasions when you have noticed yourself doing it?

- Make a working wall of the different ways to think about and work out the product of three numbers. Use speech bubbles to explain what is happening.

- Choose a number, e.g. 20, and see how it can be written as the product of three numbers. $2 \times 2 \times 5$, etc.

Ensuring progress

Supporting understanding

Work with children in a focus group to explore arrays. Ask children to model the calculations using counters. Encourage them to arrange the counters systematically and prompt them towards setting out arrays by asking questions, e.g. *How could we make it easier to count these? Is there a way to do this more quickly?*

Broadening understanding

Ask children to devise their own bar model problems, similar to those in Step 3, and share with a partner. Do they find the problems are hard or easy? Why?

✓ ## Concept mastered

Children can multiply and divide by 1, and multiply by zero. They can multiply three numbers together.

Answers

Step 1

a 0

b 3

c 0

d 8

e 30

f 100

g 48

h 56

g $48 \div 6 = 2 \times 2 \times 2$

h $8 \times 5 \times 1 = 40$

Step 3

a E.g. $8 \times 3 = 4 \times 6 = 24$

b $8 \times 2 = 4 \times 4 = 16$

c white 3, brown 24

d white 1, red 2

Step 4

Answers will vary.

Step 2

a $8 \times 1 = 8$ c $5 \div 1 = 5$

b $0 = 11 \times 0$ d $0 = 0 \div 12$

e $2 \times 3 \times 7 = 42$

f $28 = 2 \times 2 \times 7$

Written methods

- Multiply 2-digit numbers by a single-digit number using a formal written layout.
- Solve problems involving multiplying and adding.

Homework 43 and 44   Practice Book pp 81–3

Mathematical vocabulary

Sum, multiply, add, product, distributive, array, digit

Representations and resources

Whiteboards and pens, number rods, place-value counters.

Warming up

Ask children quick-fire questions to practise partitioning numbers (*Which numbers add to make 20?*), multiplication table facts (*What is the product of 6 and 7?*) and identifying place value (*How many tens are there in 348?* (34) *and what is the tens digit in 348?* (4)) Alternatively, practise using the grid method to multiply a 2-digit number by a single digit asking questions such as *63 × 6 and 28 × 9*. Children should write their method and answers on individual whiteboards.

Background knowledge

The short written method is a more efficient written method. In this concept you will use short multiplication to multiply a 2-digit number by a single digit. In 3c – Calculating on paper you made the connection with an array of counters. On page 36 of the Textbook you will find the same calculation in to provide continuity and consolidation. The progression here is from methods that support conceptual understanding, but are not efficient, towards those that are efficient but the conceptual understanding is hidden. Asking children why numbers have been recorded where they have been in these methods can help expose the conceptual understanding. The aspect of solving word problems explored here is which numbers need to be multiplied and which added. It uses the idea that multiplication is distributive over addition. Children should be aware that some items are repeated so may be multiplied and multiplying after adding means all items in the calculation are multiplied.

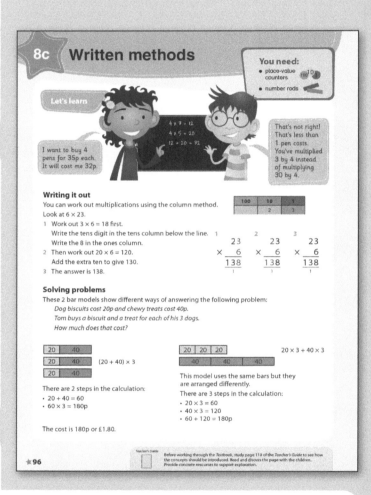

Let's learn: Modelling and teaching

Writing it out

- Refer back to the calculation on page 36 in the Textbook. Model the two calculations using place-value counters and write the corresponding step on the whiteboard. For each step in the written method ask: *What is the same and what is different about the two methods?*

- Develop the discussion by asking further questions: *Why does 18 appear in both calculations? Why does 12 (or 120) appear in one while 13 appears in the other? Where is 12 is hiding in the short written method? What has happened to the zero in the short written method?*

- Working in small groups, children identify where each digit goes in each version, using place-value counters to explain what is happening at each step.

Solving problems

- Read the problem in the Textbook. Ask children to discuss

with a partner how they would work out the answer. Take feedback. Ask children to model the problem using number rods. Invite them to model the problem again, using place-value counters to show the correct size for the numbers.

- Look at the first diagram in the Textbook. Compare it to the number rod models. Ask: *What strategy is used?* Talk through the method step by step, sketching the bars and writing down the calculations.

- Challenge children to rearrange their number rods to show a different way of finding the solution. Reveal the second diagram. Ask: *Why are the two amounts added? Why are both amounts multiplied by three?* Ask: *What is the same and what is different about each method?* Draw attention to which bars are multiplied and which are added. Discuss the advantages and disadvantages of each method.

Let's practise: Digging deeper

Step 1

Children can use whiteboards to write out their working for parts a–d, using the more familiar box or array method before transferring it to the short multiplication arrangement. This supports them in connecting the arrangement of the digits with their conceptual understanding of the process. Parts e–g may be modelled using number rods before drawing them as bar models in order to see which numbers are multiplied and which are added.

Step 2

Children can use whiteboards to draft their responses to parts a–d so that they can conjecture about what the missing digit might be before working through the calculation to check. If necessary, ask questions such as: *What number do you need to multiply by 3 to get a ones digit of 6?* They can model parts e–h using number rods, progressing to the bar model, or go straight to the bar model if they are confident. All children should be encouraged to draw bar models to embed their understanding.

Step 3

Children should use a bar model to translate the question in context into a mathematical problem. Even if children are confident they know what to do, drawing the bar model to show it is an important step in embedding their understanding. Challenge them to solve it in a different way, still using a bar model, or explain why there is only one reasonable way to approach it.

Step 4

Children develop their understanding of place value and its effect on the size of a product, which supports understanding of both ideas in this section. Encourage them to think first about which digits would make the largest product possible. Prompt them to think more deeply by asking questions such as: *Have you tried different arrangements using 4, 5 and 6? Why do you think 54 × 6 gave a larger product than 64 × 5?* The second task extends these ideas and encourages the development of systematic working to find all of the ideas.

Ensuring progress

Supporting understanding

Use coloured counters to model versions of the calculations with smaller numbers. Ask: *How can you use these counters to help you complete the same calculation with larger numbers?* When children are confident using these, introduce place-value counters and allow them to use these to to explore modelling each step in the method.

Broadening understanding

Ask children to make up a problem that is harder than those they have already attempted. They should explain why it is harder. Suggest they make up some bar diagrams and then construct some word problems to match them.

Concept mastered

Children can use a formal written method to multiply a 2-digit number by a single digit. They can solve problems involving multiplying and adding.

Let's practise

1 Calculate.

a   32 × 4 =   d   86 × 7 =   g   3 × 6 + 7 × 2 =

b   6 × 41 =   e   5 × 6 + 11 =

c   57 × 8 =   f   4 × 8 + 6 × 8 =

Remember, always multiply before you add. Draw bar models to help you.

2 Answer these.
Copy and complete.

a
```
    5 ☐
×     3
  1 5 6
```
b
```
    4 6
×   ☐
  2 7 6
```
c
```
    ☐ ☐
×     9
  7 8 3
```
d
```
    ☐ ☐
×     3
  3 9 2
```

Remember, always multiply before you add. Draw bar models to help you.

e   6 × 3 + ☐ = 23   g   63 = 2 × 9 + ☐ × 9

f   42 = 8 × ☐ + 10   h   3 × 5 + ☐ = 7 × 2 + 9

3 Solve.
Solve these word problems using multiplication and addition.

a   Ana watches 4 cartoons, each lasting 20 minutes, then a film lasting 70 minutes. How long was she watching, in hours and minutes?

b   Tom buys 6 apples at 43p each. How much does that cost altogether?

c   Peaches weigh 100 g each and oranges weigh 120 g each. How much do 7 peaches and 7 oranges weigh altogether?

d   How many days are there in 26 weeks?

e   A piece of cod costs £3.60 and a portion of chips costs £1.80. How much do 4 portions of cod and chips cost?

4 Think.

a   Use 3 of the numbers from 1 to 6 to replace the boxes in ☐☐ × ☐. Which arrangement of numbers gives the highest product?

b   Use 4 of the numbers from 1 to 6 to replace the boxes so that ☐ × ☐ + ☐ × ☐ = 24.

What if you use 4 of the numbers from 1 to 9? How many ways are there of doing it?

Teacher's Guide   See page 111 of the Teacher's Guide for ideas of how to guide practice. Work through each step together as a class to develop children's conceptual understanding.

97

Follow-up ideas

- Ask children to make up problems that look like they should be done by a formal written method but in fact are easier using a mental method.

- Children can make a presentation to explain how to do short multiplication.

- Children draw a bar model for a problem involving multiplying and adding. They then swap models and make up word problems for the model they have now.

- Children make up problems involving capacity that require both multiplying and adding.

Answers

Step 1

a   128   e   41

b   246   f   80

c   456   g   32

d   602

Step 2

a
```
    5 2
×     3
  1 5 6
```
c
```
    8 7
×     9
  7 8 3
```
b
```
    4 6
×     6
  2 7 6
```
d
```
    5 6
×     7
  3 9 2
```

e   6 × 3 + 5 = 23

f   42 = 8 × 4 + 10

g   63 = 2 × 9 + 5 × 9

h   3 × 5 + 8 = 7 × 2 + 9

Step 3

a   2 hours 30 minutes

b   £2.58

c   1540 g

d   182 days

e   £21.60

Step 4

a   54 × 6 = 324

b   6 × 2 + 3 × 4 = 24

There are three unique solutions using the numbers 1 to 9, although they can be arranged in different ways.

1 × 6 + 2 × 9 = 24

1 × 9 + 3 × 5 = 24

2 × 6 + 3 × 4 = 24

8d Scaling

- **Solve integer scaling problems.**

Homework 45 and 46   Practice Book
pp 84–6

Mathematical vocabulary

Multiplication, division, addition, scaling, integer

Warming up

Practise multiplication table facts in both multiplicative and division formats. Ask questions in a range of different ways, e.g. *What is 4 × 8? What is the product of 7 × 5? 49 divided by which number gives 7? 3 multiplied by which number gives 36? What is one third of 15? What fraction of 18 is 3? What are the factors of 30?* Children should write their answers on whiteboards.

Representations and resources

Multiplication squares, number rods, counters, straws, whiteboards, weighing scales, sand, measuring jugs, water (or pancake batter ingredients).

Background knowledge

There are two ways of looking at multiplication. One is as repeated addition. This is how children are usually introduced to multiplication and is also the way most people work out the answers to multiplication calculations. The other way is as a relation and this is the focus in this concept. It treats multiplication as an enlargement or scaling and as an operation in its own right. It is a more appropriate model for many of the applications of multiplication, particularly measurement. It is important to show that in scaling the numbers can be mapped to one another, by modelling language such as 'is 4 times as large as' and making effective use of the bar model.

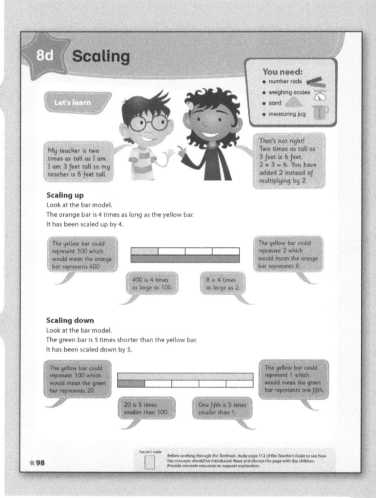

Let's learn: Modelling and teaching

Scaling up

- Look at the diagram in the Textbook, which shows a scaling of 4 times. Ask children to suggests what scaling means. Explain that when we scale we make something something larger or smaller. Explain that we can represent this relationship using bars.

- Give children number rods so they can model this. Encourage them to practically measure the shorter rod against the longer one. Encourage children to say what the relation between the two bars is and how they know, e.g. *How many times is the yellow bar as long as the orange bar? How do you know?* Try to avoid using the words 'larger than' as this could refer to the difference between them rather than the scale factor between them. Model how to record the scaling statement. Ask: *How do you know the orange bar must be 400 if the yellow one is 100?* Invite children to think of other pairs of values for the yellow and orange bars asking for another, and another. Then challenge children to find pairs of values which would not work as this helps establish the concept too.

Scaling down

- Look at the diagram in the Textbook showing scaling

down. Model how this can be recorded using the language '5 times smaller' and the language of fractions. Highlight that fractions and division are equivalent in many ways. Ask children what the scaling is and how they know that. Invite them to express it as a fraction. Encourage a deeper understanding by asking: *How do you know it is one fifth?*

- Ask children to model the example using number rods.

- Ask children to justify that the green one is 20 if the yellow one is 100. Invite suggestions for more pairs of numbers, including some involving fractions. Ask: *If the green bar is 7 what is the yellow bar? (35) If the green bar is one half, what is the yellow bar? ($2\frac{1}{2}$).*

Let's practise: Digging deeper
Step 1

Children with a secure knowledge of multiplication facts will answer these quickly. Encourage them to explain how they know by including the multiplication table fact they used and the version of it that yielded their answer, e.g. in part a they used 3 × 4 = 12 and that was the version that gave the answer. In part e they use 3 × 5 = 15 but used 15 ÷ 3 = 5 to get their answer. Using a multiplication square can support those who do not have quite such a secure knowledge base. Asking children to rephrase the question as a multiplication with a missing number can be helpful, *e.g. 8 multiplied by 6 is … or 7 multiplied by what is 84?* Ensure children represent their answers using a bar model.

Step 2

Similar strategies can support children here. Rephrasing the question as a multiplication and thinking about what fact was used to work out the answer are both helpful. Ask children

to draw a bar model as this develops their conceptual understanding of the topic and its application to solving problems. They could use number rods alongside sketching their own bar model.

Step 3

Children scale up and down in the practical context of measures. They could measure sand rather than flour, and water rather than milk; alternatively, you may wish to make pancake batter. Encourage children to compare the scaled up amounts that they have measured with the originals and one another. Ask: *Do they look right?* In part b, children should complete the scaling down calculation (using the bar model as a support) before checking their answers by measuring. Extend the task by asking them to scale the recipe up and/or down in other increments.

Step 4

Look at the two diagrams with children. Agree that the red bar is three times as long as the blue bar. You cannot match the length of one green bar to blue bars, but two green bars are five times as long as the blue bar. Ask children to use pairs of number rods to make matching lengths. They may need to use two or more of the longer bars. Encourage them to explore whether they can make matching lengths in any other way. They should realise that multiples of their original answer will also work. If necessary, refer to the diagram in the Textbook and ask questions such as: *How many blue bars would match 2 red bars?*

Let's practise

1 Answer these.
Represent each answer using a bar model.

a   What number is 3 times as large as 4?
b   What number is 7 times as large as 2?
c   What number is 6 times as large as 8?
d   What number is 8 times as large as 7?
e   What number is 3 times smaller than 15?
f   What number is 5 times smaller than 35?
g   What number is 10 times smaller than 40?
h   What number is 4 times smaller than 20?

2 Calculate.
Use the bar model to help you answer these questions.

a   How many times as large as 5 is 60?
b   How many times as large as 2 is 40?
c   42 is 6 times the size of a number. What is that number?
d   What number is half the size of 22?
e   7 is one third of the size of a number. What is that number?
f   8 is one tenth of the size of a number. What is that number?

3 Measure.

Pancakes
Serves 8
100 g flour
2 eggs
300 ml milk

a   Measure the flour and milk. Now scale each ingredient up by 3 times. Measure the flour and milk again. How much do you have now?

b   Scale the recipe down by half. How much flour will be needed? How much milk will be needed? How many eggs? Check your answers by measuring.

4 Think.

Look at the diagram.
3 blue bars match 1 red bar.
5 blue bars match 2 green bars.
Choose a pair of coloured rods. How many of each do you need to make matching lengths? Is there more than 1 answer?
Repeat with a second pair of rods. What do you notice?

Teacher's Guide
See page 113 of the *Teacher's Guide* for ideas of how to guide practice. Work through each step together as a class to develop children's conceptual understanding.

99

Ensuring progress
Supporting understanding

Expand the range of concrete resources that you use to model scaling up and scaling down, e.g. using counters or even straws.

Broadening understanding

Children can think of further examples of each type of question. Ask them to justify why their questions are appropriate. Ask another child to explain whether they would find the question hard or easy, and why.

✅ Concept mastered

Children can use multiplication as a relation when scaling.

Follow-up ideas

- Read the story of *Gulliver's Travels*. Decide what scaling is appropriate for the Lilliputians. Work out the size for their houses and other items, scaled appropriately.

- Read the story of *The Borrowers*. The people are about 6 inches tall. Decide on the scaling required and make a real life-sized (for Borrowers) house and furniture.

- Find a recipe and scale it up or down for different numbers of people.

- Explore how many desk widths wide the classroom is or how many desk heights high the classroom is, and so on.

Answers

Step 1

a   12   e   5
b   14   f   7
c   48   g   4
d   56   h   5

Step 2

a   12   d   11
b   20   e   21
c   7   f   80

Step 3

a   300 g flour; 900 ml milk
b   50 g flour; 150 ml milk; 1 egg

Step 4

Answers will vary.

Lucky numbers

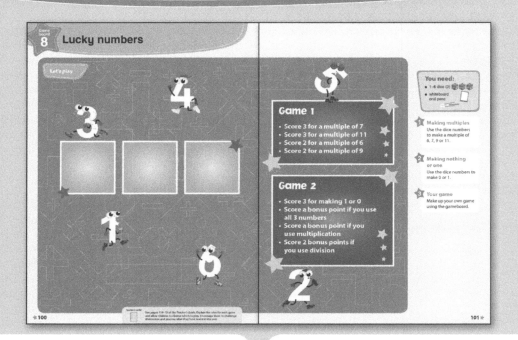

Game 1: Making multiples

Players use the dice numbers to make another number using addition, subtraction, multiplication and division as needed. The aim is to make a multiple of 6, 7, 9 or 11.

Maths focus

- Identify multiples
- Calculate with more than one operation

Resources

1–6 dice (4), whiteboard and pen (1 per player).

How to play

Players take it in turns to roll three dice. They try to make a multiple of 6, 7, 9 or 11 using all three dice numbers and any of the four operations. They score 3 for a multiple of 7 or 11, or 2 for a multiple of 6 or 9. Players keep a running total of their scores. The winner is the player with the highest score achieved during a set time (or the first player to reach a pre-agreed target such as 20). Prompt children to consider higher scoring multiples first and allow them to use a whiteboard to draft their calculations. Ask them how they know if a number is a multiple of 7 or 11. *Which numbers could you try to make first?*

Making it easier

Use a fourth dice to provide another number or have a 'wild card' that can be whatever number between 1 and 6 that the player chooses it to be.

Making it harder

Use a fourth dice and stipulate that all 4 numbers should be part of the calculation.

Game 3: Your game

Children should invent their own game designing rules that use the concepts covered in the unit. Challenge children to make their game easier or harder.

Game 2: Making nothing or one

Players use the dice numbers to make 1 or 0.

Maths focus

- Calculate with more than one operation

Resources

1–6 dice (4), whiteboard and pen (1 per player).

How to play

Players take it in turns to roll three dice. They try to make 0 or 1 using the dice numbers; the numbers can be added, subtracted, multiplied or divided. Players score 3 for making 1 or 0 successfully and can win a bonus point by using all 3 numbers or multiplication, and 2 bonus points by using division, e.g. if they throw 2, 3 and 6, they could make $3 - 2 = 1$ (scores 3), $6 - (2 + 3) = 1$ (scores 4), $6 - (3 \times 2) = 0$ (scores 5) or $6 \div (2 \times 3) = 1$ (scores 7). (Children are not expected to write number statements using brackets at this level, but they can explain what they are doing in words.) Players keep a running total of their scores. The winner is the player with the highest score achieved during a set time (or the first player to reach a pre-agreed target such as 25). Prompt children to consider inverse operations to get zero by addition and subtraction or 1 by multiplication and division. Discuss strategies, e.g. *Can you use two of the dice numbers to make the third number? Or one more or less than the third number?*

Making it easier

Allowing one other number can help a great deal. This could be generated by throwing a fourth dice, or chosen by the player (discuss what might be a sensible choice). Selecting one number that can be used when required, always 4, say, could generate some valuable discussion.

Making it harder

Set additional constraints, e.g. that the operations used to combine the numbers must be different or decided on in advance.

Unit 8 — Lucky numbers

Choose a game to play.

Game 1: Making multiples

You need:
- 1–6 dice (3)
- whiteboards and pens

How to play
- Take turns to roll 3 dice. Put them in the spaces on the gameboard.
- Use the dice numbers to make another number. You can add, subtract, multiply and divide.
  - Score 3 for a multiple of 7
  - Score 3 for a multiple of 11
  - Score 2 for a multiple of 6
  - Score 2 for a multiple of 9
- Keep a running total of your score. The player with the highest score wins.

Game 2: Making nothing or one

You need:
- 1–6 dice (3)
- whiteboards and pens

How to play
- Take turns to roll 3 dice. Put them in the spaces on the gameboard.
- Use the dice numbers to make another number. You can add, subtract, multiply and divide.
  - Score 3 for making 1 or 0
  - Score a bonus point if you use all 3 numbers
  - Score a bonus point if you use multiplication
  - Score 2 bonus points if you use division
- Keep a running total of your score. The player with the highest score wins.

Game 3: Your game

- Design your own game. Explain the rules and play with a partner.

Please help your child by reading the instructions and playing the game together.

Assessment task 1

Resources

Number rods.

Running the task

The wrong answers show some of the misconceptions children may have on the topics in this unit.

Children should be familiar with this type of task and so will know how to tackle it. If not, work through some similar examples with them, encouraging them to begin by working out the correct answer, as this can help identify the error that was made.

Ask questions as they work through the task, and expect them to explain their reasoning. This will help them formulate feedback for Tom.

For part a, ask them to put the question into words (*How many is no lots of 1? or How many is 1 lot of nothing?*).

For part b, ask them to talk you through the short multiplication method so that they can identify what Tom did not do (carry the 5 tens into the tens column).

If children cannot identify Tom's mistake in part c, give them rods so that they can model the question. They should be able to see that 7 is not 3 times as large as 4 and establish that 12 is.

For part d, encourage children to look carefully at the question and work out what they need to do. Each number needs to be used only once (Tom's mistake in part d is to multiply both 5 and 7 by 2).

Part e is a good opportunity to discuss ways of remembering the harder 11 times table facts (11×11 and 12×11).

In part f children use rods to explain that 18 is not 6 times smaller than 24, but 4 is.

Evidencing mastery

Children who can find the correct answer and also identify the mistake and write helpful feedback are evidencing mastery of the concepts covered.

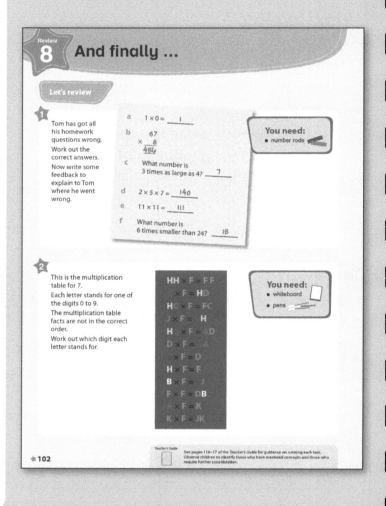

Assessment task 2

Resources

Whiteboards and pens.

Running the task

Allow children plenty of time to look for a suitable starting point, prompting them if necessary. They should notice that F stands for 7 since it appears in every line, on its own. This will enable them to work out that $H = 1$ (because $H \times 7 = 7$ and $HH \times 7 = 77$) and that $D = 4$ and $B = 9$ (because $7 \times 7 = DB$). These values in turn will reveal others.

If children guess, e.g. reasoning that since $F = 7$, $G \times F = HD$ could be $3 \times 7 = 21$, encourage them to find another fact in the table to see if it fits; e.g. $D \times F = GA$ would be $1 \times 7 = 3A$, which is clearly incorrect. This should help them see that there must be a fact in the form (letter) $\times F = F$, guiding them towards the strategy described above.

Support children who have significant difficulty getting started by suggesting that they write out the 7 times table and look for patterns. Most children will benefit from being given several copies of the task so that they can try out ideas and see if they work, or from using whiteboards to record; e.g. once they have established that $F = 7$, they can erase all the 'F's and write '7' in their place. Encourage them write the letters ($A – H$, J) along the bottom so that they can also record the value of each letter there. The use of coloured pens will also help children keep track of what they have discovered.

If children enjoy this activity, you could challenge them to make up a similar code for a friend to solve, based on another times table.

Evidencing mastery

Children who accurately crack the code, working systematically and recalling the 7 times table, are evidencing mastery.

Concepts mastered

☑ Children can count forwards and backwards in steps of 7 from any number. They can recall the multiplication facts for 7 and 11 and apply them to solve problems.

☑ Children can multiply and divide by 1, and multiply by zero. They can multiply three numbers together.

☑ Children can use a formal written method to multiply a 2-digit number by a single digit. They can solve problems involving multiplying and adding.

☑ Children can use multiplication as a relation when scaling.

Assessment task 3

Running the task

Start by looking at Ana's numbers. Then model a different group of three numbers, perhaps 1, 2 and 9. This has a product of $1 \times 2 \times 9 = 18$ which is larger than 10. They should now be able to proceed with the task to find the group of three numbers with the greatest product.

As they do so, encourage them to tell you what they notice and explain how they choose the next set of numbers to try. Expect them to reason that larger numbers will result in a larger product. They need to establish, through trial and error, that three numbers which are all as large as possible give a larger product than one large and two small numbers. Encourage them to work systematically, e.g. following 1, 1 and 10 and 1, 2 and 9 with 1, 3 and 8, then 1, 4 and 7, and finally 1, 5 and 6. They can then vary the first number in a similar way. They should conclude that 4, 4 and 4 gives the largest product.

Encourage children to use the same process when they move on to consider numbers that add up to 10. Some children may immediately suggest that 3, 3 and 4 will give the largest product; if so, ask them to test at least some combinations of numbers to check that the pattern they found when working with 12 still applies.

As a final step, children need to formulate a general rule, putting what they have noticed into their own words. They may say that all three numbers need to be as large as possible, that the numbers needs to be as close together as possible, or that you need to partition the total into thirds. This last way of putting it is perhaps the most efficient when it comes to applying the rule to other totals.

Evidencing mastery

Children who solve the problem correctly, multiplying three numbers with accuracy and confidence, are demonstrating a solid grasp of this concept.

Did you know?

Discussion of the number 7 can be extremely wide-ranging, with links to many areas of the curriculum, including spiritual, moral, historical and mythological aspects. The number 7 is special in many religions, including Christianity and other religions that tell the story of Genesis, as noted in the Textbook. In addition, there are seven wonders of the ancient world (geography and history), seven colours in a rainbow (science) and a musical 'Seven brides for seven brothers' (music). Literary references to 7 also are common and children can research some of these.

Mathematical focus

★ **Geometry: properties of shape, position and direction**

Prior learning

Children should already be able to:

- recognise and compare a variety of polygons, including all triangles and some quadrilaterals, based on their properties

- use mathematical vocabulary to describe position, direction and movement, including movement in a straight line.

Key new learning

- Compare and classify geometric shapes, including all types of quadrilaterals and triangles, based on their properties and sizes.

- Describe positions on a 2-D grid as coordinates in the first quadrant.

- Describe movements between positions as translations of a given unit to the left/right and up/down.

- Plot specified points and draw sides to complete a given polygon.

Making connections

- Coordinate pairs appear in line graphs in science when comparing two sets of numerical data such as temperature and time, e.g. children may have carried out experiments investigating the effect of different insulators on cooling.

- Computer programmers use coordinate geometry in pdf files where (x, y) coordinates of each element on the page allow them to be correctly positioned. Scanners also use coordinate geometry to reproduce the exact image of a picture in the computer.

- Children meet kite shapes in art and may have experience of actual kites, ranging from simple handheld kites to power kites, and kite surfing.

- Translated patterns appear in many examples of interior decor, e.g. fabric and tile patterns.

Talk about

It is important to use precise mathematical vocabulary from the beginning. Unlike most of the names for different quadrilaterals which are not used outside mathematics, the word kite is used in everyday speech to describe this shape of quadrilateral, so it is an easy one for children to learn and use. The other new quadrilateral is a trapezium. This is also the name for the small bone at the base of the thumb where it joins the wrist.

When a shape is translated in mathematics it means that it is moved to a new place but does not change its size or shape. Every property remains the same. Ensure that children understand this idea through plenty of mathematical discussion.

Engaging and exploring

Give children plenty of time to explore each photo and to think individually, with a partner and then share their ideas with the class. Focus on each photo in turn and engage children in discussion.

The first photo is a close-up of part of the Scottish Parliament building in Edinburgh. Ask children to describe the shapes they can see. You could also talk about the angles and look for parallel and perpendicular lines.

Use the photo as a springboard to discuss different polygons. Provide 2-D shapes to support the discussion. You could be systematic about the discussion and move through 2-D shapes, gradually increasing the number of sides and collecting examples. Ask questions such as: *What is a polygon with five sides called? Can you see one in the photo? Can you find a pentagon in the 2-D shapes? Where else do you see pentagons in everyday life?*

I wonder if you can use polygons to make a picture of *anything*?

I wonder how you can plant an orchard to look so perfect?

How could you describe the position of a chess piece on the board?

Teacher's Guide Look at the pictures with the children and discuss the questions. See pages 118–19 of the Teacher's Guide for key ideas to draw out.

105

Things to think about

- How will you organise mixed attainment pairs to give maximum opportunity for paired talk?

- How will you provide support for children who need more practice to assimilate the concepts and develop fluency?

- What will you do to ensure that the classroom is a shape-rich environment where 2-D (and 3-D) shapes can be handled in informal settings?

- What problem-solving strategies will you use to develop reasoning? These could include: Always, sometimes, never; Another, another, another; Convince me; If this is the answer, what's the question?; Odd one out; Silly answers; What do you notice? and What's the same, what's different?

The tangram is composed of a number of specific triangles and quadrilaterals that fit together to make a square. This traditional puzzle was brought to the Western world from China. Ask: *What are the names of the different shapes? How many triangles are there of each size? How many of the smallest triangles would make the largest one? Can you use the shapes to make two different quadrilaterals? If the side of the square is one unit, can you deduce the lengths of the sides of other pieces?* The seven shapes can be arranged in a huge number of ways to make a great variety of animals, people and objects. An example of each is shown and there are many more examples on the Internet. Printable tangrams and instructions on how to construct one are freely available on the Internet (e.g. www.activityvillage.co.uk/tangrams; www.enchantedlearning.com). Let children experiment with the shapes or suggest something specific to make, e.g. numbers and capital letters.

The map of the world composed of polygons is surprisingly accurate and lends itself to discussion on many levels, not least identifying individual countries and thinking about the colours that have been chosen to represent them. Ask children to look for and identify different polygons.

The question posed asks whether you can make a picture of anything from polygons and the simple answer is yes. Ask: *Which shapes would be the most useful?* Triangles are especially versatile to build up more complex shapes and rectangles would be really useful to make straight-sided shapes. This idea, where the number and shape of the polygons is unlimited, develops the previous photo showing the tangram where the pieces are exactly prescribed. Ask children to compare the two images to reinforce this connection.

The photo of the chess game highlights the importance of the chessboard. The grid is integral to the game, holding the pieces in specific positions. Ask whether any children have played chess. Can they explain how the different pieces move? Ask children to suggest how you could identify each square. Explain that every square on the board has a unique letter and number combination to identify it and this allows moves in a game to be recorded. Ask children to find specific squares using this method.

The final photo, of the orchard, shows very carefully-spaced lines of trees and asks how you can plant an orchard to look perfect. Encourage children to describe the field as an enormous coordinate grid with a tree planted at each intersection. In this way the rows and columns are evenly spaced so that the distance from one tree to the next in all four directions is identical. The pattern of the trees is repeated over and over again.

Ask children to give you other examples of where they see repeating patterns. They may suggest chairs in assembly, tiles or patterns in wallpaper and fabric. You could ask them to collect examples. This kind of awareness is ideal preparation for the work on translation.

Checking understanding

Children can compare and classify quadrilaterals, including trapeziums and kites, and other geometric shapes based on their properties and sizes. They can describe positions on a 2-D grid as coordinates in the first quadrant, plot specified points and draw sides to complete a given polygon. They can translate shapes to the left/right and up/down within the first quadrant.

Homework 47 and 48

Practice Book pp 87–90

2D Shapes

- Compare and classify geometric shapes, including all types of quadrilaterals and triangles, based on their properties and sizes.

Mathematical vocabulary

Trapezium, kite, diagonal

Representations and resources

2-D shapes, individual whiteboards and pens, geoboards and elastic bands, squared paper, rulers, scissors.

Warming up

Count in sevens from zero to 70. Ask children questions using seven times table facts, e.g. *How many sevens in 49? What is 7 × 9?* Extend the seven times table to the 70 times table and set similar questions. Write a number sentence on the board, e.g. 70 × 4 = 280 and ask children what other number facts they can deduce from it, e.g. 4 × 70 = 280, 280 ÷ 70 = 4 and 280 ÷ 4 = 70.

Background knowledge

This concept introduces children to the trapezium (a quadrilateral with one pair of parallel opposite sides) and kite (a quadrilateral with two pairs of sides of equal length that are next to each other) so they will now have learnt all seven of the different types of quadrilaterals: square, rectangle, rhombus, parallelogram, trapezium, kite and irregular quadrilateral. The the only regular quadrilateral is the square.

This Venn diagram shows how quadrilaterals are related.

All squares are parallelograms, rectangles and rhombuses. Trapeziums can never be parallelograms.

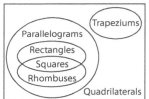

Kites are quadrilaterals with two pairs of adjacent equal sides. They are trickier to place in the diagram. They could be set in a separate ring. However, if both pairs of sides are equal, the kite becomes a rhombus and if the angles are all equal, the kite becomes a square.

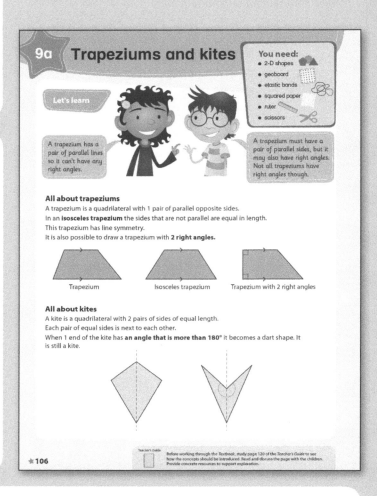

Let's learn: Modelling and teaching

All about trapeziums

- Give children individual geoboards and ask them to make sets of parallel lines of different lengths, with the shorter line on top. Join the ends with two more rubber bands to make a trapezium. Compare their trapezium with the diagrams in the Textbook and identify which one they have made. Challenge them to make the other types.

- Give children a variety of 2-D quadrilaterals. Ask questions comparing two quadrilaterals, e.g. *What's the same about a parallelogram and a trapezium and what is different?* (They are the same because they are both quadrilaterals and both have at least one pair of parallel lines. They are different because a parallelogram has two pairs of parallel lines while a trapezium has only one.)

All about kites

- Ask children to show you how to draw a line dividing a kite into two isosceles triangles on individual whiteboards. The Textbook definition for a kite states that, 'Each pair of equal sides is next to each other'. The correct mathematical term for sides that are next to each other is adjacent. Introduce this word if you feel it is appropriate.

- Children have not officially met angles greater than 180° but they will see, and may draw, concave polygons. Tell them, if they enquire, that angles greater than 180° are known as reflex angles and they will learn about them next year. A concave kite with a reflex angle is shown in the Textbook. This shape is sometimes called a dart or an inverted kite. Take the opportunity to discuss the angles in a kite. Ask: *Can a kite have a right angle? Can all its angles be acute?*

Let's practise: Digging deeper

Step 1

Prior to the task give children geoboards and elastic bands and ask them to make different trapeziums. Encourage them to compare the shapes that they make by looking at the angles and sides. Discuss which ones have a line of symmetry and why. Repeat the exercise asking them to make kites. After children have completed the task, they could review their responses and think about how they might organise the shapes in a Carroll diagram.

Step 2

This step examines the properties of the whole range of quadrilaterals and requires children to know their names. You may like to revisit the names and properties before children tackle the task. You could do this using individual whiteboards with a series of 'Show me' questions where children draw an appropriate quadrilateral. *Show me a quadrilateral with all angles equal. Show me a quadrilateral with one or more obtuse angles.* Ensure that children

have 2-D shapes to handle while they are carrying out the task.

Step 3

Give children geoboards and elastic bands to experiment with the diagonals on different kites before they design and draw their own. They could decorate their kites. If they do, ensure that their designs have a vertical line of symmetry. There are a number of observations that they can make. The longer diagonal is a line of symmetry. The shorter diagonal cuts the kite into two isosceles triangles. The diagonals intersect (cut one another) at right angles. The longer diagonal cuts the shorter one in half (bisects it).

Step 4

Children can make four isosceles right-angled triangles by drawing the diagonals on a square. They then cut carefully along the diagonals. Check that they understand how the shapes can be joined together before they begin making shapes. Two different triangles (both right-angled isosceles), and four different quadrilaterals (square, rectangle, parallelogram, trapezium) can be made, plus a number of irregular hexagons. Encourage children to be systematic in their approach and to record their findings carefully. Remind children to check that they do not list the same shape in different orientations; turning the page around may help them spot them.

Let's practise

1 **Answer these.**
Which shapes:

a   are trapeziums?

b   are kites?

c   have a line of symmetry?

d   have 1 or more right angles?

e   have 2 acute and 2 obtuse angles?

2 **Identify.**
Name the quadrilaterals:

a   with 2 pairs of parallel sides

b   with no lines of symmetry

c   with 1 or more pairs of opposite angles equal

d   with 2 pairs of equal angles.

1 quadrilateral appears in every answer, which is it?

3 **Design.**
Design 2 different kites.
Draw them on squared paper.
Add diagonal lines.
What do you notice?
Draw another kite.
What do you notice?
What about the diagonals of an inverted kite? (You will need to extend the diagonals.)
Explain the properties of the diagonals of a kite.

4 **Investigate.**
Make 4 small identical isosceles right-angled triangles.
Investigate how many different polygons you can make using all 4 triangles.
You can only join them:
• matching whole sides
• long side to long side
• short side to short side.
Draw the shapes you make on squared paper. Name them.

Teacher's Guide See page 121 of the Teacher's Guide for ideas of how to guide practice. Work through each step together as a class to develop children's conceptual understanding.

107

Ensuring progress

Supporting understanding

Display the vocabulary together with matching diagrams to support children with these challenging words. Work with children in a focus group to help them visualise the relationship between the quadrilaterals: *Close your eyes and imagine a square. Now visualise turning it through 90 degrees and then stretching it by pulling the bottom vertex downwards. What quadrilateral have you made?* Repeat with other transformations.

Broadening understanding

Ask children who can describe and compare the properties of quadrilaterals to investigate how many different length geostrips they would need to make all seven quadrilaterals. Groups of four children could also make large quadrilaterals with given properties using skipping ropes.

✓ **Concept mastered**

Children can compare and classify quadrilaterals, including trapeziums and kites, and other geometric shapes based on their properties and sizes.

Follow-up ideas

• Make a large kite with a symmetrical design in an art lesson.

• Give children pattern blocks or other manipulatives to make symmetrical and repeated patterns. They can also make repeated patterns using computer software programs.

• Children could try flying a kite. They can investigate kites and their history on the Internet. Kite festivals and competitions are held all over the world. Large kites are used in kite surfing, kite boarding and recently snow kiting.

Answers

Step 1

a   B, D, F, G   d   A, D, G, H

b   A, C, E, H   e   B, F

c   A, B, C, E, H

d   Isosceles trapezium, square, rhombus, rectangle, parallelogram. Parallelogram appears in every answer.

Step 2

a   Square, rhombus, rectangle, parallelogram.

b   Irregular quadrilateral, trapezium, parallelogram.

c   Kite, square, rhombus, rectangle, parallelogram.

Step 3

Diagonals of a kite always intersect at 90°. One diagonal is always bisected.

Step 4

Ten shapes are possible including parallelogram, square, rectangle, triangle and hexagon.

- Describe positions on a 2-D grid as coordinates in the first quadrant.
- Describe movements between positions as translations of a given unit to the left/right and up/down.
- Plot specified points and draw sides to complete a given polygon.

Homework 49 and 50   Practice Book pp 91–3

Representations and resources

0–9 digit cards, pre-drawn coordinate grids, 2-D shapes, squared paper, rulers.

Mathematical vocabulary

x-axis, y-axis, x-coordinate, y-coordinate, quadrant, translation

Warming up

Ask children to tell you the units used to measure length: centimetres, metres and kilometres. Ask them to show you with their hands one centimetre and one metre and to describe how far one kilometre is. Ask: *How many centimetres make one metre? How do you convert centimetres into metres?* Use 0–9 digit cards to generate 3-digit numbers and ask children to convert that number of centimetres to metres, e.g. 361 cm is 3.61 m. Elicit what operation they are carrying out to convert from centimetres to metres – dividing by 100. After some practice, move on to converting metres to kilometres. How many metres in a kilometre? 1 km = 1000 m. This time generate 4-digit numbers so that there is a whole number of kilometres before the decimal part, e.g. 4627 m is 4.627 km.

Background knowledge

The x- and y-axes are formed by drawing two number lines at right angles to one another with the intersection at zero. The section that children work in during Year 4 is called the first quadrant in which the values of x and y are always positive. An x-coordinate value and a y-coordinate value give a coordinate pair, (x, y), which locates a position on the grid where the lines intersect. Coordinate pairs can be used to draw shapes on a grid.

In a translation, every point of the shape moves the same distance in the same direction. The translated shape is identical to the original.

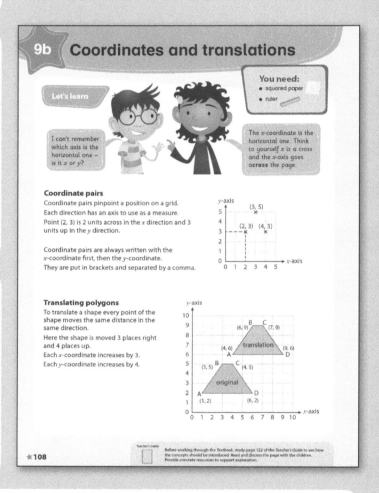

Let's learn: Modelling and teaching

Coordinate pairs

- Use the misconception cartoon to ensure that children understand the direction of each axis. The left-right (horizontal) direction is called the x-axis. The up-down (vertical) direction is called the y-axis. Move on to explain that x and y values pinpoint a position on a coordinate grid. As children look at the example in the Textbook, tell them to think, *Start at zero, go along two and up three, then plot the point.*

- There are various mnemonics to remember the order of coordinates, e.g. *x comes before y in the alphabet; go **along** the corridor, then **up** the stairs; and walk before you fly.* Ask children to draw the grid in the Textbook and to plot each point. They should trace the triangle they make with their finger.

Translating polygons

- Ask children to place a shape on a coordinate grid and draw around it. Ask them to move the shape physically left or right and up or down, and to draw around it again. Confirm that the shape has not changed in size or shape. Each point has moved the same distance in the same direction.

- Model the example in the Textbook. Move the trapezium three places to the right and ask what happens to the y-coordinates. Return the trapezium to the original position. Now move it four places up and ask what happens to the x-coordinates. Look at the translation to the right and up in the Textbook. Highlight the co-ordinates of the original and the translation. Ask children to plot a triangle and translate it three squares left and one square down. Elicit that movement left or down causes the new x and y coordinate values

Let's practise: Digging deeper
Step 1

Set out chairs in a five by five square grid to simulate coordinate points. Explain to children that you can describe an exact chair with two numbers. We describe the two directions as the x-axis, on paper that is the horizontal axis, and the y-axis, on paper that is the vertical one. Sit a child on chair (3, 2). Stand children in front of the x-axis chairs and help them to count along three columns to the child's position. Now count up two rows to see that the child's position can be exactly located as (3, 2). Challenge a child to sit on a particular chair, e.g. (1, 4). Follow this up by asking children to plot and identify points on a digital grid. When you feel they are confident, they can complete the task.

Step 2

Ask children to hold out their arm to show you the direction of the x- and y-coordinates. Ask: *What happens when a shape is translated?* Provide coordinate grids for those children who

would take a long time to draw this. Ask what they notice about the original and translated coordinates.

Step 3

Discuss codes with children. Ask if they think this would be an easy code to crack if they did not have the coordinate grid key. Look at the Textbook together and ask them to write the coordinates for the word 'Hello'. Decoding the questions and writing their own demonstrates sound understanding of coordinates.

Step 4

Read the task with children. Ask: *Which direction is the x-axis? What will happen if just the x-coordinates are doubled? Will the height of the shape change?* Children may be able to predict that the shape will move to the right and be twice as wide. Repeat with similar questions for doubling the y-coordinates, and both coordinates. If children are unable to predict the effect of doubling the x-coordinates, let them plot the points and see if they are then able to predict the effect of doubling the y-coordinates.

Let's practise

1 Plot.
Draw a 0–10 coordinate grid.
Plot these coordinates.

a (1, 2), (3, 2), (5, 5), (3, 5)

b (3, 6), (5, 7), (5, 9), (3, 10), (1, 9), (1, 7)

c (8, 1), (10, 6), (8, 9), (6, 6)

Join up the points and identify the shapes.

2 Design.
Draw a 0–10 coordinate grid.

a Plot the coordinates (6, 2), (8, 1), (8, 3).
Translate the shape 5 squares left.

b Plot the coordinates (0, 4), (1, 7), (3, 7), (2, 4). Translate the shape 6 squares right and 2 squares up.

Write the new coordinates after the translation.

Can you explain what has happened to the x- and y-coordinates?

3 Apply.
Here is a code using coordinates.

Use the code to answer these questions.

a (10, 10), (4, 5), (1, 3), (8, 2) (8, 5), (4, 6) (9, 4), (3, 1), (8, 1), (4, 9) (4, 7), (1, 3), (6, 3), (4, 2)?

b (4, 5), (3, 1), (10, 10) (3, 1), (6, 1), (7, 4) (1, 3), (4, 9), (4, 2) (9, 4), (3, 1), (8, 1)?

c Now write a question of your own.

4 Investigate.
Draw a 0–10 coordinate grid.
Plot a kite or a trapezium with all coordinate values less than 5.
Investigate what happens when you:

a double the x-coordinate value of each point

b double the y-coordinate value of each point

c double both coordinate values of each point

Teacher's Guide See page 123 of the Teacher's Guide for ideas of how to guide practice. Work through each step together as a class to develop children's conceptual understanding.

109

Ensuring progress
Supporting understanding

Consider providing a pro-forma of a zero to ten coordinate grid for the questions if drawing this is challenging. Some children may not remember how to place the x- and y-axes on the coordinate grid, despite the mnemonics. A kinaesthetic way to help them recall this is to demonstrate that the letter **y** has a **vertical** line in it, by drawing a large letter y in the air with a dramatic downward stroke.

To practise plotting coordinates in a fun setting, play coordinates 'Three in a row'. Children use a six by six coordinate grid. They throw two dice to determine a coordinate pair that they mark with a cross in their colour. The first child to get three crosses in a row is the winner.

Broadening understanding

Some children may enjoy plotting complex designs on coordinate grids. Examples of animals, types of transport, etc. are readily found on the Internet. Extend Step 3 by asking children to make up their own code for a partner to try out.

✓ Concept mastered

Children can describe positions on a 2-D grid as coordinates in the first quadrant, plot specified points and draw sides to complete a given polygon. They can translate shapes to the left/right and up/down within the first quadrant.

Follow-up ideas

- Brick wall designs involve translation of whole/part bricks and bricks of different colours. Many Victorian buildings feature beautiful brickwork. Ask children to investigate local buildings or Victorian architect Alfred Waterhouse.

- Curtains, wallpaper and clothes often have patterns that involve translation. Ask children to look for examples.

- Introduce children to the game of Battleships. This is a guessing game based on a grid where squares are identified by letter and numbers. Players secretly place their ships on their main grid and use a second grid to record their attempts to locate the ships of their opponent. When a ship is located, it is sunk. The winner is the first person to sink all their opponent's ships.

Answers

Step 1

a parallelogram

b (irregular) hexagon

c kite

Step 2

a (1, 2), (3, 1), (3, 3)

b (6, 6), (7, 9), (9, 9), (8, 6)

Step 3

a Child's first name.

b Child's age.

Step 4

a Shape moved and stretched in x direction.

b Shape moved and stretched in y direction.

c Shape moved along and up, and each side doubled in length.

Quadrilateral quest

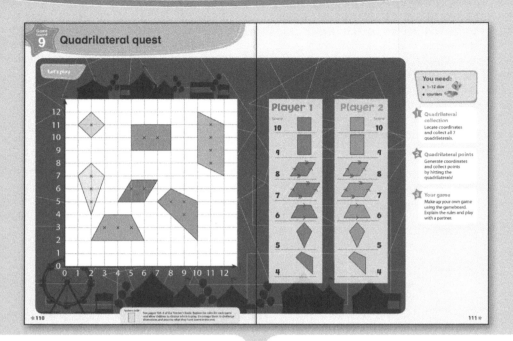

Game 1: Quadrilateral collection

Children collect a complete set of quadrilaterals, using dice rolls to determine coordinate pairs.

Maths focus

- Identify quadrilaterals
- Use coordinates in the first quadrant

Resources

7 counters per player (1 colour per player); 1–12 dice (2, of different colours, e.g. black and white).

How to play

This game is for two players. The aim of the game is to collect each of the seven different quadrilaterals on the first quadrant gameboard. Children take turns to roll the dice: the black dice gives the x-coordinate and the white dice, the y-coordinate. Any coordinate pair lying on the perimeter or inside a quadrilateral allows you to 'collect' that quadrilateral. Players keep a track of progress by covering the quadrilateral in their set with a counter. The winner is the first player to collect all the quadrilaterals.

Making it easier

Take time before beginning the game to identify and name the quadrilaterals at the side of the gameboard. Find each one on the coordinate grid.

Making it harder

After rolling one dice, children can choose to swap the x- and y-coordinates in order to have a chance of collecting a quadrilateral they still need.

Game 2: Quadrilateral points

In this version of the game, each quadrilateral has a point score. The winner is the player with the higher score.

Maths focus

- Identify quadrilaterals
- Use coordinates in the first quadrant

Resources

1–12 dice (2, of different colours, e.g. black and white).

How to play

This games is for two players. Children take turns to roll the dice: the black dice gives the x- coordinate and the white dice, the y-coordinate. They find the coordinate point and score for the quadrilateral according to the scale at the side of the gameboard. No points are scored for coordinates outside the quadrilaterals. Coordinates marked with a cross (those inside the quadrilaterals) score double points. Children keep a pencil and paper tally of their scores. The winner is the player with the higher score after a given time.

Making it easier

Take time, before beginning the game, to identify and name the quadrilaterals at the side of the gameboard and find each one on the coordinate grid.

Making it harder

After rolling one dice, children can choose to swap the x- and y-coordinates if they think they have a chance of a higher score.

Game 3: Your game

Children should invent their own game designing rules that use the concepts covered in the unit. Challenge children to make their game easier or harder.

Unit 9 Quadrilateral quest

Choose a game to play.

Game 1: Quadrilateral collection

You need:
- 7 counters per player (1 colour per player)
- two 1–12 dice (1 black, 1 white)

How to play
- Play with a partner.
- The aim of the game is to collect each of the 7 different quadrilaterals on the gameboard.
- Take turns to roll the dice:
  ▶ the black dice gives the x-coordinate
  ▶ the white dice gives the y-coordinate.
- If your coordinate pair is on the perimeter or inside a quadrilateral, you can 'collect' that quadrilateral. Cover the quadrilateral in your set with a counter.
- The winner is the first player to collect all their quadrilaterals.

Game 2: Quadrilateral points

You need:
- two 1–12 dice (1 black, 1 white)

How to play
- Play with a partner.
- Take turns to roll the dice:
  ▶ the black dice gives the x-coordinate
  ▶ the white dice gives the y-coordinate.
- Locate the coordinate point on the gameboard. Find the quadrilateral in the list at the side of the gameboard to find out your score.
  If your coordinate pair is outside the quadrilaterals, you score no points.
  If you land on starred coordinates (inside the quadrilaterals), score double points.
- Write down your scores.
- The winner is the player with the higher score after a given time.

Game 3: Your game

- Make up your own game using the gameboard.
- You could order the quadrilaterals or introduce a different scoring system.
- Explain the rules and play with a partner.

Please help your child by reading the instructions and playing the game together.

And finally ...

Assessment task 1

Resources

Squared paper, 2-D quadrilaterals.

Running the task

Begin by revisiting the properties of quadrilaterals. Ensure that 2-D shapes are available for children to handle and discuss throughout the activity. There is no single correct way to approach the task. Encourage shared discussion. You could provide a copy of the table in the Textbook. Children (and teachers) will tackle this task in different ways. If children struggle after some time to get started, help them to see that two quadrilaterals, the square and the irregular quadrilateral, can be assigned relatively straightforwardly. You could ask questions such as, *Which shape do you think might have ticks for everything? Which shape is very irregular and might have crosses for everything?*

Evidencing mastery

The completed table is given below for reference and children showing mastery will complete it correctly.

Children showing mastery will reason correctly about their decisions, making statements such as: 'There are only three crosses in the row showing "One or more lines of symmetry". The three quadrilaterals that do not have symmetry are the parallelogram, the (right-angled) trapezium and the irregular quadrilateral, let's see whether we can find which is which?'

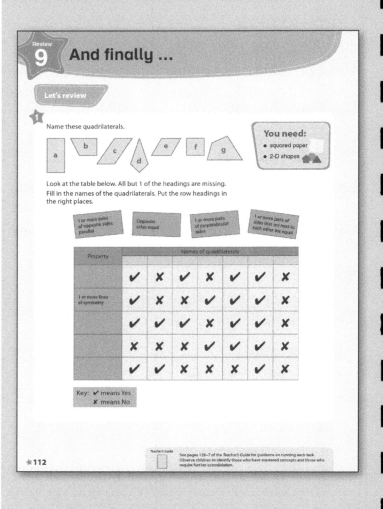

	rectangle	right-angled trapezium	parallelogram	kite	rhombus	square	irregular quadrilateral
Opposite sides equal	✓	✗	✓	✗	✓	✓	✗
1 or more lines of symmetry	✓	✗	✗	✓	✓	✓	✗
1 or more pairs of opposite sides parallel	✓	✓	✓	✗	✓	✓	✗
1 or more pairs of sides that are next to each other are equal	✗	✗	✗	✓	✓	✓	✗
1 or more pairs of perpendicular sides	✓	✓	✗	✗	✗	✓	✗

Assessment task 2

Resources

Squared paper, coloured pencils.

Running the task

Provide a zero to ten coordinate grid pro-forma for any child who will find drawing the axes challenging and/or time-consuming. Encourage children to look at the coordinates before they begin to see if they can predict the shape they are drawing. Watch children plotting the translations. It is probably best for children to work individually so that each child experiences plotting and analysing their own shapes but they should have a talking partner so that they can discuss their thinking and self- and peer-check their diagrams as their answer unfolds.

Evidencing mastery

Children showing mastery will identify the shape as a trapezium. Some children may be able to 'read' this from the coordinate values, e.g. they may notice that the first two coordinates have the same y-coordinate, so the x-coordinates give a horizontal line of five squares and second two coordinates have the same (but different to the first coordinate pairs) y-coordinate, so the x-coordinates give a horizontal line of three squares. Children showing mastery plot points with confidence, correctly translate the trapezium and quickly spot the pattern in the translations. They can explain how the values of the x- and y-coordinates have changed. Listen for children who notice that the overlap is a smaller version of the shape itself.

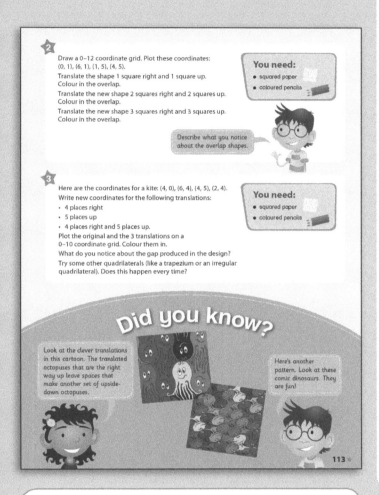

Assessment task 3

Resources

Squared paper, coloured pencils.

Running the task

To introduce the activity, ask children questions to recap the concept of translation, e.g. *Does the size of a shape change when it is translated? Do the angles remain the same? If a shape is moved sideways, which coordinates change and which remain the same? What coordinates change if a shape is moved up or down?* The first part of the task asks children to manipulate coordinates without plotting them. Make sure that they have had plenty of experience of looking carefully at the effect on x- and y-coordinates when they are translated so that they understand how to calculate new coordinates for each of the translations described. Consider providing a zero to ten coordinate grid pro-forma for children who may find that drawing their own takes too much of the available time. Support children who are less secure by asking questions, e.g. *If you are translating four places right, will both coordinates change or just one?* Suggest that children write the coordinates under each other so that the changes can be clearly seen.

Original coordinates:	(4, 0), (6, 4), (4, 5), (2, 4)
Translation 4 places right:	(8, 0), (10, 4), (8, 5), (6, 4)
Translation 5 places up:	(4, 5), (6, 9), (4, 10), (2, 9)
Translation 4 places right and 5 places up:	(8, 5), (10, 9), (8, 10), (6, 9)

Evidencing mastery

Children showing mastery can confidently write new coordinates for the translated shapes. Look for children who recognise that the gap produced in the design is an identical kite rotated through 180 degrees. Of course, this is not a coincidence because all quadrilaterals will tessellate (fit together without gaps or overlap).

Concepts mastered

☑ Children can compare and classify quadrilaterals, including trapeziums and kites, and other geometric shapes based on their properties and sizes.

☑ Children can describe positions on a 2-D grid as coordinates in the first quadrant, plot specified points and draw sides to complete a given polygon. They can translate shapes to the left/right and up/down within the first quadrant.

Did you know?

The engaging cartoon patterns are examples of tessellating patterns. Shapes that tessellate fit together without leaving any gaps and without overlapping. Many polygons – including all quadrilaterals – tessellate. Children can investigate tessellating patterns using 2-D shapes. Starting from a simple quadrilateral, they could also develop the shape to make their own cartoons. Simple instructions to do this are readily available on the Internet.

You could ask children to investigate the work of M. C. Escher (1898–1972), one of the world's most famous graphic artists, who drew some amazing pictures involving translations and tessellating shapes. Escher did not have any formal mathematical education but studied design and clearly had intuitive visual spatial understanding. He was inspired by the patterns and mathematical designs decorating the Alhambra Palace in Granada, Spain.

Number and place value in real life

Mathematical focus

★ **Number: number and place value**

★ **Measurement: money, mass, capacity/volume, time, length**

★ **Statistics: interpret and present data, solve problems**

Prior learning

Children should already be able to:

- count in multiples of 3, 4, 6, 7, 8, 9, 50 and 100
- find 10 or 100 more or less than a given number
- recognise the place value of each digit in a 4-digit number (thousands, hundreds, tens, and ones)
- identify, represent and estimate numbers using different representations.

Key new learning

- Count in multiples of 25 and 1000.
- Find 1000 more or less than a given number.
- Recognise the place value of each digit in a 4-digit number (thousands, hundreds, tens, and ones).
- Identify, represent and estimate numbers using different representations.
- Solve number and practical problems that involve all of the above and with increasingly large positive numbers.

Making connections

- This unit builds on work in Units 1 and 5 on the place value of 4-digit numbers. A solid understanding of place value, and the ability to count in steps of 1000, are both useful in the context of measures, including distance, mass, capacity, volume, and money. Children need to be able to convert between units by multiplying or dividing by 1000 (litres and millilitres, kilograms and grams, kilometres and metres) or 100 (metres and centimetres, pounds and pence).

- Working with numbers beyond 1000 means children can see a wider range of real-life applications of the skills they are learning. This includes everyday life and other subjects such as cooking and design and technology where children might work with measurements that include conversions between kilograms and grams, etc.

- Although units of time use Base 60 rather than Base 10, a knowledge of place value and how our number system works is useful in strengthening children's understanding of time and its measurement.

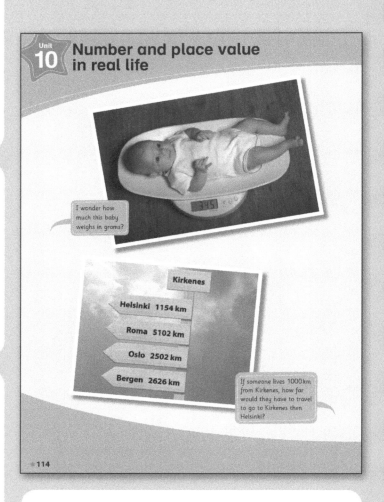

Talk about

It is important to use precise mathematical vocabulary from the start. By now children should be familiar with the four properties of place value: positional, multiplicative, additive and Base 10, but it is important to continue to encourage them to use these terms when talking about numbers.

You could also talk about the measurements we use in real life (e.g. length, distance, mass, time and money) and the words and units we use to describe them. Discuss the difference between volume and capacity. Children should know that capacity is the amount a container holds and the volume is the amount in that container at any given time.

Engaging and exploring

Look at the picture of the baby on the scales. Ask children what the numbers on the scales tell us? Agree that they show the baby's weight. Ask how much the baby weighs and agree between 3 and 4 kilograms. Ask children what they can tell you about grams and kilograms. Establish that 1000 grams are equivalent to one kilogram. Discuss how you would work out the baby's weight in grams, e.g. multiply by 1000. Agree that the baby weights 3450 grams.

Ask children if they know where the places named on the signpost are. You could show a map of Europe and identify them. Tell them that Kirkenes is a town in the north of Norway. The signpost shows that Helsinki (the capital of Finland) is 1154 km from Kirkenes, Roma (Rome, the capital of Italy) 5102 km, Oslo (the capital or Norway) 2502 km and Bergen (another large city in Norway) 2626 km. Establish that in the UK we use miles to measure distances but in other parts of Europe kilometres are used. Read the comment and ask children to tell you what is 1000 km more than the distance from Kirkenes to Helsinki; repeat with the other cities. Explain that counting in thousands is like repeatedly adding 1000 more. Rehearse counting in thousands from given numbers such as 1500, 750, 2300. Ask questions relating to the road sign, e.g. *What distance would it be to Oslo if 1000 kilometres less? 2000 kilometres more?*

Turn to the picture of the bottles. Ask children which drinks they like to drink. You could make a tally and then a table of what they say and ask them to represent the results in a bar chart or pictogram. They could choose a symbol to represent four people, or draw their scale with intervals of four; this will help them make sense of why it is useful to know their multiplication facts. Encourage them to ask questions about their representations.

Ask children to tell you how much they think each bottle could hold. Agree that drinks bottles usually hold half a litre, one litre, one and a half litres or two litres. Have a selection of bottles available to show children. Tell children that the bottles shown hold one and a half litres each. Ask: *What is that in millilitres?* Elicit that, because 1000 millilitres are equivalent to one litre and half a litre is equivalent to 500 millilitres, each must hold 1500 millilitres. Discuss how you could work out the total in all four bottles in millilitres. Agree that you could, e.g. double 1500 millilitres and double again. Agree that the total is 6000 millilitres.

Ask children to identify each coin and note in the photo of the money. Can they tell you how many pence each is worth? Give them a few minutes to work out the total amount of money shown using plastic notes and coins. Encourage them to use their individual whiteboards to keep track as they work this out. Agree there is £7.76 in coins and £45 in notes, so a total of £52.76. Ask: *How many pence is that? How did you work that out?* Write different amounts of money in pounds and pence on the board and ask children to order these from smallest to greatest. You could then ask them to round these to the nearest pound.

Look at the picture of the speed limit sign and ask children in what units we could measure distance. Agree that in this country, and a few others, we use miles, but in most countries kilometres are used. The sign showing 'your speed' indicates that the driver is driving too fast. How much too fast? Focus on the question. *If the speed limit is 25 kilometres per hour, how far would the driver travel in two hours?* Agree 50 kilometres. Can children work out from this how long it would take to travel 500 kilometres? Establish that 500 kilometres is ten times 50 kilometres, so it would take ten times as long, or 20 hours. Make up some more questions that involve children working out how far a driver would travel at 25 kilometres per hour and how long it would take to travel distances in multiples of 25 kilometres per hour.

How many millilitres do you think there are altogether in these bottles?

I wonder how much money there is altogether?

How long would it take someone to travel 500 kilometres at this speed?

Teacher's Guide: Look at the pictures with the children and discuss the questions. See pages 128–9 of the Teacher's Guide for key ideas to draw out.

115

Things to think about

- How will you adapt tasks to enable children to spot patterns, make generalisations and see the structure of the mathematics that they are learning about, e.g. a question on millilitres and litres could be adapted to use grams and kilograms.

- How will you ensure children experience practical opportunities to work on place value within the contexts of measure, e.g. length, mass, capacity/volume and money?

- In what ways will you develop questioning to encourage children to reason? Will you use problem-solving strategies, e.g. 'sometimes, always, never'?

Checking understanding

You will know children have mastered these concepts when they can count fluently in 25s and 1000s and find 1000 more or less than a given number. They will be able to explain and demonstrate the place value of 4-digit numbers and apply this to units of measure, converting between larger and smaller units.

10a 25s and 1000s

- **Count in multiples of 25 and 1000.**
- **Find 1000 more or less than a given number.**

Homework 51 and 52   Practice Book pp 94–6

Mathematical vocabulary

Multiple, one thousand, zero, more, less

Warming up

Rehearse counting in steps of six, seven and nine. Use a pendulum. As it swings from side to side, children count in steps of the chosen number from zero to the 12th multiple and back to zero. From time to time stop and ask children to tell you the related multiplication and division facts (e.g. $7 \times 6 = 42$, $6 \times 7 = 42$, $42 \div 6 = 7$, $42 \div 7 = 6$). You could take the opportunity to discuss ways of remembering any that children find difficult.

Background knowledge

Counting in steps of different sizes is an important precursor to knowing and understanding multiplication and related division facts. In this concept you will focus on 25, which has a clear relationship to 100 and 1000. This makes it relatively easy to work with quite large numbers. You will also explore counting in thousands, and find 1000 more and less than 4-digit numbers. This is helpful when working with and converting units of measure, in particular kilometres and metres, kilograms and grams, and litres and millilitres.

Let's learn: Modelling and teaching

Counting in 25s and 1000s

- Using the bar model in the Textbook, count in 25s with children from zero to 300. Discuss the repeating pattern of the tens and ones digits and establish that this happens because there are four lots of 25 in 100.

- Repeat the count, pausing occasionally to ask children how many steps they have counted, e.g. to get to 150 they have counted six steps of 25 – this means there are six lots of 25 in 150. Say this together as a multiplication statement and bring in the commutative fact as well: *25 multiplied by six equals 150 and six multiplied by 25 equals 150 because multiplication is commutative – different calculation, same answer.* Record the statements on the board.

- Look at the misconception cartoon in the Textbook and establish that both methods work, but that Tom's is an efficient mental calculation strategy. Explore how many lots of 25 there are in different numbers, in and beyond the bar model, using Tom's strategy.

- Ask children to count in steps of 1000. They should find this easy. If necessary, explain that although we have a special word for 'one thousand' (rather than 'ten hundred'), we say 10 000 as 'ten thousand'.

Representations and resources

Pendulum, place-value counters, weighing scales, classroom items weighing more than one kilogram (or sand/bags of potatoes).

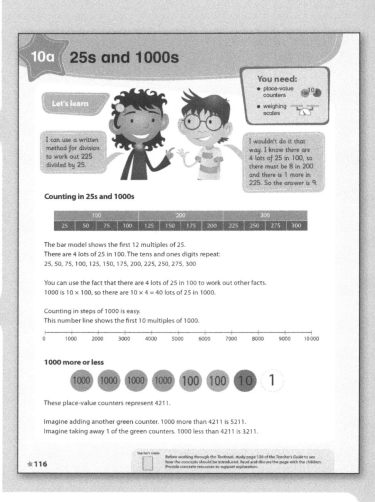

1000 more or less

- Turn to the representation of 4211 in the Textbook. Give children place-value counters so they can make the number, and add, then take away, one 1000 counter. Discuss the fact that if you add or take away 1000, the hundreds, tens and ones digits remain the same; in most cases, only the thousands digit changes.

- Give children place-value counters and ask them to make various 4-digit numbers and find 1000 more and less, writing down their answers. Encourage them to include some numbers with nine or ten thousands, exchanging ten 1000 counters for one 10 000 counter as necessary. Then write up other 4-digit numbers and ask children to find 1000 more and less, this time without using place-value counters.

Let's practise: Digging deeper

Step 1

This task asks children to work out how many 25s there are in different numbers. Allow some children to use the bar model in the Textbook to begin with. For numbers that are not on the model, encourage them to use what they know, e.g. for part g, there are 12 lots of 25 in 300 and 2 in 50, so there must be 14 in 350. Expect other children to be able to count fluently in 25s without support.

Step 2

In this task children find 1000 more, then 1000 less, than the given numbers. Observe children as they work on the numbers with tens of thousands to check they are careful to select the correct digit to add to or subtract from. In part j ten thousands becomes nine thousands.

Step 3

This task could be carried out in pairs or small groups. You might like to arrange for suitable items to be available in the classroom; alternatively, ask children to fill bags of sand or use items such as bags of potatoes. Encourage children to weigh each item to the nearest 100 grams. Ensure that children record their answers logically, either as a list or in a table. Draw out the pattern in the numbers by asking children what they notice.

Step 4

Encourage children to work systematically on this task. Ana wants to have at least one go at all three stalls, which means using 1 + 2 + 3 = 6 tokens. Children then work out how they can use the remaining four tokens, looking at each stall, and each possible pair of stalls, in turn. Some may benefit from using counters or making their own tokens to model the task. Children can count in 25s to work out the value of the tokens Ana spends at each stall, and to check that the total value in each case is £2.50.

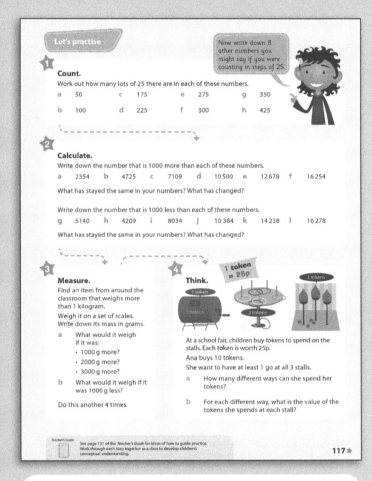

Follow-up ideas

- Ask children to pour an amount of water that they estimate to be more than 1000 millilitres into a bottle, then measure it to the nearest 100 millilitres using a measuring jug. Ask them to write down what the volume would be if was 1000 ml, 2000 ml and 3000 ml more and 1000 ml less.

- Children make cards showing the numbers 1 to 12 (or higher) and cards showing the matching multiples of 25. They shuffle these and place them face down on the table. They take it in turns to pick two cards. If they match they keep them. If they do not, they return them to the table.

- Children could make up their own scenarios and questions using tokens worth 25p. They could use such tokens to pay for items in the class shop, count in 25s to find the total amount taken and exchange this for the fewest number of coins.

Ensuring progress

Supporting understanding

Some children may need extra work on finding ten or 100 more or less before moving on to 1000; allow these children to use place-value counters to model Step 2. For Step 3, children who are more confident in measuring could work with a partner with more secure number sense, so they can support each other.

Broadening understanding

Children who can count fluently in 25s could be given larger numbers to tackle in Step 1. You could extend Step 4 by asking children to explore Ana's options if she doesn't mind whether she has a go on three stalls.

 Concept mastered

Children can count fluently in 25s and 1000s and find 1000 more or less than a given number.

Answers

Step 1

a	2	e	11
b	4	f	12
c	7	g	14
d	9	h	17

8 other multiples of 25, e.g. 25, 75, 125, 150, 200, 250, 325, 375

Step 2

a 3354

b 5725

c	8109	h	3209
d	11 500	i	7034
e	13 678	j	9384
f	17 254	k	13 238
g	4140	l	15 278

In most of the numbers, the ten thousands digit (if applicable), hundreds, tens and ones digits stay the same; the thousands digit changes. In part j the ten thousands digit also changes.

Step 4

Ana can spend her tokens in 4 different ways.

Tombola		Hoops		Coconut shy	
Tokens used	Value	Tokens used	Value	Tokens used	Value
1 + 1 + 1 + 1 + 1	£1.25	2	£0.50	3	£0.75
1 + 1 + 1	£0.75	2 + 2	£1.00	3	£0.75
1 + 1	£0.50	2	£0.50	3 + 3	£1.50
1	£0.25	2 + 2 + 2	£1.50	3	£0.75

- Recognise the place value of each digit in a 4-digit number (thousands, hundreds, tens and ones).
- Identify, represent and estimate numbers using different representations.
- Solve number and practical problems that involve all of the above and with increasingly large positive numbers.

Homework 53 and 54 · Practice Book pp 97–9 · Place Value & Abacus

Representations and resources

Counting stick, coins and notes, place-value grids, digit cards.

Mathematical vocabulary

Place value, positional, multiplicative, additive, zero, place holder, analogue, digital, money, litres, millilitres, kilograms, grams, kilometres, metres

Warming up

Rehearse counting in thousands using a counting stick. Tell children that zero is at one end of the counting stick. Ask them what will be at the other. Agree 10000. Point to the divisions and as you do so children count in thousands to 10000 and back to zero. Jump your finger around the stick. Pause on some positions and ask children to tell you the multiplication and division statements that can be made, e.g. $4 \times 1000 = 4000$, $1000 \times 4 = 4000$, $4000 \div 1000 = 4$, $4000 \div 4 = 1000$. Ask: *What is 1000 more? What is 1000 less?* Point to positions between the divisions and ask children to estimate what could go there.

Background knowledge

Place value is key to developing an understanding of how the units of measure relate to each other. This concept spread builds on previous work on 4-digit numbers (Units 1 and 5) and applies it to litres and money, with scope to include units of mass and length. Time is our only area of measurement that does not use Base 10. Use this opportunity to touch on Base 60 to make the connection with time.

Let's learn: Modelling and teaching

1000s and measures

- Look at the measuring jug in the Textbook. Remind children that there are 1000 millilitres in a litre. Ask: *How many millilitres are there in two litres? Three litres?* Link to counting in thousands. Agree that each small division on the jug represents 0.25 litres, or 250 millilitres, so it contains 1.75 litres or 1750 millilitres of water. Look at the two place-value grids and ask children to explain what they show, referring to the positional, multiplicative and additive aspects of the numbers.

- Model the money shown in the Textbook with plastic notes and coins. Ask children to count it. Agree that there is £31.56. Look at the two place-value grids and ask children to explain what they show. Highlight that money is different from litres because there are 100 pence in a pound. 1000p is equivalent to £10.00.

- What other units of measure can children think of, and how would they convert them? Give them opportunities to measure volumes, masses and lengths practically, and

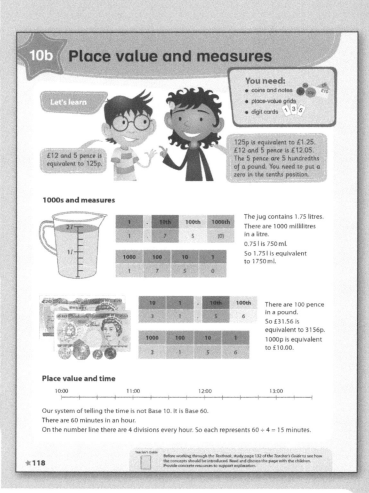

make amounts of money. They can use resources such as place-value grids, partitioning cards and Base 10 apparatus to represent their measures in different ways.

Place value and time

- Explain that our system for time does not work in the same way as our number system. In time we count to 59 before moving to the next position, which is 60. The next position would be 60×60 (3600). This is Base 60, which was developed by the ancient Babylonians. Rehearse converting time in minutes to hours and minutes, e.g. 80 minutes, 145 minutes, 180 minutes.

- Discuss the number line in the Textbook and establish that each division represents 15 minutes. Ask questions, e.g. *What is the difference between 10:30 and 12:00?* Children can draw number lines to find time differences and durations.

Let's practise: Digging deeper
Step 1
This task asks children to convert amounts in pence to pounds and pence, positioning the digits of the new amounts into place-value grids. When they describe the place value of each amount encourage them to refer to the positional, multiplicative and additive aspects. The next parts require children to convert from litres to millilitres and grams to kilograms. Discuss how these measures differ from pounds and pence. Remind them, using place-value grids, that 0.5 litre is equivalent to 500 millilitres, 0.25 kilograms to 250 grams, and so on.

Step 2
Remind children that when finding time differences they need to count on to the next hour, which is to 60, not 10 or 100. Briefly recap 24-hour clock times, reminding children that analogue clock times work in blocks of 12 hours and digital

time 24 hours – so one o'clock in the afternoon would be 13:00, two o'clock 14:00 and so on. Encourage children to draw number lines with divisions every 15 minutes, as in the Textbook, and estimate the position of the times given.

Step 3
Children must work out how far Olli has walked. Before children tackle the task, work through a similar scenario with different lengths. Once they have found the sum of the distances, they record these in three ways: as kilometres and metres, metres and kilometres. Encourage children to use place-value grids if needed.

Step 4
This task asks children to explore Base 5, in which the numbers increase and decrease in powers of five. If appropriate, work through some further examples before children begin: draw a Base 5 place-value grid on the board, write in some digits, and ask children to work out the value of each and then add them together, e.g. 1111 in Base 5 represents $125 + 25 + 5 + 1 = 156$; 2143 represents $250 + 25 + 20 + 3 = 298$. Emphasise that you can only use the digits zero to four.

Ensuring progress
Supporting understanding
In Step 1, give children money so they can make the first few amounts using £10 notes and £1, 10p and 1p coins. Some children may benefit from using place-value grids (1, 10th, 100th, 1000th) or another resource of their choice. In Step 2, you could ask children to focus on finding the time difference to five minutes.

Broadening understanding
Extend Step 3 by asking children to make up an imaginary plan of a town of village, with distances between points of interest. They then make up their own routes and work out the distances between them. In Step 4, you could ask children to explore other bases, such as Base 20.

✓ Concept mastered
Children can explain and demonstrate the positional, multiplicative and additive properties of place value in the context of measures, including volume and money. They recognise that there are other systems of place value, including Base 60 for time.

Follow-up ideas
- Ask children to find out more about the Babylonian number system. They could do this on the Internet.
- Children could play a matching game. Give them 20 pieces of card. On ten they write amounts in pence and on the other ten they write the equivalent amounts in pounds and pence. They shuffle the cards and lay them face down on the table. They pick two. If these match they keep them, if they do not, they return them to the table. The winner is the player with the most pairs.
- Ask children to make up time difference and duration word problems for a partner or the class to solve.

Answers
Step 1
a	£2.45	i	3250 ml
b	£7.89	j	4750 ml
c	£16.75	k	3 kg
d	£53.54	l	4.5 kg
e	£90.63	m	8.5 kg
f	6000 ml	n	7.25 kg
g	7500 ml	o	9.75 g
h	9500 ml		

Step 2
a	1 hour 50 minutes
b	1 hour 45 minutes
c	2 hours 20 minutes
d	3 hours 25 minutes
e	2 hours 15 minutes
f	2 hours 38 minutes
g	5 hours 17 minutes

Step 3
5 km 900 m, 5900 m, 5.9 km

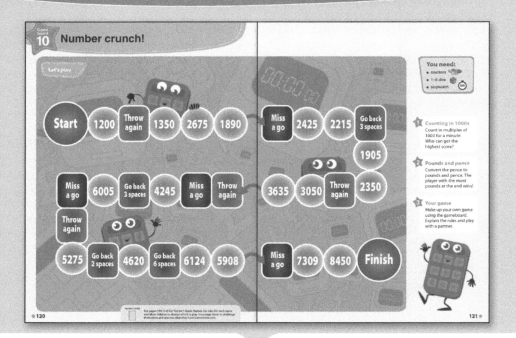

Game 1: Counting in 1000s

This game gives children practice in counting in 1000s from different numbers.

Maths focus

- Count in multiples of 1000

Resources

1 counter per player (1 colour per player), 1–6 dice (1), stopwatches (or minute timers).

How to play

Children play in pairs, placing their counters on Start. They take it in turns to roll the dice and move their counter that number of spaces. If they land on an instruction they follow it. If they land on a number, they count in steps of 1000 from that number for one minute. Their partner times them and counts the numbers they say. The number of steps they manage in their minute is their score for that go. Play continues like this until both players reach Finish. They find the sum of all their scores. The player with the higher sum is the winner.

Making it easier

Children could focus on counting in thousands only, ignoring the hundreds, tens and ones digits.

Making it harder

Children could aim to count to the tenth step and then back to their starting number in one minute. If they do, they score a point. The winner is the player with the higher total of points at the end.

Game 3: Your game

Children should invent their own game, designing rules that use the concepts covered in the unit. Challenge children to make their game easier or harder.

Game 2: Pounds and pence

This game helps children reinforce, rehearse and consolidate their understanding of place value in the context of money. Before they begin, tell children that the numbers on the board represent amounts of money in pence.

Maths focus

- Recognise the place value of each digit in a 4-digit number (thousands, hundreds, tens and ones)

Resources

1 counter per player (1 colour per player), 1–6 dice (1), calculators.

How to play

This game should be played in pairs. Children place their counters on Start. They take it in turns to roll the dice and move their counter that number of spaces. If they land on an instruction they follow it. If they land on a number, they convert the pence to pounds and pence and round the amount to the nearest pound. They write down the number of pounds. They continue in this way, making a running total of their number of pounds, until they both land on Finish. The winner is the player with the most pounds.

Making it easier

Children could focus on changing the pence to pounds and not worry about rounding. Ask them to write the whole amount (pounds and pence) down each time. At the end of the game they can use a calculator to add the pounds from each amount.

Making it harder

Rather than rounding, children could write down each amount in pounds and pence. At the end of the game, they order all the amounts they made and then find the total amount in pounds and pence. The player with the highest total is the winner.

Number crunch!

Choose a game to play.

Game 1: Counting in 1000s

How to play

- Each place your counter on Start.
- Take turns to roll the dice. Move your counter that number of spaces.
- If you land on an instruction, do what it says.
- If you land on a number, count in steps of 1000 from that number for 1 minute. Ask your partner to time you and count the numbers you say to find your score, e.g. if you count 7 steps from the number on the gameboard, you score 7.
- When you both reach Finish, add up your scores. The winner is the player with the higher total score.

You need:

- 1 counter per player (1 colour per player)
- 1–6 dice
- stopwatch

Game 2: Pounds and pence

How to play

- Each place your counter on Start.
- Take turns to roll the dice. Move your counter that number of spaces.
- If you land on an instruction, do what it says.
- If you land on a number, convert it to pounds and pence. Then round the amount to the nearest pound. Write down the number of pounds.
- When you both reach Finish, add up the pounds you have made. The winner is the player with the most pounds.

You need:

- 1 counter per player (1 colour per player)
- 1–6 dice

Game 3: Your game

- Make up your own game using the gameboard.
- What else could the numbers on the board represent? e.g. they could be millilitres.
- What are the rules for your game? Explain them to someone.

Please help your child by reading the instructions and playing the game together.

Assessment task 1

Running the task

Before children begin the task, reinforce the importance of place value in terms of converting between measures, counting in thousands and finding thousands more and less than a given number. Practise counting in thousands, then write a 4-digit number on the board, e.g. 8650. Ask children to tell you the number that is 1000 more and less, 3000 more and less and 5000 more and less.

The first part of the task asks children to convert the kilogram masses to grams. You may wish to practise a few conversions first. Remind children that there are 1000 grams in one kilogram, so amounts with .5 at the end are 500 grams, .25 are 250 grams and so on. Children need to choose the correct number of grams from the options given. Expect them to be able to explain their choice to you, e.g. there are 1000 grams in a kilogram, and $5 \times 1000 = 5000\,g$, so five kilograms is equivalent to 5000 grams.

At this stage, expect children to deal with the kilograms and grams separately (e.g. 10×1000 is $10\,000\,g$ and $0.75\,kg$ is $750\,g$, so $10.75\,kg$ is equivalent to $10\,750\,g$). Multiplying and dividing whole numbers and decimals by 10, 100 and 1000 will be introduced in Year 5, and this work on counting in thousands, relating the steps the multiples, leads into that concept. Some children will be beginning to see for themselves that when multiplying by 1000 all the digits move three places to the left. If any children struggle with the conversions, make a note of their names and work with them in a focus group next time you do any work on mass.

The second part of the task asks children to find 4000 grams more and then 4000 grams less than their new amounts. They can do this by counting on and back; as they do so, encourage them to focus solely on the digits in the thousands position (and, if applicable, ten thousands) and to ignore the other digits because they are not relevant.

Evidencing mastery

Children who can convert from kilograms to grams and find thousands more and less than a given amount are evidencing mastery.

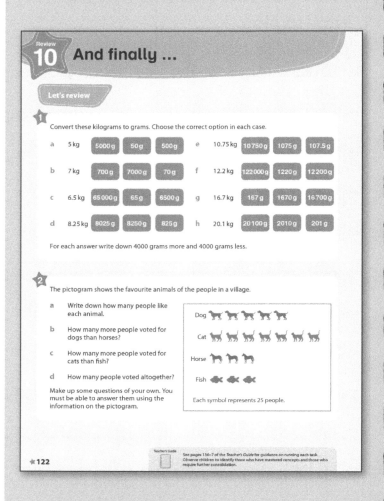

Assessment task 2

Running the task

Before children begin the task, ask them to explain what a pictogram is. Expect them to be able to tell you that a pictogram is a way of representing data that uses symbols; each symbol represents a given number. Discuss the fact that the pictogram in the task is about people's favourite animals and that each symbol represents 25 people. Rehearse counting in 25s from zero to the 12th multiple and back to zero. Ask questions, e.g. *If 150 people voted, how many symbols would there be? If there were 11 symbols how many people would that represent?*

The task asks children to list how many people voted for each animal. They can do this by counting in 25s. Observe whether any children can identify that 75 people like horses or fish simply by noting that there are three symbols for

each, without needing to count. Children then answer some questions about the data. You could discuss different ways of doing this. To find how many more people voted for dogs than horses, you could subtract the total for horses from the total for the dogs or identify how many more symbols there are for dogs and count them in 25s. Ask children which method they prefer to use? Ask children to identify which is the most efficient. Finally, children can write their own questions that can be answered using the information provided on the pictogram.

Evidencing mastery

If children can fluently count forwards and backwards in intervals of 25s they are evidencing mastery. Children with a particularly strong grasp of the concept may be able to recall some of the multiples of 25 without counting.

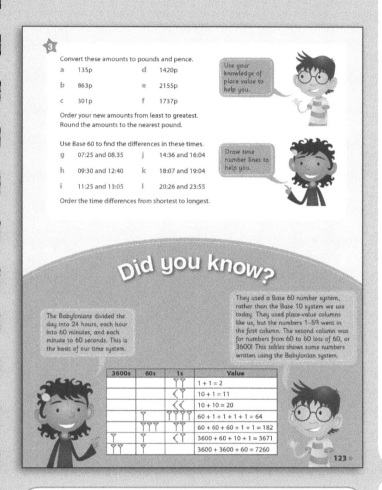

Assessment task 3

Running the task

Remind children that our number system is Base 10. Ask them what this means. Agree that our numbers increase and decrease in powers of ten. Write some numbers on the board and ask children to write down what these would be if they were ten and 100 times larger and smaller. Recap the positional, multiplicative and additive elements of place value. Expect children to be able to tell you what these are. Then remind them that for time we use Base 60. Ask them what this means. Expect them to tell you that there are 60 minutes in an hour.

The first part of the task asks children to use their understanding of place value in our number system to convert amounts in pence to pounds and pence. If necessary they could use place-value charts as in 10b – Place value and measures. They then need to order the amounts, which they can do by considering the number of whole pounds only. Finally, they round the amounts to the nearest pound. This reinforces work carried out in Unit 7 where they were comparing and rounding numbers with decimal places. Put into the context of money most children will be able to do this without any problem.

The second part of the task asks children to use Base 60 to work out time differences. Encourage them to draw time number lines to help them count on to the next hour (60 minutes). Once they have found these differences they order them from shortest to longest.

Evidencing mastery

If children can explain and demonstrate how place value works in the context of money, including order and rounding, they are evidencing mastery. They can explain how time is different from other measures and work out and order time intervals.

Concepts mastered

☑ Children can count fluently in 25s and 1000s and find 1000 more or less than a given number.

☑ Children can explain and demonstrate the positional, multiplicative and additive properties of place value in the context of measures, including volume and money. They recognise that there are other systems of place value, including Base 60 for time.

Did you know?

The Babylonians lived in Mesopotamia, a region that is now Iraq, Syria and Kuwait, about 5000 years ago. They divided the day into 24 hours, each hour into 60 minutes, and each minute to 60 seconds. This form of counting has survived for 4000 years and is the basis of our time system.

The Babylonians also used Base 60 for calculations. Even by today's standards, their system was very advanced. Their numbers were made from just two symbols. The numbers 1–59 went in the first column; for 60 and beyond marks were made in the second column. The third column was used when they reached 60 lots of 60, or 3600 (compared with ten lots of ten, or 100 in our own system). The table in the Textbook shows some numbers written using the Babylonian system. You could challenge children to write some more numbers using Base 60.

Mathematical focus

★ Number: addition and subtraction

★ Measurement: money, volume/capacity, mass

★ Statistics: interpret and present data

Prior learning

Children should already be able to:

- add and subtract numbers mentally using knowledge of place value and related facts

- recognise the place value of each digit in a 4-digit number (thousands, hundreds, tens and ones)

- use representations to add and subtract numbers with up to four digits, relating it to the formal written method

- find 10, 100 and 1000 more or less than a given number.

Key new learning

- Add and subtract numbers with up to four digits using the formal written methods of columnar addition and subtraction where appropriate.

- Estimate and use inverse operations to check answers to a calculation.

- Solve simple measures and money problems involving fractions and decimals to two decimal places.

- Estimate, compare and calculate different measures including money in pounds and pence.

- Solve addition and subtraction two-step problems in contexts, deciding which operations and methods to use and why.

Making connections

- Estimating, comparing and calculating different measures, including money in pounds and pence, has many applications in everyday life. Children may have seen people comparing prices of items in a shop or estimating how much of a particular ingredient is needed for a recipe or how much time they have to catch a train. It is important that children recognise that estimating, comparing and calculating are skills that are used outside the mathematics classroom.

- Solving two-step problems can involve interpreting discrete and continuous data presented in many different ways, including tables, bar charts, pictograms and other graphs. There are clear links here to other subjects, such as science or geography (e.g. line graphs showing change over time).

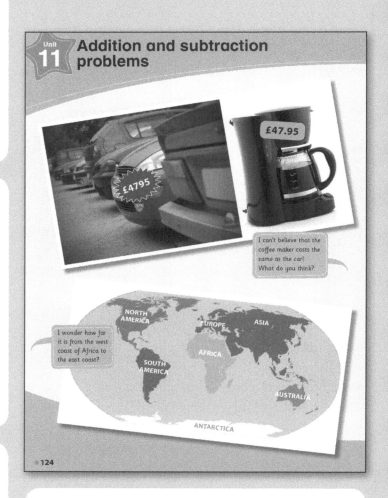

Unit 11 Addition and subtraction problems

£47.95

£4795

I can't believe that the coffee maker costs the same as the car! What do you think?

I wonder how far it is from the west coast of Africa to the east coast?

NORTH AMERICA · EUROPE · ASIA · AFRICA · SOUTH AMERICA · AUSTRALIA · ANTARCTICA

★124

 Talk about

It is important to use precise mathematical vocabulary from the beginning so that children refer to the value of each digit when comparing and calculating. They have been working with measurements with up to two decimal places and should relate these to a tenth of a pound (0.1) and hundredth of a pound (0.01) when working with money and, e.g. a tenth of a metre and a hundredth of a metre when working with metres and centimetres for length.

When they are solving problems, encourage children to discuss the language used in the problem and how they can use this to help determine the required operations.

Engaging and exploring

Ask children to look at each picture and talk about the questions with a partner before discussing them as a class. Focus on each photo in turn.

Ask children to describe the similarities and differences between the two prices £4795 and £47.95 and use what they know about rounding to give an approximate price for each item. Children should identify that the car is nearly £5000 and the coffee maker is nearly £50.

Challenge children to show the value of the car and the coffee maker on a place-value grid with digit cards. Which columns or positions will they need to use for each? Focus on the position of the digits and compare the multiplicative and positional properties of each, i.e. for the digit 9, it is in the tens position for the car and its true value is found when we multiply nine by ten, but it is in the tenths position for the coffee maker and its true value is found when we divide nine by ten.

You could also ask children to estimate the difference in price between the two items or the total price. They should explain why a formal written method is inappropriate for 5000 + 50 and 5000 – 50.

Look at the world map and focus on Australia. Explain that the distance from the easternmost point to the westernmost point is 4100 km. Ask children to estimate the distance from the easternmost point to Alice Springs in the central part of Australia. Link this to halving and look at partitioning to halve 4100 as 4000 ÷ 2 and 100 ÷ 2 which is equal to 2050 km.

Return to the question in the Textbook and challenge children to use what they know about the distance across Australia to help them make an estimate about the easternmost point to the westernmost point of Africa. This is an approximate distance of 7400 km. Children could use rulers to help them decide how much greater the distance is than 4100 km. They can also compare the distances and calculate the difference, relating this to the fact 74 – 41 = 33.

Discuss the different types of clocks shown and how they differ. Ask children to describe how the time for Wednesday can be written in 24-hour notation or how 16:55 for Friday would be shown on an analogue clock. Tell children that Tom always starts his homework at a quarter past four; the clocks show the time he finished on three different days. Ask: *Which day did Tom spend the longest on his homework? The shortest?* Discuss how you could work out how long he took each day. Compare the values and challenge children to make statements about them, e.g. It took Tom 15 minutes longer to do his homework on Wednesday than on Monday. How long do children spend on their own homework?

The table shows the capacities of two of the courts at Wimbledon. Ask children to compare the value of the digit 9 in the capacities of the two courts. Children could also show each of the capacities on a place-value grid, noting that both the Centre Court and Court 1 have capacities greater than 10 000.

Discuss how the question about the first tournament can be answered and the strategies that could be used. Children could represent the problem using the bar model and use a number line to count up from 1877 to, e.g. 2016, using number bonds to support their calculating. Depending on the current year, children explain whether a mental method or a written calculation is more appropriate.

Checking understanding

You will know children have mastered these concepts when they can solve addition and subtraction problems in different contexts. They appropriately choose and use number facts, showing understanding of place value, counting and mental and written methods. They explain their decision making and justify their solutions.

Things to think about

- How will you model and encourage the use of precise mathematical vocabulary when explaining thinking and reasoning? How will you share the language requirements with other adults?

- How will you make connections with measurement and statistics so that children recognise a purpose for applying methods of calculation? How will you ensure that children continue to develop mental methods even after a written method has been introduced?

- How will you use manipulatives and visual representations to help all children to continue to develop their conceptual understanding of the formal written method?

- How will you make effective use of additional adults?

- How will you build in problem solving so that children apply what they have learnt, in a range of contexts?

- Add and subtract numbers with up to four digits using the formal written methods of columnar addition and subtraction where appropriate.
- Estimate and use inverse operations to check answers to a calculation.
- Solve simple measures and money problems involving fractions and decimals to two decimal places.
- Estimate, compare and calculate different measures including money in pounds and pence.

Homework 55 and 56   Practice Book pp 100–3

Mathematical vocabulary

Addition, subtraction, total, sum, difference, decimal, whole, tenth, hundredth, pound, pence

Representations and resources

Bead strings, Base 10 apparatus or place-value counters, coins, place-value grids, digit cards.

Warming up

Practise number bonds to 20 using a range of calculations in which children need to find the missing number. Make sure the missing number is in different places, e.g. $9 + \boxed{} = 12$ and $\boxed{} - 10 = 8$, etc. Children can use bead strings to model the number bonds they are using each time and explain which group of beads represents the missing number. Ask children to make up a contextualised maths story to go with some of their bonds.

Background knowledge

Children are introduced to decimals in Year 4. Continue to give them plenty of opportunities to describe the value of each digit and use this to order and compare decimals. In the context of measurement, e.g. one pence is one-hundredth of a pound so it has the value £0.01.

Decimal numbers are related to fractions. Like fractions written with a numerator and denominator (rational fractions), the decimal fractions that make up decimal numbers are also related to parts of the whole. A numerator divided by the denominator of a fraction will always give the decimal equivalent of the fraction.

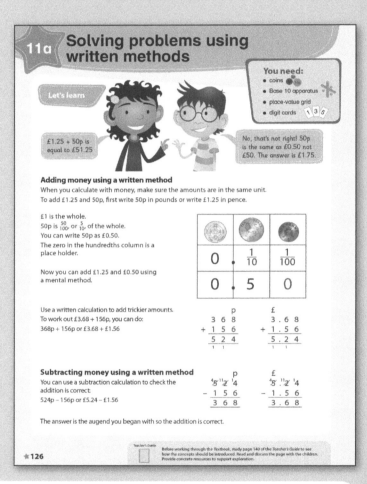

Let's learn: Modelling and teaching

Adding money using a written method

- Look at the way the place-value grid in the Textbook has been used to show pounds and pence. Discuss the relationship between the units. Agree that there are 100 pence in a pound so each pence is worth one-hundredth of a pound. Link this to the relationship between $\frac{1}{10}$ and $\frac{10}{100}$, using Base 10 apparatus.

- Explore the calculations given, ensuring that children recognise that both units have to be the same, i.e. both in pounds or both in pence. Focus on pounds to model calculating with decimal numbers. Encourage children to explain why a mental method can be used to add 50 pence but a written method is more efficient for £3.68 + £1.56. Discuss a useful estimate, e.g. £4 + £2 = £6 and ask: *Will the answer be more or less than this?* Using Base 10 apparatus and a large copy of a place-value grid

as in the Textbook, work through the column calculations, modelling each step with the Base 10 apparatus. Emphasise that the two answers are equivalent, just written in different units. Discuss how the final answer of £5.24 compares to the estimate.

Subtracting money using a written method

- Discuss the relationship between addition and subtraction. Focus on the language 'undo' to help children make sense of inverse so that subtraction undoes an addition calculation and vice versa, e.g. 70 + 30 = 100 and 100 – 30 undoes this and brings you back to your starting number, 70.

- Model the subtraction calculations in both pounds and pence so that the relationship between the units is explicit. Base 10 apparatus or place-value counters can also be used to represent the calculation and support decomposition.

Let's practise: Digging deeper

Step 1

Children use coins and a place-value grid with digit cards to support their understanding of decimals. Ensure that children make an estimate before adding £2.35. Encourage children to decide whether a total will be more or less than the estimate made. They add the coins as they go and write down the calculation they use each time, e.g. £1.22 + £2.35 = £3.57. A subtraction calculation should be used to check each of the additions.

Step 2

The first three calculations are set out in the column method. Children should represent the calculations using Base 10 apparatus, adding or subtracting the hundredths of a pound first. They should remember to make estimates and check each calculation using the inverse. For parts d and e, children must set

out the calculations themselves, remembering to line up the decimal points, but must first convert the units so both are the same.

Step 3

There is an opportunity to consider doubling as a strategy to find out the amount that Ana saves in two weeks and then add a further £2.35 for three weeks. Children apply subtraction in the context of change. Coins and Base 10 apparatus can be used to represent the calculation and the bar model could be used to represent the problems.

Step 4

This is an open task as children select 11 coins (£1, 10p and 1p) each time to create four different amounts. They use the values to make as many sums and differences as they can, exploring the greatest and smallest total or the greatest and smallest difference. Children should reason about the size and number of coins involved and explain their thinking. You could discuss how a table could be used to organise results and avoid repeats.

Let's practise

1 Calculate.
Use coins to make the following amounts:

a £1.22   b £1.45   c £2.72   d £3.07

Add £2.35 to each amount.
Write the calculations you use.
Check your answers using the inverse subtraction.

Remember to make an estimate first.

2 Calculate.
Copy and complete these calculations. Use Base 10 apparatus.
Make an estimate first. Check your answers using the inverse calculation.

a £
   3 . 4 7
+ 1 . 3 6

b £
   4 . 7 2
− 1 . 4 9

c £
  1 5 . 2 8
− 1 2 . 6 4

Answer these calculations using the formal written method.

d £4.17 + 164p   e 635p − £2.62

3 Solve.

a Ana saves £2.35 each week for 3 weeks. How much more money will she need to buy a game costing £12.49?

b Tom has £9.75 and buys 2 books. One book costs £5.29 and the other costs £2.45. How much money does he have left?

4 Think.

Use £1, 10p and 1p coins.
Take 11 coins. Make up a value, e.g.: five £1 coins, four 10p coins and two 1p coins to make £5.42.
Make up 4 different values in this way.

a Use the values to make 5 different addition and subtraction calculations.

b Find the largest and smallest total you can make using any 2 values from 11 coins.

c Now investigate the largest and smallest difference.

Teacher's Guide | See page 141 of the *Teacher's Guide* for ideas of how to guide practice. Work through each step together as a class to develop children's conceptual understanding.

127

Follow-up ideas

- Give children a budget to plan a party or to restock a pencil case. They should use addition and subtraction to calculate the amount spent and the amount left, first estimating whether they have enough. Encourage them to think about mental and written methods. Use catalogues and other price lists to ensure realistic prices.

- Look at data representations involving money and ask children to estimate and calculate sums and differences in response to a series of questions.

Ensuring progress

Supporting understanding

Children continue to use the place-value money headers (as shown in the Textbook) to explore adding single-digit amounts, multiples of ten pence and multiples of one pound. Amounts can be represented in coins and Base 10 apparatus.

Broadening understanding

The problem in Step 4 can be extended so that children reason about how best to change one rule in the task to allow for a greater total or greater difference, e.g. change £1 coins for £2 coins; 10p for 20p coins or increase the number of coins to 12 rather than 11. They can investigate how this changes the possibilities.

✓ Concept mastered

Children can represent an amount shown in pounds, e.g. £3.25, using coins and Base 10 apparatus. They can explain why one pence is $\frac{1}{100}$ of a pound and why ten pence is $\frac{1}{10}$ of a pound. They represent the equivalence between $\frac{1}{10}$ and $\frac{10}{100}$ and can explain why money is shown to two decimal places.

Answers

Step 1

a £3.57   c £5.07

b £3.80   d £5.42

Step 2

a £4.83

b £3.23

c £2.64

d £5.81 or 581p

e £3.73 or 373p

Step 3

a £5.44   b £2.01

Step 4

b Largest total is
£11.00 + £10.10 = £21.10 and smallest is 11p + 20p = 31p.

c Largest difference is
£11 − 11p = £10.81and smallest is a difference of 9p, e.g. 20p − 11p.

- **Solve addition and subtraction two-step problems in contexts, deciding which operations and methods to use and why.**

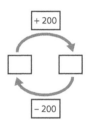

Homework 57 and 58   Practice Book pp 104–7

Mathematical vocabulary

Addition, subtraction, total, difference, multiple, boundary, two-step problem

Representations and resources

Place-value counters, Base 10 apparatus, bead strings, place-value grid.

Warming up

Challenge children to complete the diagram in as many ways as they can to show the result of adding and subtracting 200, e.g. 1250 + 200 = 1450 and 1450 – 200 = 1250. This will allow children to draw on their knowledge of place value, and could be extended to cover adding and subtracting 2000. Reinforce the inverse relationship between addition and subtraction.

Background knowledge

When making choices about when to use a mental method and when to use a written method, it is important to look for calculations that require the addition or subtraction of a single digit, a multiple of ten or a multiple of 100 or 1000. Be sure to challenge children when they use the written method inappropriately, so that children continue to develop their sense of place value. Use place-value apparatus to represent what stays the same and what changes in a number when one of these multiples is added or subtracted. It is often useful to role-play word problems and sketch a bar model to help children make sense of the steps required.

Let's learn: Modelling and teaching

Solving two-step problems mentally

- Discuss the word problem in the Textbook. Ask questions, e.g. *How many visitors were there on Wednesday?* to check children understand the table. Ask what you need to know in order to answer the question. Establish that you need to know the combined total for Tuesday and Wednesday (addition) and the difference between that total and the total for Thursday (subtraction).

- Look at the bar models in the Textbook. The first shows which days need to be considered and the second gives the associated numbers of visitors. Check children understand how the bar models relate to the problem. Next discuss how to complete the first step. Refer back to recent calculations that required a mental method and others that did not. Discuss what was different about them and establish that calculations involving a multiple of 10, 100 or 1000 can often be done mentally. So, 3400 + 4000 can be found by counting on 4000. Model the addition using place-value counters, ensuring that children recognise which part of the number changes and which

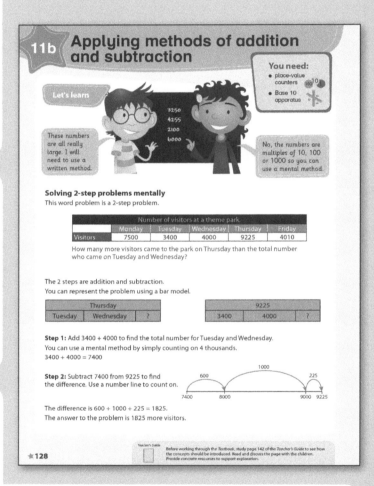

stays the same as a multiple of 1000 is added. Sketch the bar model to match this step.

- Encourage children to make an estimate before they carry out Step 2 of the calculation. Discuss why the counting-on strategy is a good one to use to find the difference between 9225 and 7400, establishing that the numbers are close together on the number line and also close to hundreds boundaries. Recap the strategy by recording each step on the whiteboard.

- You could also consider alternative ways to solve the problem, e.g. working out 9225 – 4000 – 3400. Discuss suitable strategies and whether each step can be done mentally.

- Ask children to make up some similar word problems about the table. When could they use mental methods and when would they need a written method?

Let's practise: Digging deeper

Step 1

Children complete a set of addition and subtraction calculations, using and developing knowledge of place value or partitioning. They should represent each calculation using place-value counters or Base 10 apparatus, and model adding or subtracting the values given. They should explain which parts of the number stay the same and which change each time as different multiples are added or subtracted.

Step 2

Children solve a set of two-step calculations, building on the mental strategies they have used in Step 1. They should recognise when it is not necessary to recalculate as some answers have already been obtained in Step 1.

The calculations develop to include a calculation in the context of measurement and a two-step word problem. Encourage children to explain the operations they will need to use and to make appropriate estimates before carrying out the calculations.

Step 3

Children solve a two-step problem, explaining to their partner how many steps there are. Observe many work out 9500 – 3198 – 5319 and how many first find the total for Tuesday and then subtract it from 9500. Encourage them to represent the problem using the bar model to help them make sense of it and make decisions about how best to calculate. Again, Base 10 apparatus can be used to support calculating. They are also required to make up their own two-step problem for their partner to solve. Ask questions such as: *What would a hard problem be? What would an easy problem be? Why?*

Step 4

The bar model represents a two-step operation. This involves an addition and a subtraction or two steps of subtraction to give a difference of 250. It may be useful to represent the difference first and then think about the possible numbers that would result in this difference. Children are asked to find solutions where a mental method can be used, but this can also be extended to find examples that may best be completed using a written method.

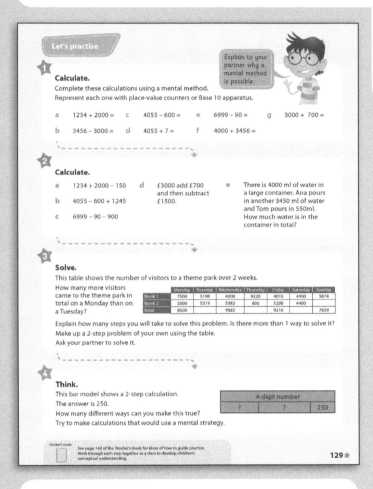

Ensuring progress

Supporting understanding

Bead strings can be used to support partitioning a single-digit number over a tens boundary.

Base 10 apparatus should continue to be used to support adding and subtracting multiples of 10, 100 or 1000. It may also be useful to represent the numbers on a place-value grid so that the zero place holders can be seen as you calculate.

Broadening understanding

For Step 4, you could change the difference to, e.g. 249, so children have to reason about how they will need to change their set of solutions so that the calculations remain true. Encourage children to adapt their solutions rather than starting from scratch each time.

 Concept mastered

Children can solve addition and subtraction two-step problems in contexts. They can decide which operations to use and explain when and why a mental method is appropriate.

Follow-up ideas

- Look at other statistical representations, e.g. bar charts and time graphs that use scales that are labelled in multiples of 100 or 1000 with intervals of 25 or 50 and 250 and 500 respectively. Children can find sums and differences and make up and solve a set of one and two-step problems.

- Use practical tasks involving mass and capacity to add and subtract multiples of 10, 100 and 1000 millilitres or grams. Children should apply mental methods to calculate.

Answers

Step 1

a	3234	e	6909
b	456	f	7456
c	3455	g	3700
d	4062		

Step 2

a	3084	d	£2200
b	4700	e	8000 ml
c	6009		

Step 3

983. Two steps.

Step 4

Answers will vary,
e.g. 4000 – 2000 – 1750 = 250
or
2000 + 1750 = 3750 and
4000 – 3750 = 250

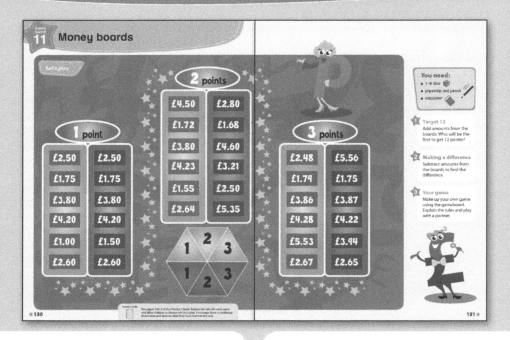

Game 1: Target 12

Players must correctly add amounts from the boards, determined by the dice and spinner, to score points.

Maths focus

- Adding money

Resources

1–6 dice (2), paperclip and pencil, calculators, Base 10 apparatus.

How to play

Play with a partner. Each player takes it in turn to use the spinner. To do this they place one end of a paperclip over the dot in the centre of the spinner and position the sharp end of a pencil on the dot. They flick the paperclip. Where it lands shows them which board to use and how many points they can score. After each spin, both players roll two dice to find which amounts on the board they need to add, counting from the bottom, e.g. if a player gets a red three on the spinner and rolls a two and a four on the dice, they must add £3.94 and £3.87. A dice roll of double two would result in the calculation £3.94 + £3.94 or double £3.94. Both players then complete their calculations, using either a mental or a written method, at the same time.
They check their partner's answer with a calculator. A correct answer scores the points available for the board being used. The players then spin again. The winner is the first player to score 12 points.

Making it easier

Players can represent the calculations using Base 10 apparatus or decide which board (i.e. level of difficulty) they would like to try rather than spinning.

Making it harder

An additional step could be added in which a bonus point can be scored each time if the change is calculated from £10, e.g. after a calculation £3.94 + £3.87 = £7.81, find the change from £10 using the subtraction £10 − £7.81 = £2.19.

Game 2: Making a difference

Players must correctly find the difference between two amounts from the boards.

Maths focus

- Subtracting money

Resources

1–6 dice (2), paperclip and pencil, calculators, Base 10 apparatus.

How to play

Play in the same way as for Target 12. This time, after each spin, both players roll two dice to find which amounts on the board they need to find the difference for, counting from the bottom. Both players then complete their calculations, using either a mental or a written method, and check their partner's answer with a calculator. A correct answer scores the points available for the board being used. The players then spin again. The winner is the first player to score 12 points.

Making it easier

Players can represent the calculations using Base 10 apparatus or decide which board (i.e. level of difficulty) they would like to try rather than spinning. The winning score could also be reduced to the first to eight points.

Making it harder

Players play as above but roll only one of the dice. They must then make up a subtraction calculation which gives that amount as the answer. Their partner must decide if they are to use a written or mental method.

Game 3: Your game

Children should invent their own game designing rules that use the concepts covered in the unit. Challenge children to make their game easier or harder.

Unit 11 — Money boards

Choose a game to play.

Game 1: Target 12

You need:
- two 1–6 dice
- paperclip and pencil
- calculator

How to play

- Place one end of a paperclip over the dot in the centre of the spinner and position the sharp end of a pencil on the dot. Spin the spinner. The number it lands on shows you which board to use.
- Both players roll the 2 dice. Your scores tell you which amounts on the board you need to add, counting from the bottom, e.g. on the red '3 points' board, a 2 and a 4 on the dice mean you must work out £3.94 + £3.87.
- Choose whether to use a mental or written method.
- Do your calculations at the same time, then check each other's answer with a calculator.
- If your answer is correct, you score the points available for the board you are using.
- The winner is the first to 12 points.

Game 2: Making a difference

You need:
- two 1–6 dice
- paperclip and pencil
- calculator

How to play

- Play in the same way as Target 12 above.
- This time, after each spin, roll 2 dice to find which amounts on the board you need to find the difference for, counting from the bottom, e.g. on the red '3 points' board, a 2 and a 4 on the dice mean you must work out £3.94 – £3.87.
- Choose whether to do use a mental or written method.
- Do your calculations at the same time, then check each other's answer with a calculator.
- If your answer is correct, you score the points available for the board you are using.
- The winner is the first to 12 points.

Game 3: Your game

- Make up your own game using the gameboard.
- You could roll 3 dice to make an addition using 3 numbers.
- One player could always use the red board and the other the yellow board.

Please help your child by reading the instructions and playing the game together.

Assessment task 1

Resources

Place-value grid, Base 10 apparatus.

Running the task

Talk about some of the calculations you have been doing recently involving money. You may want to also assess children's understanding of the place value of money by asking them to represent some of the amounts shown on a place-value grid using pence and pounds.

Remind them that making an estimate is always a good way to get a sense of the size of your answer. Children could make an estimate for each of Ana's calculations, explaining the rounding they have done and why they have made a useful estimate. They should use their estimates and reason about the accuracy of Ana's calculations compared to their estimates. If they do not do so, ask them to explain whether the actual answers will be smaller or greater than the estimates, encouraging them to give their reasons. Alternatively, they could use an inverse calculation to check Ana's calculations. Note that they should be able to tell at a glance that the third is incorrect because the amounts have been incorrectly placed in the columns.

You may wish to ask children to represent each calculation using Base 10 apparatus and match this to Ana's working as they first work with the digits in the ones positions and then tens, etc. Any incorrect workings by Ana should be amended and also checked against the estimates. Children should explain the mistakes that Ana has made.

Evidencing mastery

Children should be able to describe the place value of an amount given in pounds and use this to help them represent calculations. They use number bonds to add and subtract numbers within 20. Those who can readily identify that all Ana's answers are incorrect and also explain where Ana has gone wrong are demonstrating a strong grasp of the concept.

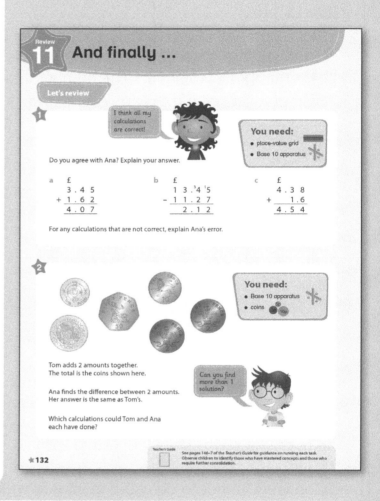

Assessment task 2

Resources

Base 10 apparatus, money (coins).

Running the task

This task can be completed in pairs or within a group so that children can compare and reason about possible solutions. They should first discuss what the problem is asking them to do and present it using a bar model so that they can make sense of the value £3.64 as a sum and as a difference for Tom and Ana's calculations.

You could begin by looking at values that would require adding or subtracting a whole number of pounds or a multiple of ten pence only. This will help children to make further sense of the problem and provide assessment opportunities for recognising the effect of adding or subtracting multiples of 100 or 10 to any given number. Ask children to use Base 10 apparatus and coins to model and prove solutions. Children can then work in pairs to think of other sets of solutions that would work in the same way, i.e. adding or subtracting a multiple of 10 or 100. Discuss the use of mental methods here and why a written method would be inappropriate.

You could ask children to use a table to organise their possible solutions and look for any patterns in the numbers. Consider ways that a set of solutions could be adjusted to provide further solutions rather than always starting from scratch, e.g. if we know that £1.64 + £2.00 = £3.64 then this can be adjusted to £1.65 + £1.99, etc.

Evidencing mastery

Children should be able to represent a value of money shown in coins as a value shown in £.p notation. They represent the values using Base 10 apparatus and use this to explore adding and subtracting multiples of 100 and 10 as pounds and ten pence.

Children who use estimating to reason about sums and differences and can produce a wide range of solutions to the problem are demonstrating mastery.

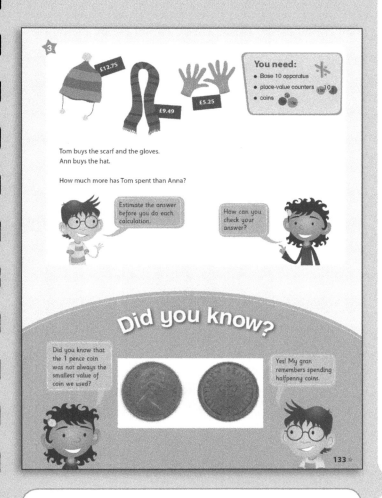

Concepts mastered

✓ Children can represent an amount shown in pounds, e.g. £3.25, using coins and Base 10 apparatus. They can explain why one pence is $\frac{1}{100}$ of a pound and why ten pence is $\frac{1}{10}$ of a pound. They represent the equivalence between $\frac{1}{10}$ and $\frac{10}{100}$ and can explain why money is shown to two decimal places.

✓ Children can solve addition and subtraction two-step problems in contexts. They can decide which operations to use and explain when and why a mental method is appropriate.

Assessment task 3

Resources

Base 10 apparatus, place-value counters, money (coins).

Running the task

Discuss the problem and which operations to use. Encourage children to explain whether they think it is a one- or two-step problem and why. Invite children to represent the prices using coins and then with place-value counters or Base 10 apparatus.

Discuss how the problem can be solved and then consider possible strategies to add £9.49 and £5.25, making an estimate first. Look for children who can explain that the actual total will be more than £14. Children should carry out a mental or written method to add these values, discussing how close the answer is to the estimate. Look for children who confidently line up the decimal points and can explain why this is important.

Talk about the second step in the problem and the strategies that children can use. They may decide to find the difference between £14.74 and £12.75 using the counting-up strategy. Look for children who recognise that 74p is one less than 75p and begin to reason about the value of the difference being nearly two pounds. Children should also think about ways to check the calculation, including the use of inverse calculations.

Evidencing mastery

Children who can explain what the problem is requiring and how they will carry it out are showing mastery of this concept. They should be able to make decisions about which method to use, drawing on mental and written strategies as appropriate. They should be able to use number bonds to help them carry out the calculations and check the validity of a solution by referring to estimates and checking using the inverse.

Did you know?

The smallest value coin used in the UK is the one pence coin; however, between 15 February 1971, when decimal currency was introduced, and 1984 we also had a decimal halfpenny coin. Like the one penny, it was made of bronze. It weighed only 1.78 grams. Children might find it interesting to find out about our currency before 1971 and how the decimal halfpenny was needed to help convert some of the previous coins more accurately. You could also discuss what number of halfpennies is equivalent to 10p, 50p and £1, or find out about the introduction of the 20p and £2 coin, and the withdrawal of the £1 note.

In the past, coins were sometimes cut in halves or quarters when smaller values were needed. It was once believed that the first halfpenny coins were produced in the reign of King Edward I (1272–1307) but earlier silver halfpennies have been found that date back to the reign of Henry I (1100–1135) and Henry III (1216–1272). These are very rare and not much is known about them.

Mathematical focus

★ Number: fractions (including decimals)
★ Measurement: length, mass, volume/capacity, money

Prior learning

Children should already be able to:

- count up and down in tenths and hundredths, recognise that tenths arise from dividing an object into ten equal parts and dividing single-digit numbers or quantities by ten; recognise that hundredths arise when dividing an object by one hundred and dividing tenths by ten

- recognise and write decimal equivalents of tenths, hundredths, a quarter, half and three-quarters

- recognise and show, using diagrams, families of some common equivalent fractions

- add and subtract fractions with the same denominator.

Key new learning

- Recognise and write decimal equivalents of any number of tenths or hundredths.

- Recognise and write decimal equivalents to quarter, half and three-quarters.

- Recognise and show, using diagrams, families of common equivalent fractions.

- Add and subtract fractions with the same denominator.

- Round decimals with one decimal place to the nearest whole number.

- Compare numbers with the same number of decimal places up to two decimal places.

Making connections

- Fractions and decimals are used frequently in everyday life, and in subjects such as science and geography. The obvious context is measurement. In length children work with numbers with one decimal place when dealing with centimetres and millimetres, and numbers with two decimal places when dealing with metres and centimetres. They also work with numbers with two decimal places when working with money.

- An understanding of fractions and decimals is essential for children's further mathematical study, underpinning work on ratio, proportion, statistics and algebra.

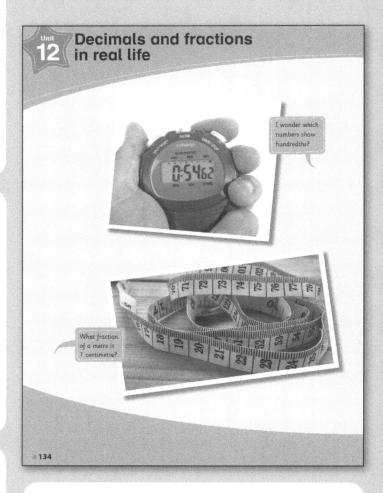

Unit 12 Decimals and fractions in real life

I wonder which numbers show hundredths?

What fraction of a metre is 1 centimetre?

 134

💬 Talk about

It is important to use precise mathematical vocabulary from the beginning. Remind children about the Base 10 aspect of place value and ensure they understand that when we multiply and divide numbers by ten, they increase and decrease by powers of ten. Ask them to multiply and divide different numbers by ten and then 100 and to explain the effect. Focus on the decimals that are made and expect children to be able to describe the positional and multiplicative elements of place value for these.

Engaging and exploring

Ask children if they have ever used a stopwatch and if so when. Establish that a stopwatch is used to time events that need recording to the nearest minute or second. Ask children how many seconds there are in one, two and three minutes. Discuss how they can do this, e.g. using their knowledge of multiplication facts for six. Look at the picture of the stopwatch and agree that the zero represents minutes and the 54 seconds. For smaller units of time we used tenths and hundredths of a second. Agree that the six represents six tenths of a second and the two represents two hundredths of a second. Give pairs of children a stopwatch and ask them to time themselves doing different tasks, e.g. making a tower of 20 interlocking cubes. Expect them to record the time it takes them in seconds and hundredths of seconds.

Look at the picture of the tape measure and ask children to tell you what units of measure they can see. Agree that they are centimetres and between the centimetres there are millimetre divisions. Agree that 100 centimetres are equivalent to one metre, so one centimetre must be one hundredth of a metre. Establish that a tape measure is used to measure length. Discuss other pieces of apparatus that could be used to measure length, e.g. rulers, metre sticks. Give children the opportunity to measure items around the classroom. Ask them to record their measurements in metres, as decimals. Ask children to tell you what fraction of a metre different centimetres are, e.g. 10 cm, 50 cm, 25 cm. You could also give children different centimetres to convert to fractions and their equivalent decimal representations, e.g. 10 cm = $\frac{1}{10}$ m = 0.1 m, 45 cm = $\frac{45}{100}$ = 0.45 m.

For the photo of the food, ask children to identify the fractions that the watermelon and pie have been divided into. Look at the fraction equivalents, e.g. one quarter and two-eighths, one third and two-sixths. *What would be equivalent to half?* Agree four-eighths and three-sixths, so half the watermelon would be four pieces and half the pie would be three pieces. Give the watermelon and pie values, e.g. £4.80, and ask children to work out the price of each piece. Discuss why, despite the whole being £4.80, the slices are different prices. Establish that sixths are greater than eighths in this instance, so will be worth more. Give two different prices for the items, so that the eighths are worth more (e.g. £5.60 for the watermelon and £3.00 for the pie), and discuss why this is.

Next look at the photo of the fruit and drinks and find out if children can identify each fruit. Can they tell you how 750 millilitres would be represented in litres? Elicit that 750 millilitres is three-quarters of a litre, or 0.75 litres. Ask them to work out the total volume (2250 millilitres or 2.25 litres). Invite children to share how they worked this out. If different children used different methods, you could discuss the advantages and disadvantages of each.

Give children the opportunity to fill containers with water and then measure them to the nearest 100 millilitres. Ask them to record their answers in two ways, e.g. litres and millilitres and then litres, using decimals. You could also ask children to count the apples and work out the fraction each child would get if they were shared between two, three or four children. You could repeat this for the other fruit.

Turning to the money photo, ask children to work out the total amount using plastic notes and coins. Then focus on each coin less than £1 and ask children to tell you what fraction it is of £1. Begin with 1p ($\frac{1}{100}$), 2p ($\frac{2}{100}$) and 5p ($\frac{5}{100}$). For 10p, 20p and 50p, ask: *How many hundredths? How many tenths?* Agree that each of these coins is ten times the value of one of the smaller coins. Then ask what fraction each coin is of £2. This time the whole is 200 pence, so one pence is $\frac{1}{200}$, two pence is $\frac{2}{200}$ and so on. Ask children what they notice. Can children reduce $\frac{2}{200}$? Use coins to model the generalisation developed in Unit 7 – Fractions and decimals. $\frac{2}{200}$ is equivalent to twice $\frac{1}{100}$.

If I wanted half the watermelon and half the pie would I get the same number of pieces?

How much money is here?

If each glass holds 750 ml, I wonder what the total volume is?

Teacher's Guide Look at the pictures with the children and discuss the questions. See pages 148–9 of the Teacher's Guide for key ideas to draw out.

135 ▶

Things to think about

- How will you ask questions and give tasks that encourage problem solving within the context of measures when children are working with decimals?

- What practical activities will you use for length, mass and capacity/volume that involve fractions and decimals?

- How will you ensure all children master the concepts studied in this unit? What support can you give children who need it? What challenges can you develop for those children who grasp concepts quickly?

Checking understanding

You will know children have mastered these concepts when they can recognise and write decimal equivalents of tenths, hundredths, one quarter, half and three-quarters. They will be able to explain and demonstrate what a fraction is and find families of common equivalent fractions. They will be able to add and subtract fractions with the same denominator. They will be able to round numbers with one decimal place to the nearest whole number and compare numbers with up to two decimal places.

- Recognise and write decimal equivalents of any number of tenths or hundredths.
- Recognise and write decimal equivalents to quarter, half and three-quarters.
- Recognise and show, using diagrams, families of common equivalent fractions.
- Add and subtract fractions with the same denominator.

Homework 59 and 60

Practice Book pp 108–11

Fraction Wall

Representations and resources

Interlocking cubes, rulers, tape measures (or metre sticks), dominoes (optional), card strips

Mathematical vocabulary

Denominator, numerator, equivalent

Warming up

Recap finding fractions of amounts, reminding children that they need to divide the whole by the denominator to find the value of one part and then multiply by the numerator to find the amount required. Ask children to find different fractions of one hour, e.g. twelfths, fifths, quarters and thirds. Before you begin, ask children what they need to know in order to do this. Agree that they need to know there are 60 minutes in an hour. You could then move on to finding fractions of a metre, e.g. tenths and fifths.

Background knowledge

You can find equivalent fractions by multiplying the numerator and denominator by the same number. This is true for unit and non-unit fractions. Equivalent fractions can also be found by simplifying or reducing, by dividing both parts of the fraction by the same number.

Adding fractions outside a whole gives improper fractions. This is not a requirement for Year 4, however, you could nevertheless introduce the concept of mixed numbers. Children should know how many of a particular fraction make a whole and be able to find the fraction that is left. Some children may realise dividing the numerator by the denominator gives a whole number and proper fraction.

Let's learn: Modelling and teaching

Equivalent fractions

- Look at the cartoon in the Textbook. Can children explain Ana's reasoning? Can they tell you why Tom is correct?

- Look at the models in the Textbook. Discuss similarities and differences between these and the models in Unit 7 – Fractions and decimals. They both show fractions, but that the fractions are different. Explore equivalences between fifths, tenths and fifteenths. Give children interlocking cubes and ask them to find as many fractions as they can that are equivalent to fifths. Can they remember the generalisation for finding equivalent fractions? Tell children the whole represents different measurement amounts (e.g. £45, 90 metres). Ask questions such as: *What is one-fifth? Three-fifteenths?*

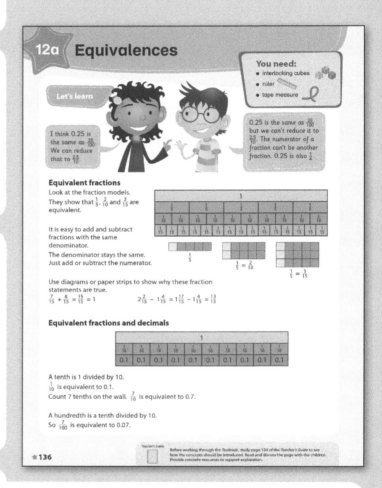

- Give children some fractions with the same denominator to add and subtract. Remind them that any improper fractions should be changed to mixed numbers. Include some subtraction statements where a whole number needs to be exchanged (e.g. $2\frac{3}{5} - \frac{4}{5}$).

Equivalent fractions and decimals

- Look at the fraction wall and agree that ten of one-tenth and ten of 0.1 each make one whole, so one-tenth is the same as 0.1. Emphasise that they are both tenths, just written differently. Ask children to convert different tenths to decimals, counting along the wall at first.

- Give pairs measuring equipment and the opportunity to measure lines in centimetres and millimetres and masses and volumes in kilograms and grams and litres and millilitres, recording the results using decimal notation.

Let's practise: Digging deeper

Step 1

Recap finding equivalent fractions: you multiply (or divide) the denominator and numerator by the same number. During the task, some children may benefit from looking at the models in the Textbook. If necessary, prompt children to consider whether a fraction (e.g. $\frac{3}{15}$) can be reduced or simplified to make an equivalent fraction, as well as multiplied. Children write an explanation of how they worked out the equivalent fractions, putting the generalisation into their own words.

Step 2

Begin by rehearsing adding and subtracting fractions that include mixed numbers (e.g. $2\frac{1}{5} + 1\frac{3}{5}$ and $3\frac{1}{5} - 2\frac{4}{5}$). Discuss when you can deal with the whole numbers separately and when you need to convert to an improper fraction or exchange one whole number. Tell children that the answers must be in positive

integers, so for the subtraction statements they first need to identify the larger fraction.

Step 3

Provide pairs of children with tape measures or metre sticks. It might be helpful to select items around the classroom that are over a metre in length for them to measure. Children need to estimate, measure and record the lengths using decimal notation, then work out the difference between their estimates and the actual measurements. Some children may need support in constructing a suitable table and you might want to model this.

Step 4

This task asks children to use domino patterns to investigate fractions. If you have dominoes in the classroom, give these to children to use. Make sure they understand that the top half of the domino represents the numerator and the bottom the denominator. Ask questions to draw out reasoning, e.g. *How will you know if two dominoes are equivalent? How else might you know? How can you find out how to order these? What do you need to consider? Would making them all fractions with the same denominator help?*

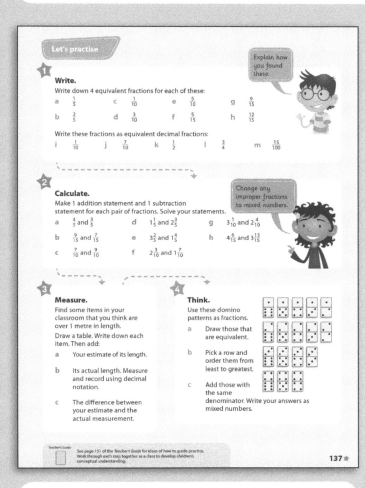

Ensuring progress

Supporting understanding

In a focus group, work with children to make strips of card that are divided into fifths, tenths and fifteenths. Discuss the equivalence as you make the strips together. Allow children to use their strips throughout teaching and practising the concept. If children cannot change improper fractions to mixed numbers in Step 2, let them present their solutions as improper fractions.

Broadening understanding

Ask children to make up some of their own addition and subtraction calculations that involve mixed numbers.

✓ Concept mastered

Children can show and explain how to find equivalent fractions and add and subtract fractions with the same denominator. They can recognise and write decimal equivalents to quarter, half, three-quarters, tenths and hundredths.

Follow-up ideas

- Children write pairs of equivalent fractions on cards. They shuffle them together, place them face down and pick two: if they match they keep the pair. The winner has the most pairs at the end.

- Give children water, bottles and a measuring jug. They pour some water into a bottle, estimate how much is in there and then measure to the nearest 100 millilitres. They record this using decimal notation.

- Give children clock faces. They explore the different fractions that they can make by cutting them into fractional parts, e.g. half, one-third, quarter, one-fifth, one-sixth and so on. They then explore the equivalences that they can make.

Answers

Step 1

For example:

a $\quad \frac{1}{5} = \frac{2}{10}, \frac{3}{15}, \frac{4}{20}, \frac{5}{25}$

b $\quad \frac{2}{5} = \frac{4}{10}, \frac{6}{15}, \frac{8}{20}, \frac{10}{25}$

c $\quad \frac{1}{10} = \frac{2}{20}, \frac{3}{30}, \frac{4}{40}, \frac{5}{50}$

d $\quad \frac{3}{10} = \frac{6}{20}, \frac{9}{30}, \frac{12}{40}, \frac{15}{50}$

e $\quad \frac{5}{10} = \frac{10}{20}, \frac{15}{30}, \frac{20}{40}, \frac{25}{50}$

f $\quad \frac{5}{15} = \frac{1}{3}, \frac{10}{30}, \frac{15}{45}, \frac{20}{60}$

g $\quad \frac{9}{15} = \frac{3}{5}, \frac{18}{30}, \frac{27}{45}, \frac{36}{60}$

h $\quad \frac{12}{15} = \frac{24}{30}, \frac{36}{45}, \frac{48}{60}, \frac{60}{75}$

i $\quad 0.1$

j $\quad 0.7$

k $\quad 0.5$

l $\quad 0.75$

m $\quad 0.15$

Step 2

a $\quad \frac{7}{5} = 1\frac{2}{5}; \frac{1}{5}$ e $\quad 4\frac{6}{5} = 5\frac{1}{5}; 1\frac{3}{5}$

b $\quad \frac{16}{15} = 1\frac{1}{15}; \frac{2}{15}$ f $\quad 3\frac{10}{10} = 4; \frac{6}{10}$

c $\quad \frac{16}{10} = 1\frac{6}{10}; \frac{2}{10}$ g $\quad 5\frac{5}{10} = 5\frac{1}{2}; \frac{7}{10}$

d $\quad 3\frac{4}{5}; 1\frac{2}{5}$ h $\quad 7\frac{19}{15} = 8\frac{4}{15}; \frac{8}{15}$

Step 4

a $\quad \frac{1}{2} = \frac{2}{4} = \frac{3}{6}; \frac{1}{3} = \frac{2}{6}$

c $\quad \frac{10}{6} = 1\frac{4}{6}; \frac{10}{5} = 2; \frac{10}{4} = 2\frac{1}{2};$
$\quad \frac{6}{3} = 2; \frac{3}{2} = 1\frac{1}{2}$

Comparing and rounding decimals

- Round decimals with one decimal place to the nearest whole number.
- Compare numbers with the same number of decimal places up to two decimal places.

Homework 61 and 62

Practice Book pp 112–15

Mathematical vocabulary

Compare, round, decimals

Representations and resources

Base 10 apparatus, place-value grids, partitioning cards, string, scissors, rulers, sand, plastic bags, weighing scales, 1–6 dice.

Warming up

Rehearse counting in steps of different tenths and hundredths. Begin counting in tenths from zero to one and back to zero. Then start at different numbers (e.g. 2.3, 12.9 and 25.8) and count in tenths for 15 to 20 steps and back again. Repeat for counting in hundredths. Begin at zero and then other starting numbers such as 2.13, 8.38 and 24.96.

Background knowledge

A conceptual understanding of place value is vital for ordering and rounding numbers. When ordering numbers such as 25.8 and 25.4, some children will view the decimal parts as whole numbers and conclude that 25.8 is larger than 25.4 because eight is larger than four. This may lead to misconceptions in future when they need to compare, e.g. 25.49 and 25.8. Develop children's understanding of place value to include tenths and hundredth. Recap the positional, multiplicative and additive aspects of place value at this point. Rounding tenths and hundredths works in the same way as rounding whole numbers, so that they are not thrown by the presence of the decimal point.

Let's learn: Modelling and teaching
Comparing numbers with decimal places

- Look at the cartoon in the Textbook and discuss Ana's explanation. Then ask children to take their finger for a walk on the Gattegno chart: *Start on four, multiply by ten, subtract 20, divide by 100, add 0.6, divide by ten.* Are they all on 0.08? Discuss what happens to the numbers as you move along each row and up or down each column.

- Ask children to make pairs of numbers using the chart and compare them using the > and < symbols. Start with numbers made from the top three rows, then move on to numbers made from the bottom three rows. Encourage children to make some pairs where the whole number part is the same. Expect them to be able to tell you which digit (tens, ones, tenths or hundredths) they looked at in order to decide which number is the larger.

- Use Base 10 apparatus to reinforce children's understanding that, e.g. 0.8 is greater than 0.6. Ask children to make more pairs of numbers using the apparatus. Again, ask them to compare their numbers and explain how they know their statements are correct.

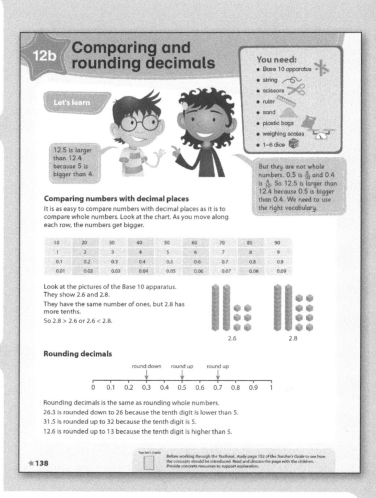

Rounding decimals

- Ask children to tell you all they know about rounding numbers to the nearest ten. Agree that numbers with the ones digit five and above are rounded up and others are rounded down. Explain that we round decimal numbers to the nearest whole number in exactly the same way, except that we look at the tenths digit to decide whether to round up or down.

- Ask children to look at the number line in their Textbooks. Together, decide whether 0.3, 0.5 and 0.7 round down to zero or up to one, then look at the other examples. Ask children to make up five numbers with one decimal place and round them to the nearest whole number. They can draw the appropriate number lines and use them to check their answers.

Let's practise: Digging deeper

Step 1

Before children begin the task, recap the greater than and less than symbols. During the task, ask children to explain some of their answers; expect them to talk about the place value of the tenths and hundredths. The last two questions are presented as a challenge. Some children may find place-value grids or partitioning cards helpful here. For part j you could remind them that 87.6 could be written as 87.60. Once they have used > and < to compare the numbers, they then need to work out what they should do to make the numbers equal. They do this by adding to one and subtracting from the other, e.g. 2.4 + 0.4 = 2.8 and 2.8 – 0.4 = 2.4.

Step 2

Ask children to tell you how they know whether to round up or down to the nearest whole number. Agree that if the digit in the tenths position is less than five we round down, if it is five or more we round up. During the task, allow children to draw number lines if they find these helpful. Again, the last two questions are presented as a challenge. You could discuss how numbers such as 231 are rounded to the nearest ten and 100 or use a number line to show that the hundredths digits can be ignored.

Step 3

Children work in pairs. For the first part, give each pair a length of string about one metre long for them to cut into six pieces of different lengths. For both parts, encourage children to measure the lengths and masses accurately. Some children may need support in constructing a suitable table, and you might want to demonstrate measuring and recording the information for one length and one mass first.

Step 4

Give each child or pair two dice. Ask them to throw two dice ten times, make two numbers and round them like Tom does. Do they think Tom is correct? Explain that they need just one counter-example to prove Tom is incorrect, but they cannot say he is correct without exploring all the possibilities. If children have already found the counter-example, ask them to explore all the possibilities anyway to see if there are any others. Encourage them to work systematically, recording their results in a table that gives all the relevant information.

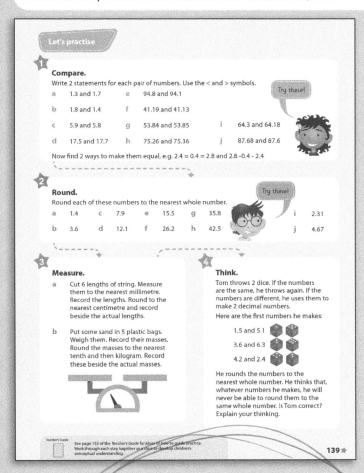

Ensuring progress

Supporting understanding

You could simplify Step 1 by asking children to compare only numbers with one decimal place. For Step 2, you could provide blank number lines to support them. Children who find these tasks difficult need not attempt the final two parts of the first two steps.

Broadening understanding

Extend Step 1 by asking children to work out what they could do to the numbers in each pair to make them equal. In Step 3, you could ask them to find the difference between the actual and rounded measurement in each case.

✓ Concept mastered

Children can explain and demonstrate how to compare numbers with one or two decimal places and round numbers with one decimal place to the nearest whole number.

Follow-up ideas

- Ask children to make sets of cards with numbers that have one decimal place. They place these in a pile face down on the table and take it in turns to pick a card, turn it over and place it so that the cards that are face up are in ascending order. They could repeat this with numbers with two decimal places.

- You could ask children to use the cards they made with one decimal place and round each to the nearest whole number. Does this make a difference to the order?

- Ask children to carry out the task in Step 3 of the Textbook, but this time within the context of volume. Provide bottles, measuring jugs and water.

Answers

Step 1

a	1.3 < 1.7, 1.7 > 1.3
b	1.8 > 1.4, 1.4 < 1.8
c	5.9 > 5.8, 5.8 < 5.9
d	17.5 < 17.7, 17.7 > 17.5
e	94.8 > 94.1, 94.1 < 94.8
f	41.19 > 41.13, 41.13 < 41.19
g	53.84 < 53.85, 53.85 > 53.84
h	75.26 < 75.36, 75.36 > 75.26
i	64.3 > 64.18, 64.18 < 64.3
j	87.68 > 87.6, 87.6 < 87.68

Step 2

a	1	f	26
b	4	g	36
c	8	h	43
d	12	i	2
e	16	j	5

Step 4

Tom is incorrect. 4.5 and 5.4 both round to 5.

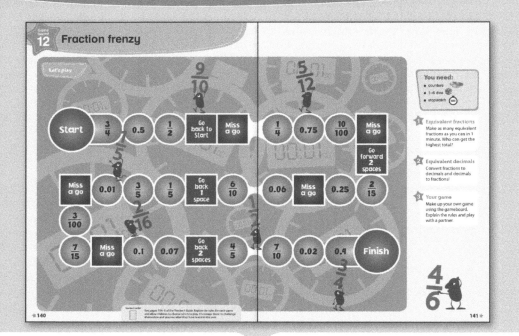

Game 1: Equivalent fractions

This game challenges children to find as many equivalent fractions as they can within one minute.

Maths focus

- Find equivalent fractions

Resources

1 counter per player (1 colour per player), 1–6 dice (1), stopwatches (or minute timers).

How to play

Children play in pairs. They place their counters on Start. They take it in turns to roll the dice and move their counter that number of spaces. If they land on an instruction they follow it. If they land on a decimal they do nothing. If they land on a fraction their partner times them as they write down as many equivalent fractions as they can in one minute. Their partner checks to see if they agree with the equivalences made. The child who made the equivalent fractions counts how many and scores that number of points. Play continues until both players reach Finish. They find their final score. The winner is the child with the higher score.

Making it easier

You could replace the non-unit fractions on the gameboard with unit fractions for those children who still find equivalent fractions difficult.

Making it harder

You could replace the instructions on the gameboard with fractions that could be reduced or simplified (e.g. $\frac{24}{36}$ $\frac{12}{15}$).

Game 2: Equivalent decimals

This game gives children practice in converting between fractions and decimals.

Maths focus

- Recognise and write decimal equivalents of any number of tenths or hundredths
- Recognise and write decimal equivalents to quarter, half and three-quarters

Resources

1 counter per player (1 colour per player), 1–6 dice (1).

How to play

This game should be played in pairs. Children place their counters on Start. They take it in turns to roll the dice and move their counter that number of spaces. If they land on an instruction they follow it. If they land on a fraction they convert it to a decimal. If they land on a decimal number they convert it to a fraction. They score one point for each correct conversion; their partner should check the player's conversion to ensure it is correct. Play continues like this until both players reach Finish. They find their final score. The winner is the player with the higher score.

Making it easier

You could alter the gameboard so that children focus on finding equivalences for tenths, quarter, half and three-quarters.

Making it harder

Ask children to list all their conversions as they play. At the end of the game they could order them from least to greatest. They could also pick pairs and write some comparison statements using the symbols < and >. You could time them for one minute, and award one point for each correct comparison statement, to be added to their total from the main game.

Game 3: Your game

Children should invent their own game, designing rules that use the concepts covered in the unit. Challenge children to make their game easier or harder.

Unit 12 — Fraction frenzy

Choose a game to play.

Game 1: Equivalent fractions

How to play

- Each place a counter on Start.
- Take turns to roll the dice. Move your counter that number of spaces.
- If you land on an instruction, do what it says.
- If you land on a decimal, do nothing. If you land on a fraction:
  - ▶ make up as many equivalent fractions as you can in 1 minute (your partner can time you)
  - ▶ check your fractions with your partner
  - ▶ count how many you made and score that number of points.
- Play until you both reach Finish. The winner is the player with the higher final score.

You need:

- 1 counter per player (1 colour per player)
- 1–6 dice
- stopwatch

Game 2: Equivalent decimals

How to play

- Each place a counter on Start.
- Take turns to roll the dice. Move your counter that number of spaces.
- If you land on an instruction, do what it says.
- If you land on a decimal, convert it to a fraction. If you land on a fraction, convert it to a decimal.
  - ▶ Check your conversion with your partner. If you are correct, score 1 point.
- Play until you both reach Finish. The winner is the player with the higher final score.

You need:

- 1 counter per player (1 colour per player)
- 1–6 dice

Game 3: Your game

- Make up your own game using the gameboard.
- Perhaps it could involve rounding decimals, or adding and subtracting fractions?
- What are the rules for your game? Explain them to someone.

Please help your child by reading the instructions and playing the game together.

Assessment task 1
Running the task

The first part of the task asks children to write down five equivalent fractions for eight given fractions. Recap this with children before they begin the task. Write some equivalent fractions on the board and ask children to talk to a partner about what they notice about them. *What are their similarities and differences?* Agree that although they look different, they are the same value. Recap the generalisation for finding equivalent fractions. Emphasise that this will always give an equivalent fraction whether the fraction is a unit or non-unit fraction. During the task, encourage children to consider whether a fraction can be reduced or simplified by division.

The second part of the task asks children to write and solve addition and subtraction calculations using the given pairs of fractions. You might want to work through an example before children tackle the questions in the Textbook, e.g. write up $3\frac{2}{5} + 1\frac{4}{5}$. $\frac{2}{5} + \frac{4}{5} = \frac{6}{5}$, which is an improper fraction, equal to $1\frac{1}{5}$, so the answer to the addition is $5\frac{1}{5}$. If appropriate, encourage children to change any improper fractions they make during the task to mixed numbers – this is good practice, though not required for mastery at this level.

For subtraction, some of the calculations will require exchanging a whole. You could use $3\frac{2}{5} - 1\frac{4}{5}$ as an example to demonstrate and discuss this. Agree that you cannot subtract $\frac{4}{5}$ from $\frac{2}{5}$, so you need to exchange one of the ones in $3\frac{2}{5}$ for fifths, giving $2\frac{7}{5}$. You can now subtract the whole numbers, 2 – 1 = 1, and the fractions, $\frac{7}{5} - \frac{4}{5} = \frac{3}{5}$, giving a final answer of $1\frac{3}{5}$.

Evidencing mastery

If children can demonstrate and explain how to find equivalent fractions, and add and subtract fractions with the same denominator, explaining how they achieved their results, they are evidencing mastery. Those who can convert any improper fractions in their answers to mixed numbers have a particularly strong grasp of the concept and are exceeding mastery for Year 4.

Assessment task 2
Resources

Individual whiteboards, number lines, fraction strips.

Running the task

By now children should be able to simply recall the decimal equivalents of quarter, half and three-quarters, and also $\frac{1}{10}$ and $\frac{1}{100}$. They should also be able to convert any number of tenths or hundredths, although for some this may require a little more thought. Before children begin the task, you could practise counting on and back in tenths and hundredths from different starting numbers, stopping from time to time and asking children to write that number of tenths or hundredths as a fraction and as a decimal. Emphasise that the values are the same, but we have two different ways of writing them.

You could also write different fractions on the board in tenths and hundredths and ask children to convert these to decimals, writing them on their individual whiteboards. You could repeat this for converting decimals to fractions.

During the task, take the opportunity to check children's understanding by asking them about the place value of the numbers they write. If any children write, e.g. $\frac{15}{100}$ and 0.015, remind them that $\frac{10}{100}$ is equivalent to $\frac{1}{10}$ and ask them to describe to you the positional, multiplicative and additive properties of 0.15. Children who have not mastered this may benefit from additional small-group work using number lines and fraction strips. In the second part, encourage those who can to reduce or simplify the fractions to their lowest term.

Evidencing mastery

Children who can explain and demonstrate how to change fractions to decimals and vice versa, and can fluently recall the decimal equivalents to quarter, half, three-quarters, tenths and hundredths, are evidencing mastery of this area of mathematics.

3
Write 2 statements for each pair of numbers.
Use the < and > symbols.

a   2.4 and 2.8   d   24.68 and 24.28

b   6.9 and 6.3   e   25.34 and 25.35

c   12.25 and 12.35   f   36.12 and 36.17

Round each of these numbers to the nearest whole number.

g   6.7   j   15.1

h   8.3   k   24.5

i   12.6   l   32.9

Draw a number line to help you.

Did you know?

A lot of the mathematical vocabulary we use comes from an old language called Latin.

The word 'fraction' comes from the Latin word *fractio* which means 'to break'. 'Decimal' comes from the Latin *decimus* meaning 'tenth'.

143

Concepts mastered

☑ Children can show and explain how to find equivalent fractions and add and subtract fractions with the same denominator. They can recognise and write decimal equivalents to quarter, half, three-quarters, tenths and hundredths.

☑ Children can explain and demonstrate how to compare numbers with one or two decimal places and round numbers with one decimal place to the nearest whole number.

Assessment task 3
Resources
Number lines.

Running the task
The first part of the task asks children to compare numbers with one or two decimal places using the 'is greater than' and 'is less than' symbols < and >. Before they begin, discuss the two symbols and check they remember which is which. Write pairs of numbers on the board and invite children to place the correct symbol between them. Does everyone agree? Invite individual children to explain a correct statement to the rest of the class.

During the task, ask children to explain how they know their statements are correct. In both cases, expect them to talk about the importance of place value and to describe comparing the numbers in each position in turn until they get to those that are different.

The second part of the task asks them to round numbers with one decimal place to the nearest whole number. Check they understand that numbers with a tenths digit of less than four are rounded down, and those with a tenths digits of five or more are rounded up. Allow those who find them helpful to use number lines.

Evidencing mastery
If children can compare numbers with one and two decimal places and round numbers with one decimal place to the nearest whole number they are evidencing mastery.

Did you know?

Most of the mathematical vocabulary we use today comes from Latin, a classical language with roots in Etruscan and Greek. Etruria was an area in ancient Italy, and there were Greek colonies in southern Italy in ancient times. Latin was the language of the Latins, who occupied an area called Latium, centred on Rome, which grew to become the capital of the Roman Empire and what we now call Italy. In the days of the Roman Empire Latin became the dominant language, initially in Italy and subsequently throughout the Roman Empire. It eventually developed into other languages, such as French, Italian, Portuguese, Spanish and Romanian.

The word 'fraction' comes from the Latin word *fractio* which means to break. We get the word 'fracture' from this too. You could ask children if they have ever fractured a bone in their body. The word 'vinculum', which we use to mean the line that separates the numerator and denominator of a fraction is the Latin word for 'bond'. The vinculum bonds the numerator and denominator together, making a complete fraction. 'Denominator' comes from the Latin prefix *de* and *nomen* which means name. The denominator names the number of parts a whole is broken into. 'Numerator' comes from the Latin *numeratus* which means 'to number'. The numerator numbers the parts being considered. 'Decimal' comes from the Latin *decimus* meaning tenth.

Multiplication tables

Mathematical focus

★ **Number: multiplication and division**

★ **Measurement: money, volume/capacity, length**

Prior learning

Children should already be able to:

- multiply 2-digit numbers by a single digit using a formal written method

- solve simple problems involving multiplying and adding including integer scaling and correspondence problems

- recall multiplication table facts for the two, three, four, five, six, seven, eight, nine, eleven and twelve times tables.

Key new learning

- Count in multiples of 25 and 1000.

- Recall multiplication and division facts for multiplication tables up to 12 × 12.

- Multiply 2-digit and 3-digit numbers by a single-digit number using a formal written layout.

- Solve problems involving multiplying and adding, including integer scaling problems and harder correspondence problems such as *n* objects are connected with *m* objects.

Making connections

- Counting in multiples of 25 links with percentages as 25 per cent is equivalent to one quarter. Counting in 1000s links with metric units.

- Fluency with multiplication facts will support children when working with fractions and ratio later in Key Stage 2, as well as in future work on proportion in a wide variety of contexts. Recognising factors and multiples will similarly help children with work in algebra later.

- Using formal written methods for multiplication relies on and reinforces an understanding of place value and provides a foundation for work in Upper Key Stage 2.

- Children are required to solve problems involving the four operations throughout the maths curriculum, when mathematics is used in other subjects and in daily life. The ability to translate word problems into the correct operations is required in many circumstances.

- Developing ideas about scaling links to scale diagrams. These are used in the construction trade by architects and builders in order to communicate information. Photographers need an understanding of scaling so that images will look right and fit in the space required.

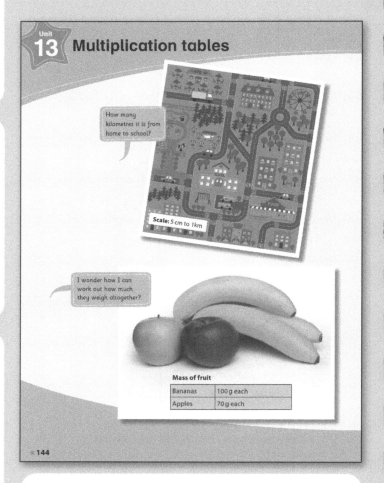

Talk about

The language of scaling is a key idea in this unit. It builds on the interpretation of multiplication as a relation rather than as repeated addition. Highlight the relationship between two sets of numbers by modelling language as 'a number is five times as large as another number'. Make the connection to correspondence problems in which there are two (or more) sets of things which are matched or compared in some way. The word 'correspondence' is worth exploring. The idea of a mapping between two sets is the basis for work on functions and this leads to how items in one set *correspond*, or match with, items in another set. It may be a mapping such as five cakes shared between three people.

Engaging and exploring

Begin by looking at a map of your local area that has a scale showing kilometres. Ask children to find the scale and invite them to suggest what it shows. Explain that one kilometre is 1000 metres and ask if they can identify a length or distance that is one metre in the classroom. Ask them to imagine 1000 of them and gather ideas about what distance around the school that might be. Ask children if they ever travel along the motorway. Have they noticed the small signs at the side which show how many kilometres you are from the start of the motorway? Suggest that next time they try to estimate when they will reach the next kilometre sign using landmarks they can see ahead.

Look at the map in the Textbook and discuss its scale. Decide where 'home' might be and ask children how you could work out how many kilometres it is from home to school. One option is to measure the distance with a piece of string and then measure this against the scale. Return to the map of your local area. Repeat the activity using locations that children know.

There are many occasions when it is necessary to calculate the mass, length or cost of several items where the masses, lengths and costs are repeated because there are several items that are the same. Ask children to come up with examples. Look at the picture of the fruit. Ask: *How would you work out the total mass of the fruit?* Discuss the strategies that children suggest, focusing on which would be the most efficient. Repeat with further examples (e.g. five apples and three bananas, apples weigh 100 grams each, bananas weigh 110 grams each). Then ask questions such as *What if I take one banana away – what is the total mass now?* You could model each example using plastic fruit. Challenge children to think of examples where they may have to work out 'puzzles' like this. Are they more likely to involve mass, length or cost?

Photos are often scaled up or down. Ask children if they have ever needed to change the size of a photo and why. Look at the photo and frame in the Textbook and establish that the photo needs to be doubled in size (two times bigger) in order to fit the frame. Ask children to work out how they would do this by asking question: *Would you double just the length? Would the photo fit the frame then? Would the photo look right?* Demonstrate this on an interactive board by dragging the corner of a picture. It allows children to see that both sides need to be doubled.

Use the photo of the clothing to explore structure and working systematically. Tell children that you'd like to find out how many different outfits can be made with the items of clothing shown. Ask children to think about how they could work this out and take feedback. Review children's ideas and highlight the most systematic approaches. Focus on approaches that involve counting or listing the possibilities. Invite children to represent the possibilities using manipulatives (e.g. counters) or pictures. Develop the discussion further by asking: *Would it be useful to be able to work out the number of outfits without listing all of the possibilities?*

Ask children for examples of computer games that reward success by giving points. Do any of these give extra rewards for accumulating a given number of points? Give children the following scenario: One computer game has 8 levels. You score 45 points at each level. How could you work out your total score? Agree that they need to multiply, which they could do mentally using known facts ($4 \times 8 = 32$, so $40 \times 8 = 320$, and $5 \times 8 = 40$, so $45 \times 8 = 320 + 40 = 360$) or on paper using the formal written method of short multiplication. Ask children to tell you scores they have achieved in games at home. Explore similar multiplication calculations using their real-life scores.

How many times bigger does the photo need to be to fit this frame?

How many different outfits could someone choose to wear?

I scored 45 points on the first level of my computer game. I wonder what my total will be if I score that on the first 8 levels?

Teacher's Guide Look at the pictures with the children and discuss the questions. See pages 158–9 of the Teacher's Guide for key ideas to draw out.

145

Things to think about

- Will you encourage the use of calculators to check work and explore ideas?
- Will you use rich tasks that require the use of multiplication as a relation rather than repeated addition?
- How will you check for conceptual understanding of scaling?
- How will you support children who struggle to recall the multiplication table facts?
- Will you encourage children to use reasoning to work out multiplication table facts?
- What concrete resources will you offer to support conceptual understanding?
- What images will you habitually use throughout?

Checking understanding

You will know that children have mastered these concepts when they can solve problems involving multiplication and division in different contexts, including scaling and correspondence problems. They can appropriately choose and use number facts, showing an understanding of place value, as well as a range of mental and written methods. Children can explain their decision making and justify their solutions.

- **Count in multiples of 25 and 1000.**
- **Recall multiplication and division facts for multiplication tables up to 12 × 12.**

Homework 63 and 64   Practice Book pp 116–19

Mathematical vocabulary

Multiple, multiplication, division, thousands, digit

Representations and resources

Counters, coins, place-value counters, place-value grid, 1–6 dice.

Warming up

Using a pendulum, practise counting in steps of 10 and 5, from zero and numbers other than zero. Occasionally stop the count and ask children how they could partition the number they have stopped on. Ask for one way, and another, and another.

Background knowledge

Children have now learnt all of their multiplication table facts up to 12 × 12. Consolidate those by looking at the connections between the multiplication tables. Knowledge of multiplication facts supports later learning in that it makes calculation easier and also enables children to recognise patterns, both in results and in the workings of examples presented to the class.

Counting in 25s supports mental calculation of percentages and decimal conversions of quarters, eighths, and sixteenths. When counting in 1000s, only the thousand digit changes (and, when crossing a boundary, the ten thousands digit). This reinforces the the power of a place-value number system.

Let's learn: Modelling and teaching

Count in 25s and 1000s

- Ask children to count in steps of 25 from zero. They should model the count using coins.

- Revisit the count again, this time using the number line in the Textbook. Look at the last two digits of the numbers they count. Ask children to explain why these digits follow the sequence 00, 25, 50, 75. *Will that pattern continue forever?* Explore what happens when starting the count from a number other than zero and count in 25s.

- Use a different number to start from and count on and back in 1000s. Begin by using place-value counters to represent the numbers and move on to showing the sequence on a number line. Children should quickly be able to tell you that only the digit in the thousands column changes. Reinforce this by writing the numbers in a place-value grid. Compare this to counting in tens and hundreds, again using a place-value grid. Move on to counting in multiples of 1000 from zero. Invite children to explain the pattern that they see.

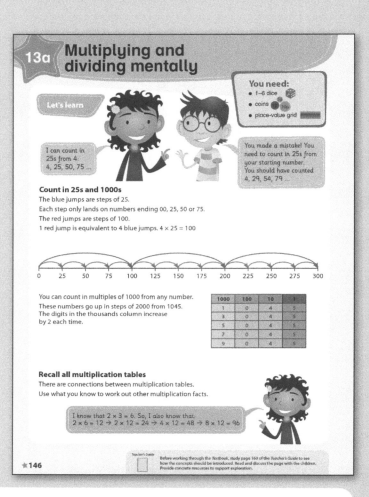

- **Recall all multiplication tables**

- Write 3 × 3 = 9 on the board. Ask: *How can we show this using counters?* Agree a 3 by 3 array. Ask: *What else can we work out if we know this fact?* Draw out the idea of doubling by repeating the array of 9 counters. Ask children to give the calculation that this represents.

- Progress to larger multiples with counters and images, e.g. represent 3 × 3 as a square on squared paper and build it up until it reaches 12 × 12 = 144.

- Ask children use the same process to identify the facts that can be derived from 2 × 3 = 6. Check their answers using the Textbook.

Let's practise: Digging deeper

Step 1

Encourage children to write down jottings if they find doing the full calculation mentally too challenging. Support the calculations involving 25 by encouraging children to ask themselves questions, e.g. *What is 4 × 25? How can that help?* Encourage children to use a place-value grid to record the numbers for b and d.

Step 2

In this step, children use known multiplication facts to work out other facts. Remind them to model the calculation using an array of counters. Provide extra support by asking: *What if we place another array like that next to it? What calculation have you made?* For e and f encourage children to begin with a known multiplication fact. For f children may choose to sketch their model rather than making it with counters.

Step 3

Children should use their multiplication tables to interpret the pictogram. Some children may struggle to work out the amount of points for the whole squares. Ask them to count in sixes, pointing to the whole squares as they go. For those who have difficulty with the parts of squares ask: *If you know that one square is worth six points, how much is half a square worth? How could you show one point?* If children need further support, you could suggest that they represent the pictogram using counters, with six counters representing each whole square.

Step 4

Children can use the 3 dice numbers in any order to make a 3-digit number. Before they begin, discuss possible strategies, such as partitioning the target number in different ways and making the parts. Explore different ways of making the same number, e.g. 150 = 25 × 6 and 100 + 25 × (8 − 6). If children find the task challenging, allow them to use the numbers more than once, or include 10 and 5. Some numbers will be harder to make than others, so praise children who get close. The second part of the activity gives children the opportunity to explore further how to work out multiplication table facts from other facts for seven that they know. Encourage them to reflect on which approaches are more efficient and which will help them memorise the facts.

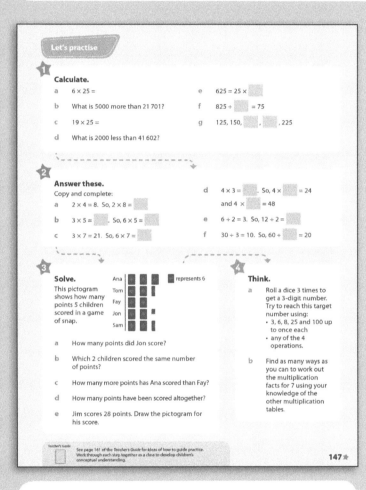

Ensuring progress

Supporting understanding

Children can use counters to support working out multiplication table facts and then count in multiples in order to obtain the answer. Making counters with value 25, or drawing them, allows children to group the appropriate number of 25s in sets of four and so count up in 100s.

Broadening understanding

Challenge children to fill in a ten by ten grid with multiplication facts or division facts that give each of the numbers from one to 100.

✓ Concept mastered

Children can count in steps of 25 and 100 and recall multiplication facts up to 12 × 12.

Follow-up ideas

- Children choose a fact from the multiplication tables that they find hard to recall and make a poster for it. The poster should show diagrams of it and how it is connected to other facts as well as word problems that require it to be the calculation.

- Find an online version of the 'Countdown' numbers game and encourage children to have a competition.

- Children fill in a 12 by 12 multiplication table as quickly as they can and note the time that it takes them. They then try to improve upon that.

Answers

Step 1				**Step 3**	
a	150	e	25	a	13
b	26 701	f	11	b	Tom and Sam
c	475	g	175, 200	c	6
d	39 602			d	73

Step 2

a	16	e	6
b	15 and 30	f	3
c	42		
d	12, 6 and 12		

e

- Multiply 2-digit and 3-digit numbers by a single-digit number using a formal written layout.
- Solve problems involving multiplying and adding.

Homework 65 and 66   Practice Book pp 120–1

Mathematical vocabulary

Multiply, product, add, subtract, divide

Representations and resources

Whiteboards and pens, number rods, place-value counters.

Warming up

Enable children to practise their multiplication table facts in a wide variety of forms, e.g. *What do I multiply four by to get 48? What are the factors of 60? What number is a multiple of both seven and nine?* Counting in sixes from numbers other than six develops a feel for the size of a step of six as well as the structure of linear sequences. You could repeat this for other numbers, such as seven, nine and eleven. Throughout, use a variety of vocabulary and question forms, e.g. *What is 14 more than three lots of nine?*

Background knowledge

Children met the grid method for multiplying 2-digit numbers by a single digit in Unit 3. They built on this in Unit 8 with the formal written method of short multiplication. Now they extend this to multiplying 3-digit numbers by a single digit.

Children have solved problems using a mixture of addition and multiplication; now they move this to problems with the same structure but subtraction and division are used as it is no longer the 'whole' that is required, but one of the 'parts'. This means that the inverse operations are required but the use of the bar model to illustrate it shows that the relationship between the quantities involved is the same.

Let's learn: Modelling and teaching

Column method for 3-digit numbers

- Give children place-value counters and ask them to make the array shown in the Textbook. Ask children to suggest what it shows. Agree that the counters represent hundreds (red), tens (blue) and ones (green); there are 4 lots of 587, so the array represents 587×4. Next look at the grid. Ask: *How does it relate to the array?* e.g. $500 \times 4 = 2000$, which is represented in the array by 20 hundred counters. Both the array and the grid method result in the number statement $2000 + 320 + 28 = 2348$.

- Remind children they met the column method in Unit 8. Work through the example in the Textbook. Remind the children that for this method we start with the ones and work to the left. Encourage them to model the calculation with their place-value counters, e.g. exchanging 20 ones counters for 2 tens; this will help them understand the need to carry digits.

- Ask children to multiply other 3-digit numbers by a single digit (e.g. 236×8) using these methods. Check they can explain each step in their working.

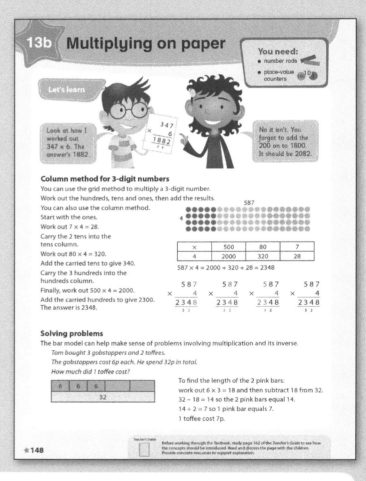

Solving problems

- Invite children to look carefully at the bar model and discuss how the numbers relate to the word problem. Ask questions such as: *Why are three bars purple? Why do they have 6 written in them?* You could read through the problem sentence by sentence, drawing the bar model on the board as you go. Then discuss how to solve the problem, using the working in the Textbook and referring to the bar model at each step. You could amend the model on the board, e.g. erasing the '6's and vertical lines to make one bar worth 18.

- Give children similar problems and ask them to draw bar models and solve them. Encourage them to write down all their calculations. Some could involve 3-digit numbers that children multiply using the column method. Finally, ask children to make up their own word problems and draw bar models to go with them.

Let's practise: Digging deeper

Step 1

Allow children to draft their work before committing it to paper, using whiteboards. For parts a–c they could use an array model to discover the answer before reworking the question using the formal written method. Ask them to tell you what is the same and what is different about the two methods. Observe how children tackle parts d–f. The most efficient strategy is to ask, e.g. *What do I need to multiply 1 by to get 6?* Encourage them to check their answer works for the whole calculation. The final part is the most challenging as children need to notice the carried 2 and ask: *What do I need to multiply 4 by to get 28?*

Step 2

Children may find it helpful to model parts a and b using number rods; this will help ensure they perform the operations in the correct order. For parts c–e, encourage them to draw bar models and to see if putting the calculation into words helps (e.g. 8 lots of 7 is the same as 3 lots of 7 and how many lots of 7?).

Step 3

It is helpful to draw a bar model (or other diagram) to represent the problems, before attempting to solve them. Some children may be able to unravel the process required without one however you should still encourage them to draw diagrams for one or two of the questions in order to deepen their understanding and to prepare for later work on algebra. Ensure that children check that their answers are sensible. A bowl with a mass of ten kilograms would not be practical!

Step 4

There are two possible answers for the first question and children may find a systematic approach helpful here , e.g. they could try substituting the digits 1–9 in turn into the first box and then ask: *What do I need to add to make 41? Is it a multiple of 7?* Can children think of other methods? They may find it helpful to make a list of the multiples of 3 and 7 to refer to. Children should have had enough experience of maths questions to be able to make some up for the bar model. They might find it helpful to give values to the yellow and brown bars, and hence the orange bar, and then write their question. Alternatively, they could adapt Step 3 part d.

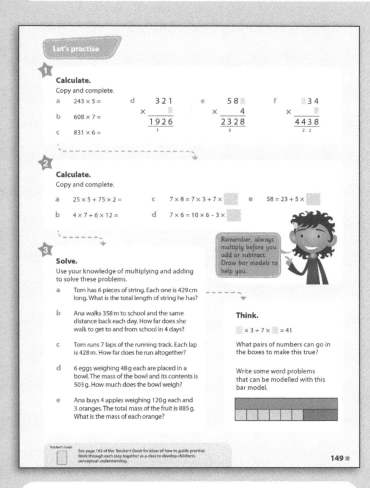

Ensuring progress

Supporting understanding

Work with children in a focus group to provide further opportunities to work through examples. Encourage them to use place-value counters and number rods to help them to make sense of the calculations. Place-value grids can support children in setting out their calculations.

Broadening understanding

Ask children to draw a bar model for a calculation such as $4 \times 7 + 6 \times 12$ and make up a word problem to match it. Allow them to vary the numbers if they wish.

✓ Concept mastered

Children can use the formal written method of short multiplication to multiply a 3-digit number by a single digit. They can solve problems involving subtraction and division as the inverse operations of addition and multiplication.

Follow-up ideas

- Children could make a poster showing examples of calculations involving multiplication and addition in other subject areas and real life.

- Children can write a 'Parent's guide' on how to do short multiplication.

- Children could check their answers to some the questions in Step 3, or to similar questions, by measuring or weighing.

Answers

Step 1				Step 3	
a	1215	d	6	a	2574 cm or 25 m 74 cm
b	4256	e	582	b	2864 m or 2 km 864 m
c	4986	f	634×7	c	2996 m or 2 km 996 m
Step 2				d	215 g
a	275	d	6	e	135 g
b	100	e	7	**Step 4**	
c	5			Pairs of numbers:	
				2 and 5 or 9 and 2	

- Solve problems involving multiplying and adding, including integer scaling problems and harder correspondence problems such as *n* objects are connected with *m* objects.

Homework 67 and 68   Practice Book pp 122–4

Mathematical vocabulary

Scaling, correspondence, multiply, divide

Representations and resources

Number rods, counters, whiteboards.

Warming up

Practise strategies to support mental calculation of multiplication, e.g. partitioning. Ask a series of quick-fire questions such as: *Use 12 = 10 + 2 to work out 12 × 15, 12 × 8; Use 15 = 10 + 5 to work out 6 × 15, 9 × 15; Use 8 = 10 – 2, use this to work out 8 × 6, 8 × 9.* Children should write their answers on whiteboards and receive immediate feedback.

Background knowledge

Children met integer scaling problems in Unit 8 and in this concept you will develop the idea of multiplication as a relation (scaling). Use vocabulary accurately. *How many times as large?* and *how many times larger?* are different questions with different answers. The second question is ambiguous, potentially referring to the comparison between the difference and the original. Children will often look for an additive relationship whereby four times as large means adding four. Looking at the relative sizes of number rods is a way to address this.

In correspondence problems, two sets of objects are compared. The problems can be linked to multiplication (e.g. if I have 3 hats and 12 scarves, I have 36 possible outfits) or division (e.g. if I have 3 cakes and 12 children, each receives $\frac{1}{4}$ of a cake). You can deepen children's understanding of multiplicative relationships by exploring correspondence problems.

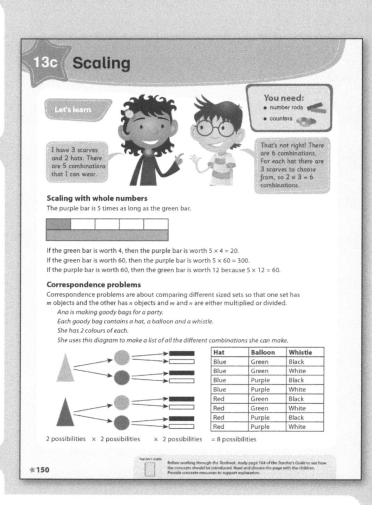

Let's learn: Modelling and teaching

Scaling with whole numbers

- Give children number rods such that one is 5 times the length of the other. Ask them to work out the relationship between them by lining up several of the shorter rods alongside the longer one. Agree that 5 of the shorter bars are equivalent to the longer bar, so the longer bar is 5 times as long. Tell children the shorter bar is worth 4. Ask: *What is the value of the longer bar now?* Agree 20 (5 × 4).

- Give other values to the shorter bar, and then the longer bar, and discuss how to find what the other bar is worth in each case. Encourage children to start sketching their bar models rather than creating them from the rods.

- Repeat, using different pairs of bars to show other relationships; include some with fractional answers.

Correspondence problems

- Present children with the scenario described in the Textbook and ask them to explore how many different combinations Ana can make, using coloured counters. Can they find all eight possibilities? Invite children to tell you how they tackled the problem. Agree that a systematic approach is best, as it means you can be sure you have found all the possibilities. Look at the diagram in the Textbook and discuss how it is structured and that it more efficient than making or drawing all eight possibilities. Ask children to read out what each path shows, and ensure they understand how this relates to the list. Discuss the fact that the total number of possibilities is the product of the possibilities for each item. Return to the counters and add (or take away) a possibility for one of the items to confirm this.

Let's practise: Digging deeper
Step 1

Before children begin the task, recap the use of number rods or bar models to represent scaling, e.g. use 6 short and 1 long rod to model the relationship $6 \times 4 = 24$. Model questions that the children could ask themselves as they answer the questions, e.g. *What is 6 times as large as 4? 24 is how many times as large as 4? 24 is 6 times as large as what? What is 6 times as large as 4?* Encourage children to model the questions using number rods when they tackle the task independently.

Step 2

Expect most children to need to model each situation using coloured counters or by drawing a diagram. Encourage them to work systematically and create a list as they go. If any children have the confidence to work out the number of possibilities by multiplication, encourage them to list the options to check their answer.

Step 3

In this task children measure their classroom (to the nearest metre) and scale down the measurements by ten times. Encourage them to work systematically and collaborate by asking questions, e.g. *What shall we do first? Can you estimate of the length of the room? Does everyone agree with the estimate? How can we work out the length for the model?* Children should record their measurements and, if possible, draw the floor plan as a check of their answers. As an extension they could make a simple model.

Step 4

Suggest that children begin by modelling the ice-cream and cones using plastic cubes. Provide opportunity for discussion by asking them to work in pairs. Encourage children to be systematic and ask: *How can you be sure you have found all the possibilities?* Together, draw a diagram to show the possibilities. In the second part of the task, ensure that children look at one variable at a time. Encourage them to draw their own diagram to show the possibilities.

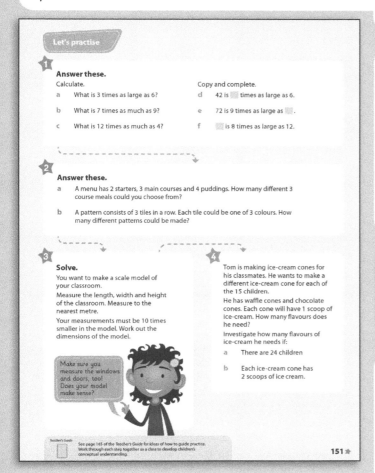

Let's practise

1 Answer these.
Calculate.
a   What is 3 times as large as 6?
b   What is 7 times as much as 9?
c   What is 12 times as much as 4?

Copy and complete.
d   42 is ☐ times as large as 6.
e   72 is 9 times as large as ☐.
f   ☐ is 8 times as large as 12.

2 Answer these.
a   A menu has 2 starters, 3 main courses and 4 puddings. How many different 3 course meals could you choose from?
b   A pattern consists of 3 tiles in a row. Each tile could be one of 3 colours. How many different patterns could be made?

3 Solve.
You want to make a scale model of your classroom.
Measure the length, width and height of the classroom. Measure to the nearest metre.
Your measurements must be 10 times smaller in the model. Work out the dimensions of the model.

Make sure you measure the windows and doors, too! Does your model make sense?

4
Tom is making ice-cream cones for his classmates. He wants to make a different ice-cream cone for each of the 15 children.
He has waffle cones and chocolate cones. Each cone will have 1 scoop of ice-cream. How many flavours does he need?
Investigate how many flavours of ice-cream he needs if:
a   There are 24 children
b   Each ice-cream cone has 2 scoops of ice cream.

Teacher's Guide See page 165 of the Teacher's Guide for ideas for how to guide practice. Work through each step together as a class to develop children's conceptual understanding.

151

Ensuring progress
Supporting understanding

Some children may benefit from exploring the number of possibilities arising from two 'choices', before adding a third.

Broadening understanding

Encouraging children to describe and explain how they solve the problems is an excellent way of deepening understanding. They should also think of examples in everyday life or other parts of the curriculum where the same problems would need to be solved.

✓ Concept mastered

Children can solve problems involving multiplying and adding, including those involving integer scaling and correspondence problems.

Answers

Step 1			
a	18	d	7
b	63	e	8
c	48	f	96

Step 2
a   24   b   27

Step 3
Answers will vary.

Step 4
15 children, 8 flavours needed

a   24 children, 12 flavours needed

b   24 children + 2 scoops each:
4 flavours + 2 cones gives 12 options,
5 flavours + 2 cones gives 20 options,
6 flavours + 2 cones gives 30 options

Follow-up ideas

- Children can find a story that involves a variety of sizes such as *Goldilocks and the Three Bears* and write questions about them.

- Ask children to research dinosaurs and their heights to see how much larger they were than humans.

- Ask children to look around the classroom to see the correspondence between chairs, tables, pencils, pencil sharpeners, etc. that are provided for them, e.g. there might be one table for every two children, but each child has one chair.

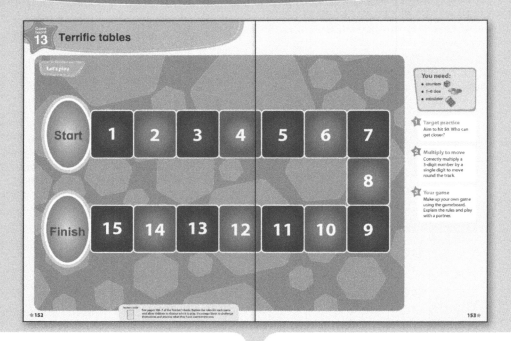

Game 1: Target practice

In this race game, players estimate what they need to multiply a number by to make 50. Players who can easily recall their multiplication table facts will have an advantage, although the game also involves an element of luck, in that some multiplication facts are 'easier' than others.

Maths focus

- Use multiplication as scaling
- Estimate answers

Resources

1 counter per player (1 colour per player), 1–6 dice (1), calculators.

How to play

This is a game for two players. Players place their counters on Start. Player 1 rolls the dice, adds two, and estimates what they need to multiply the result by to reach 50 (or as near as possible to it). Player 2 also estimates what the multiplier should be, but cannot use the same answer as Player 1, e.g. if Player 1 rolls a four, adding two to make six, Player 1 might estimate nine and Player 2 might estimate eight. They can use decimals if they choose but do not suggest this.

Player 1 then uses a calculator to check whose estimate is closest. The winner moves one space along the track. Player 2 then takes their turn, and play continues like this until one of the players reach the Finish, winning the game. Since a roll of the dice can generate only six numbers in total, each will come up an average of five times per game; this repetition will help children learn to recognise multiples of the numbers three to eight.

Making it easier

You could use the number on the dice and not add two, or change the target to 20.

Making it harder

Change the target to 100.

Game 2: Multiply to move

Players must multiply 3-digit numbers by single-digit numbers in order to move round the game board. The game provides plenty of practice in short multiplication and is also an opportunity to identify repeated mistakes.

Maths focus

- Use the formal written method of short multiplication

Resources

1 counter per player (1 colour per player), 1–6 dice (1), calculators.

How to play

This is a game for two players. Players place their counters on Start. Player 1 rolls the dice three times to make a 3-digit number (the first roll gives the hundreds digit, the second the tens and the third the ones). They then roll the dice again and add three to the dice number to get a single digit to multiply by. They work out the answer using short multiplication. Player 2 checks the answer using a calculator. If they are correct they move one space. It is then the turn of Player 2. The first player to reach the Finish wins the game.

Making it easier

You could use the final dice throw without adding three. You could allow children to use a 2-digit number instead by only throwing the dice twice to get the multiplicand.

Making it harder

If a player gets the multiplication wrong, they miss their next turn.

Game 3: Your game

Children should invent their own game, designing rules that use the concepts covered in the unit. Challenge children to make their game easier or harder.

Choose a game to play.

Game 1: Target practice

How to play

- Each place your counter on Start.
- Player 1 rolls the dice once and adds 2.
- Player 1 estimates what number to multiply the result by to reach 50.
- Player 2 also estimates. This must be different to Player 1's estimate.
- Use the calculator to decide who is nearer.
- The winner moves 1 place along the track.
- Now it is Player 2's turn to roll the dice.
- Continue playing until one of you reaches the Finish and wins the game.

You need:

- 1 counter per player (1 colour each)
- 1–6 dice
- calculator

Game 2: Multiply to move

How to play

- Each place your counter on Start.
- Player 1 throws the dice 3 times to get a 3-digit number.
- They add 3 to this to get a single digit to multiply by.
- They work out the answer using short multiplication.
- Player 2 checks the answer using the calculator.
- If Player 1 gets the answer right, they move 1 place along the track.
- Now it is Player 2's turn to roll the dice.
- Continue playing until one of you reaches the Finish and wins the game.

You need:

- 1 counter per player (1 colour each)
- 1–6 dice
- calculator

Game 3: Your game

- Make up your own game using the gameboard.
- Can you think of a different way to generate numbers to multiply?
- What are the rules for your game? Explain them to someone.

Please help your child by reading the instructions and playing the game together.

Assessment task 1

Resources

Place-value counters, number lines.

Running the task

The wrong answers show some of the misconceptions children may have on the topics in this unit. Children should be familiar with this type of task and so will know how to tackle it. If not, work through some similar examples with them, encouraging them to work out the correct answer to identify the error.

Ask questions as they work through the task, and expect them to explain their reasoning. This will help them formulate feedback for Ana.

For parts a and b, children can find number lines or place-value counters to help them. You could also suggest they find the difference between the numbers in the sequence, and between 4901 and 4601.

For part c, ask them to talk you through the short multiplication method so that they can identify what Ana did wrong (writing the carried 1 hundred on the answer line rather than beneath it). Some may benefit from modelling the calculation as an array, using place-value counters.

For part d, encourage children to read the question sentence by sentence, drawing a bar model as they do so. This should help them to see that Ana must have added the two prices and then multiplied the answer by the total number of pieces of fruit.

For part e, again encourage children to draw a bar model. Discuss how to recast the information, e.g. *Ana has 4 times as many counters as Tom*, and then (because Tom has 5 counters) *Ana has 4 times 5 counters*. Stress the difference between this and Ana has 4 more counters than Tom.

Evidencing mastery

Children who can find the correct answer and also identify the mistake and write helpful feedback are evidencing mastery of the concepts covered.

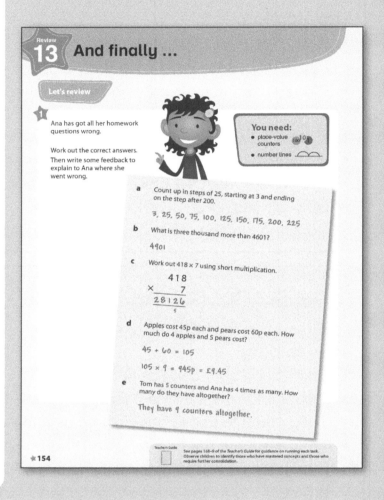

Assessment task 2

Resources

Coloured counters.

Running the task

Discuss the task with children before they begin. Agree that there are lots of possible codes, but only one will open the door. Agree that the best way to crack the code would be to try each different combination in turn. Discuss systematic ways of doing this. Give children counters to model the possibilities and encourage them to draw a diagram like the one in 13c – Scaling. Some will need to make all the possible codes using the counters, but others may only need to make a few to help them construct the diagram and list all 16 possibilities.

For the second part of the task, ask children to look at their diagram and list for four positions. What do they need to add to it to find the possibilities for five positions? Agree that you could add a red counter to one end of each of the codes with four positions; you could also add a blue counter to each in

the same place. This means that the number of possible codes doubles. Allow children to add to their diagrams, modelling the additional codes with counters, if necessary, to confirm this.

Finally, children need to recognise that you can find the total number of possibilities by multiplying the number of possibilities in each position, and explain this in their own words. Encourage them to consider the number of possibilities for a code with two and three positions and compare these with those for four and five. They should see that the total doubles as the number of positions increases. Discuss what happens if there is only one option for one of the positions (e.g. red) or a third option (e.g. green).

Evidencing mastery

Children who work systematically to create a list of the possible codes, and explain the relationship between the number of options for each position and the total number of possibilities, are demonstrating mastery of this concept.

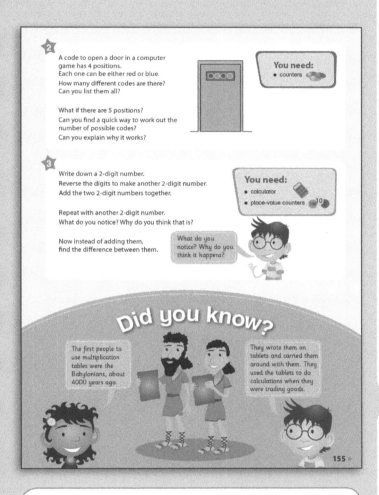

Assessment task 3

Resources

Calculator, place-value counters.

Running the task

Encourage children to try a variety of 2-digit numbers with the aim of finding one that does not give a multiple of 11 when added to its reverse. Some multiples of 11 may be beyond the multiplication facts they need to know but children can use a calculator to check or use a mental method to multiply larger numbers by 11 (ten times then one more) to see if they give the multiple of 11 that is being tested. They should try these larger numbers as they are seeking an example that does not work, a counter-example. A possible misconception is that all multiples of 11 have repeated digits whereas this is only the case up to 9×11. The multiplicand has two digits and the tens digit is 'carried' across to the tens column and added into the next product. Offer children place-value counters to help them explain why the pattern works. Expect them to tell you that each digit is in the tens and the ones, and so that is eleven lots of it overall.

Working out the difference may be done using the column method or a mental method. The multiples of nine that appear should be readily recognised. Again, expect children to explain why the pattern works with reference to place value.

Evidencing mastery

Children who can carry out the calculations accurately, recognise the multiples of 9 and 11 and explain the patterns, are evidencing mastery.

Did you know?

One of the earliest uses of mathematics was in trading. Calculations needed to be quick and accurate and so quick recall of the correct facts was vital. The Babylonians wrote their times tables on clay tablets which they could carry around with them to help them. However, those who could do the calculations quickly, perhaps because they knew the answers by heart, had an advantage over other traders. The Babylonians worked in Base 60 instead of Base 10, which meant they needed to know up to the 59 times tables.

Since calculators arrived on the scene, traders' ability to calculate mentally has become less important. You could have a debate in class about whether there is still a need for learning multiplication tables. Ideas that are worth airing include:

- it is easier to see patterns and relationships if you do know your multiplication tables
- finding quick ways to work out the few you do not remember may give a better understanding of numbers
- the laborious task of learning them all is not worth it
- it is really hard to remember them all.

Concepts mastered

- ☑ Children can count in steps of 25 and 100 and recall multiplication facts up to 12×12.

- ☑ Children can use the formal written method of short multiplication to multiply a 3-digit number by a single digit. They can solve problems involving subtraction and division as the inverse operations of addition and multiplication.

- ☑ Children can solve problems involving multiplying and adding, including those involving integer scaling and correspondence problems.

Perimeter, area and symmetry

Mathematical focus

★ Geometry: properties of shapes

★ Measurement: perimeter, area, time, money

Prior learning

Children should already be able to:

- measure the perimeter of simple 2-D shapes
- identify lines of symmetry in 2-D shapes presented in different orientations
- recognise acute, right and obtuse angles.

Key new learning

- Measure and calculate the perimeter of rectilinear figures (including squares) in centimetres and metres.
- Find the area of rectilinear shapes by counting squares.
- Identify acute and obtuse angles and compare and order angles up to two right angles by size.
- Complete a simple symmetrical figure with respect to a specific line of symmetry.

Making connections

- Area and perimeter have many real-life applications, e.g. floor plans. You could use floor plans of the school or collect information from local estate agents about new houses in the local area. Children may even have floor plans for their own homes if they have moved recently or had an extension built. The floor plans could be the stimulus for questions about addition and multiplication practice. There is a connection to art and design, e.g. you could let children design their own floor plans for a house or an activity centre.
- Children meet symmetry in many areas of everyday life. Ask them to be aware of symmetry for a set period of time and to collect specific examples of symmetry that they encounter at school and home. They could make a display of the artefacts or sketch them.
- In the Year 4 art curriculum children are expected to create sketchbooks to record their observations and to find out about great artists, architects and designers in history. Symmetry is such an important aspect of art that they could study it through the work of particular artists, architects or designers.

Unit 14 — Perimeter, area and symmetry

I wonder how farmers calculate how much fencing they need?

How can you describe this car park?

★156

Talk about

It is important to use precise mathematical vocabulary from the beginning. In geometry, the word perimeter describes the sum of the length of each side of a polygon. Outside maths, the word is used to describe the outside of an area, e.g. the perimeter of an airfield.

The word area is used in maths to describe the size of a plane (2-D) surface enclosed within a specific boundary or perimeter. However, it is also used widely in everyday language where it can simply mean a section or part of something, e.g. her particular area of study is British raptors.

Engaging and exploring

Ask children to look at each picture and discuss the questions with a partner before discussing them as a class. Focus on each photo in turn.

The first photo shows fencing and questions how farmers calculate the required length. Ask children to explain this and listen for those who can explain that they need to measure the distance all the way around the edge of the field. Some children may recall from Year 3 that the mathematical word for this is perimeter. For a rectangular field farmers would add together length + width + length + width. Establish that the perimeter of a field would be measured in metres. Discuss with children how the fence encloses an area of land. They could estimate and measure the perimeter of their school playground.

The question about the photo of the car park asks how the car park could be described. Elicit that the most important

attributes are its shape and size, the number of cars it can hold, their arrangement and where the entrance and exit might be located. This is a great way to lead into thinking about area. Ask children to think about other car parks or open spaces, perhaps the school car park or playing field and how they can be described. They could investigate the perimeter and area required for a single car. Disabled spaces and parent and child spaces are larger.

In the game action shot you can see line markings and the off-court player looking to pass to someone in her team. The question asks, 'Why are line markings so important in team games?' Encourage children to share their ideas. They may say that the lines define the size of the court/pitch and this is important so that players know that the court is always the same size and therefore know how they can use the space. Some lines indicate areas that are only for certain players, e.g. the third markings in a netball court. The perimeter lines show when the ball is out of play. Children could investigate the perimeters of different courts/pitches and compare their dimensions. The Sport England website lists the dimensions of most courts and pitches and includes additional information, e.g. spaces required around courts. Present children's findings as posters with statements that include terms such as 'greater than' and 'less than'.

Butterflies are the quintessential choice for discussions on symmetry and this is justified because they are so beautifully detailed. Ask children to describe the patterns in each of the examples. The question asks if lines of symmetry can be in any direction. Collect feedback on whether children agree or disagree with the question and display their responses as a tally chart. Display the photos on the whiteboard and together identify the lines of symmetry and agree the direction of the lines. Children learnt to identify lines of symmetry presented in different orientations earlier in the year in Unit 4 – 2-D shapes, angles and symmetry, but thinking that the lines must be vertical or horizontal is a common misconception so this is useful reinforcement. Most animals, including humans, have bilateral symmetry. It is a characteristic of organisms that are capable of moving freely through their environments.

The final photo shows an aerial shot of a large number of people carefully arranged to look like the head of a panda. Collect ideas from children on how many people there are in the picture and how they think it was achieved. Their suggestions may include scale drawings and chalk marking or spraying the pattern on the ground. Listen for them explaining that the design is perfectly symmetrical. Ask them to point out the line of symmetry. Challenge them to produce their own aerial shot picture. They could plan something simple, involving only their own class, or something more ambitious with a greater number of children.

Why are line markings so important in team games?

I wonder if lines of symmetry can be in any direction.

How do the people in the photo know where to stand?

Teacher's Guide. Look at the pictures with the children and discuss the questions.
See pages 170–1 of the Teacher's Guide for key ideas to draw out.

157

Things to think about

- How will you organise groupings for practical measuring activities, making best use of adult support?
- How will you check perceptual understanding of area?
- How will you support children carrying out investigative tasks to record their own representations?
- Will you need to check that children know how to use measuring equipment accurately?
- What opportunities will you give children to explain their reasoning and build fluency?
- Which problem-solving opportunities are most appropriate for this unit?

Checking understanding

You will know children have mastered the concepts in this unit when they can use centimetres or metres to measure and calculate the perimeter of rectilinear figures. They will be able to find the area of rectilinear shapes by counting squares and are beginning to understand the relationship of area to arrays and multiplication. They will be able to identify angles as acute, right or obtuse, and order them up to two right angles. They will be able to complete a simple symmetrical figure with respect to a specific line of symmetry.

14a Perimeter and area

- **Measure and calculate the perimeter of rectilinear figures (including squares) in centimetres and metres.**
- **Find the area of rectilinear shapes by counting squares.**

Homework 69 and 70   Practice Book pp 125–8

Representations and resources

0–9 digit cards, 5 cm square cards, cm² squared paper, rulers, metre sticks or tape measures, calculators.

Mathematical vocabulary

Perimeter, area, cm² – centimetres squared,
m² – metres squared

Warming up

Ask children to tell you the units used to measure time, starting with the smallest unit: seconds, minutes, hours, days, weeks, months and years. Ask: *How many seconds make one minute? How do you convert seconds into minutes?* Use 0-9 digit cards to generate 3-digit numbers and ask children to convert that number of seconds to minutes, e.g. 482 seconds is eight minutes two seconds. Elicit what operation they are carrying out to convert from seconds to minutes – dividing by 60. After some practice, ask about conversions between other units of time and practise some examples.

Background knowledge

Area measures the surface within a fixed perimeter. It is a 2-D measurement, measured in square units. The common standard metric units are cm² and m². One m² is 10000cm² (100 cm × 100 cm). Perimeter is a measure of distance. Its units are cm or m. Model use of the correct units from the outset so that children establish good practice.

Shapes with the same perimeter length may or may not have the same area. Similarly shapes with the same area may or may not have the same perimeter. For a given perimeter the largest area is the shape nearest to a square.

Let's learn: Modelling and teaching

Area

- Using the definition in the Textbook, explain that area measures the surface within a fixed perimeter. It is measured in 'square' units (mm², cm², m², km²).

- Introduce the concept of area using non-standard units. Prepare some 5 cm squares and draw some rectangles of different sizes that are multiples of 5 cm, e.g. 10 cm × 20 cm, 20 cm × 30 cm. Explain to children that they can use the 5 cm squares to compare the areas of the rectangles. Ask them to cover each rectangle with the squares without overlapping. They will discover the smaller rectangle requires eight (5 cm) squares to cover it completely while the larger one needs 24. This shows that the larger one is exactly three times bigger. Try other rectangles.

- When children have grasped the concept of square units, explain that the standard units are 1 cm² and 1 m². Explain that using these units allows areas to be directly

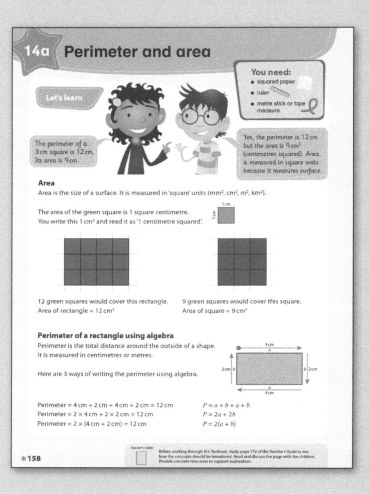

compared. Use the squares in the Textbook to illustrate finding area by counting squares (cm²).

Perimeter of a rectangle using algebra

- Revisit the definition of perimeter and the units it is measured in. In the Textbook, the left-hand column shows the expression for a specific rectangle and the right-hand column has the same expression shown algebraically. This is a very visual way to help children develop algebraic understanding and begin to learn how to manipulate equations. Explain that the letters a and b have been used to take the place of any number.

- Discuss what the three different ways of writing the perimeter show. Work through some examples together.

Let's practise: Digging deeper

Step 1

Remind children that perimeter is the length of the outside of the shape and is measured in centimetres. Use your finger to draw an outline of a square in the air. Explain that, although the squares in the diagram do not measure 1 cm by 1 cm, they represent centimetre squares. To measure area, children count the number of squares. Remind them to include the units, cm². Some children may want to draw the questions in d and e – help them to try to visualise the shapes first and then draw them for confirmation.

Step 2

This step uses representations to determine missing information and helps children to build their ability to visualise problems. Each question covers a different aspect of perimeter and area and their relationships. Explain to children that they should expect an element of trial and error when answering the questions. They should think about how to adjust their rectangle if the first one

they draw does not fit the criteria. When looking for possible dimensions of a given area, they should think about factor pairs. You could pose similar exercises for children to solve.

Step 3

This practical task gives children the opportunity to measure larger shapes with larger perimeters and areas and enables them to handle bigger numbers. Rounding to the nearest ten centimetres means that children should be able to carry out the relevant multiplication calculations. Observe how confidently children use the context of measures to find the cost of the edging and backing fabric for each board.

Step 4

This investigation allows children to see the pattern in which perimeters and areas of squares 'grow'. As they complete the table, ask them to pause and read the number sequences. Ask: *Can you recognise the pattern? What are the differences between successive numbers?* The pattern in the perimeters of squares is the four times table. The pattern in the areas is square numbers and children may notice that the numbers grow much more rapidly.

Let's practise

1 Calculate.
Find the perimeter and area of these shapes. Each square is 1 cm.

a, b, c

d   Square with sides of 5 cm.

e   Rectangle with length 9 cm and width 1 cm.

2 Draw.
Draw diagrams on squared paper to show the missing measurements.

a   A square has an area of 16 cm². Show the length of its sides.

b   The length of a patio is 6 m. The area is 12 m². Show the width of the patio.

c   2 different rectangles have a perimeter of 10 cm. Show their lengths and widths. Find their areas.

d   2 different rectangles that have an area of 6 cm². Show their lengths and widths. Find their perimeters.

3 Measure.
Look at the display boards in your classroom. Measure the length and width in centimetres. Round to the nearest 10 cm. Calculate the cost of covering the boards in your classroom.

Silver edging £1.00 per m²

Coloured backing fabric £5.00 per m²

4 Think.
Copy and complete the table. Show the perimeter and area of squares as they increase in size.

Length of side	1 cm	2 cm	3 cm	4 cm	5 cm	6 cm	7 cm	8 cm	9 cm	10 cm
Perimeter										
Area										

Describe any patterns you can see in the answers.

Teacher's Guide   See page 173 of the Teacher's Guide for ideas of how to guide practice. Work through each step together as a class to develop children's conceptual understanding.

159

Ensuring progress
Supporting understanding

Measurement of area using square units is a new concept for children. Begin by revisiting the work that children have done previously in making informal judgements of the relative size of surfaces, e.g. they could sort paper of different sizes. Help them to understand how using standard units enables them to compare areas exactly.

Broadening understanding

Ask children to make up their own area and perimeter problems similar to those in Step 2. The ability to do this demonstrates a deep level of understanding.

✓ Concept mastered

Children can measure and calculate the perimeter of rectangles and squares in centimetres and metres. They can find the area of rectilinear shapes by counting squares and know that area is measured in cm² or m².

Answers

Step 1

a $P = 20$ cm; $A = 21$ cm²

b $P = 18$ cm; $A = 20$ cm²

c $P = 20$ cm; $A = 16$ cm²

d $P = 20$ cm; $A = 25$ cm²

e $P = 20$ cm; $A = 9$ cm²

Step 2

a   4 cm

b   2 m

c   4 cm × 1 cm, $A = 4$ cm²
    3 cm × 2 cm, $A = 6$ cm²

d   2 cm × 3 cm, $P = 10$ cm
    1 cm × 6 cm, $P = 14$ cm

Step 4

Length of side	1 cm	2 cm	3 cm	4 cm	5 cm	6 cm	7 cm	8 cm	9 cm	10 cm
Perimeter	4 cm	8 cm	12 cm	16 cm	20 cm	24 cm	28 cm	32 cm	36 cm	40 cm
Area	1 cm²	4 cm²	9 cm²	16 cm²	25 cm²	36 cm²	49 cm²	64 cm²	81 cm²	100 cm²

Patterns:

$P =$ numbers in the 4 times table.

$A =$ square numbers.

Follow-up ideas

- The concept of perimeter as an outer boundary can be extended to boundaries of places; e.g. the grounds of a house, a village, a parish, a town, county or country. Children can find out about the old custom of 'beating the bounds' (walking the boundaries of a parish).

- Children can try finding the approximate area of irregular shapes, e.g. the approximate area of their hand. They use cm² paper to draw around their hand and count the whole squares within the outline plus the number of part squares that are more than half a square.

Perimeter and angles

Homework 71 and 72   Practice Book pp 129–33

Mathematical vocabulary

Perimeter, rectilinear, acute, obtuse, algebra, algebraic

Representations and resources

Two 1–6 dice, cm² paper, rulers, centimetre cubes, protractors.

The lesson objectives are:
- Measure and calculate the perimeter of a rectilinear figure (including squares) in centimetres and metres.
- Identify acute and obtuse angles and compare and order angles up to two right angles by size.

Warming up

Draw a simple animal on the board, e.g. a fish, and mark the length, e.g. 8 cm. Roll two dice and add the two numbers to determine a scaling factor, e.g. rolling a three and a four gives a scaling factor of seven so the new length of the fish is 8 cm × 7 = 56 cm. Ask children to calculate the new length and to estimate that length with their hands. Change the length of the fish to give practice with another starting number. This warm up gives children practice with their tables and with estimating length.

Background knowledge

Rectilinear figures are composite shapes made up from rectangles. Therefore, all the angles are right angles. The perimeter is the distance around the outside of a shape, measured in centimetres or metres. Continue to model use of the correct units from the outset so that children establish good practice.

Shapes with the same perimeter length may or may not have the same area. Similarly shapes with the same area may or may not have the same perimeter.

Angles measure an amount of turn. The standard unit is degrees (°). A right angle equals 90°. Angles less than 90° are called acute angles. Angles greater than 90° but less than 180° are known as obtuse angles. 180° is two right angles or a straight line angle.

Let's learn: Modelling and teaching

Perimeter of rectilinear shapes

- Provide children with two cardboard rectangles, 5 cm × 2 cm and 3 cm × 2 cm. Ask children to tell you the perimeters (14 cm and 10 cm respectively, giving a total of 24 cm).

- Now ask them to join one whole side of the smaller rectangle to the other rectangle to give a new rectilinear shape. A number of different shapes are possible. If both short sides are joined, it will make a long thin rectangle that is 8 cm × 2 cm. The other shapes are all composite rectilinear shapes that are 'L' or 'T' shaped. Ask children to calculate the perimeter of the new shapes. When the 3 cm side is joined, the new perimeter is 18 cm. Two lots of 3 cm have become part of the internal shape, 24 – (3 × 2). When the 2 cm side is joined, the perimeter is 20 cm, 24 – (2 × 2). This shows how the joined sides become part of the shape and are no longer part of the perimeter.

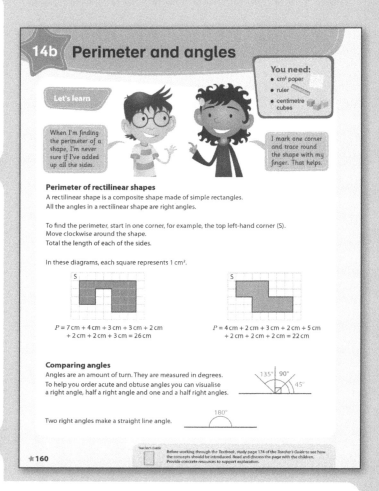

- Look at the more complex rectilinear shape in the Textbook. Use the diagram and the misconception cartoon to discuss a good starting point for finding the area. Talk through the worked example.

- Practise with other rectilinear shapes on cm² paper until children are confident.

Comparing angles

- The Textbook shows a 180° straight line angle, with 45°, 90° and 135° and another with 180° clearly marked. This is in preparation for using a protractor next year.

- Prepare a selection of laminated acute and obtuse angles. Ask children to sort and order them in different ways, e.g. largest/smallest; acute/obtuse; less than 45°/half a right angle/between 45° and 90°. Encourage them to find two angles together to make a straight-line angle.

Let's practise: Digging deeper
Step 1

Before children carry out this question, practise some examples together. It is easy to miss out a measurement when totalling the sides. Suggest to children that they count the number of sides that the polygon has and check that they have the same number of sides in their calculation. Starting at the same place is good practice (often the top left is used) and helps children to know when they are back at the start. When children draw their own crosses, ensure that they are symmetrical and that children have identified the correct measurements of each side.

Step 2

This question reinforces children's understanding of acute, obtuse and right angles and their ability to order them. Children who are still establishing their ability to recognise angle size can use an angle tester to decide on the size.

Step 3

Give children 24 square tiles to test possible arrangements of the slabs. They can record each arrangement on squared paper. Once they have three possible answers, ask them to compare the perimeters. Ask them to explain why the perimeters vary. Ask how they can be sure that they have found all possible arrangements. Elicit from children that they need to find all the factor pairs.

Step 4

Read through the question to check that children understand what they need to do. Support them by asking questions such as: *What is the perimeter of the smallest rectangle that encloses the cubes? Can you make a rectilinear shape with a smaller perimeter? What about the area of the shapes you have drawn?* Encourage children to tackle this task with a partner so that they can discuss their discoveries.

Ensuring progress
Supporting understanding

Work with children in a focus group. Put together 2-D rectangles to make compound rectilinear shapes. Ask children to show the perimeter by tracing around it with their finger. Some children may try to include internal lengths so reinforce the definition of perimeter as the length of the outside edge.

Broadening understanding

Children are not officially introduced to protractors to measure angles until Year 5 but some children may already have encountered them, in maths sets for example. By examining a protractor they can develop their understanding of angle as a continuous measurement that describes an amount of turn and is numerically measured in degrees.

✓ Concept mastered

Children can measure and calculate the perimeter of a rectilinear figure (including squares) in centimetres and metres. They can identify acute and obtuse angles and compare and order angles up to two right angles by size.

Follow-up ideas

- Use a trundle wheel to measure the perimeter of places inside the school and in the school grounds, e.g. school hall, netball and football pitches. Every school has annotated floor plans. Find the plans for your school and compare children's measurements with the plans.

- Ask children to calculate the perimeter of regular polygons. This gives practice of recalling the names of polygons together with multiplication tables practice.

- Look at newspapers with children to see how each page is divided into a combination of different news stories and advertisements. Children could cut out the rectilinear shape of an article and find its perimeter.

Answers

Step 2

a 24 cm

b 42 cm

Step 1

a c (acute), a (acute), b (obtuse)

b d (acute), f (right), e (obtuse)

c i (acute), g (right), h (obtuse) and j (obtuse),

Step 3

Possible arrangements are:

1 row of 24 slabs (or 24 rows of 1 slab), P = 50 m;

2 rows of 12 slabs (or 12 rows of 2 slabs), P = 28 m;

3 rows of 8 slabs (or 8 rows of 3 slabs), P = 22 m;

4 rows of 6 slabs (or 6 rows of 4 slabs), P = 20 m.

The largest perimeter is the long thin shape because it has most outside edges on the perimeter. The smallest perimeter is 4 × 6 which is the closest to a square.

- **Complete a simple symmetrical figure with respect to a specific line of symmetry.**
- **Find the area of rectilinear shapes by counting squares.**

Homework 73 and 74   Practice Book pp 134–7

Mathematical vocabulary

Symmetry, line of symmetry, symmetrical, orientation, rectilinear.

Representations and resources

Coins (optional), cm^3 cubes, cm^2 paper, rulers, mirrors, pattern blocks or coloured counters, blue and yellow pencils, coloured counters, camera.

Warming up

Discuss the coins used in the UK. There are eight different coins, in decreasing order of value: £2, £1, 50p, 20p, 10p, 5p, 2p and 1p. Write an amount of money on the board such as £2.38 and ask children to tell you the smallest number of coins that are required to make this sum. In the example, it is six coins (£2, 20p, 10p, 5p, 2p 1p). Now ask children to tell you how much is required to make the sum up to £5, in this example £2.62. Repeat with different amounts.

Background knowledge

In Year 4 children are expected to measure area by counting squares and the non-statutory guidance for the National Curriculum suggests that children start to relate area to arrays and multiplication. Counting the squares of a simple rectangle drawn on cm^2 paper gives its area, e.g. a rectangle measuring 3 cm × 4 cm has an area of 12 cm^2. Looking at the rectangle shows that it is 3 rows of 4 squares (3 × 4). Children are familiar with arrays and they may spot that using multiplication to find area is a useful shortcut. The new mathematics in this concept spread is to complete a simple symmetrical figure with respect to a specific line of symmetry. Be aware that children do not always recognise lines of symmetry that are not horizontal or vertical. Completing a simple symmetrical figure with respect to a specific line of symmetry can be done by eye, by counting squares or measuring or by using coordinates.

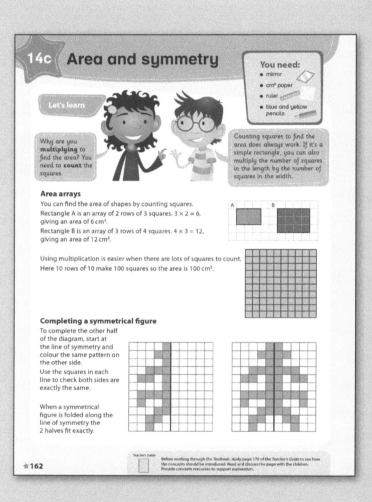

Let's learn: Modelling and teaching

Area and arrays

- Give children cm^3 cubes. Discuss that the surface of the cube has an area of 1 cm^2. Make a square with 4 cubes and ask them to give the area of the top surface. Count the squares and also say that 2 cm × 2 cm makes 4 cm^2. Repeat with more squares and rectangles. Once confident, ask them to predict the area of a particular rectangle and then check using cubes.

- Look at the diagrams in the Textbook and confirm that multiplication of the number in the row by the number of rows gives the area. Ask them to tell you what the areas of other rectangles are, e.g. six squares by three squares. Encourage children to see that this method becomes quicker and more reliable than counting squares as the size of the rectangles increases.

Completing a symmetrical figure

- The Textbook shows half an insect pattern. Show children how to count squares in each line to check that both sides are identical but a mirror image. Some children with good spatial awareness will be able to do this by eye. However, all children should establish the habit of looking carefully at the finished diagram or picture to check that an error has not slipped in.

- Both sides have the same area and the same perimeter length. Line symmetry is also known as reflective symmetry or mirror symmetry. Make sure that mirrors are available for children for checking purposes.

Let's practise: Digging deeper

Step 1

Children can use the counting squares method for finding the area of each shape. However the areas of the simple rectangles a and c can also be calculated using multiplication. Ask children to explain which method they will use before finding the answers. Ask: *Why will that method be the most efficient?* Check that children include the units in their answers.

Step 2

In this step, children use coordinates to make symmetrical polygons. Before they begin, ask them to explain how to plot a point to recall the correct order of coordinates. The line drawn at $x = 5$ gives a vertical line of symmetry. The examples in the Textbook are an irregular hexagon and an irregular octagon. Ensure that children record the missing coordinates.

You could ask children to plot different half polygons for their partner to complete.

Step 3

Encourage children to be imaginative and creative when drawing their half pictures. They are using squared paper so the drawings are pixelated diagrams. They can draw them with horizontal, vertical or diagonal lines of symmetry. You could suggest that they do one picture with each. If children are working on loose paper they can fold the diagram along the line of symmetry to check that the two halves fit exactly or use a mirror to check.

Step 4

The investigation asks children to find shapes with an area of $10\,cm^2$. There are many possibilities. The squares must make a single shape; there cannot be any detached squares. Ask questions to help children think more deeply, e.g. *How many squares must your shape enclose to give an area of $10\,cm^2$? How many rows can be completely filled? If you fill the top 2 rows, how many ways are there of placing the final 2 squares? Which of your shapes are symmetrical? What about if you have different rows completely filled? Are all your shapes different or are some the same when rotated? Can you find pairs of shapes that are mirror images?*

Let's practise

1 **Answer these.**
Find the area of these shapes. Each square is 1 cm.
Explain your method.

a   b   c   d

2 **Plot.**
Draw a coordinate grid with *x*- and *y*-axes labelled 0–10.
Draw a mirror line at *x* = 5.
Each shape is half of a symmetrical polygon.
Complete each polygon and name it.
List the missing coordinates.

a   (4, 1), (2, 2), (4, 3)

b   (5, 5), (3, 6), (4, 7), (3, 8), (5, 9)

3 **Draw.**
Work with a partner.
On squared paper, draw half a house, half a face and half an insect.
Swap papers. Complete the drawings so they are symmetrical.

4 **Investigate.**
This diagram shows a rectilinear shape with an area of 10 cm².
Find 8 different ways to draw shapes within a 4 cm × 4 cm square that have an area equal to 10 cm².

Colour the shapes with a line of symmetry yellow.
Colour the shapes with no line of symmetry blue.

Teacher's Guide
See page 177 of the *Teacher's Guide* for ideas of how to guide practice. Work through each step together as a class to develop children's conceptual understanding.

163

Follow-up ideas

- Many of the art deco and art nouveau artists, e.g. Charles Rennie Mackintosh, executed beautiful symmetrical designs. Children could study these periods and collect some of their favourite examples.

- Collect pictures from magazines, e.g. of people, buildings or landscapes, cut them in half and ask children to draw or paint the missing half, making it symmetrical.

- Discuss with children the different sizes of newspapers. The larger-sized newspapers are the broadsheets (*Daily Telegraph and Financial Times*) while the smaller ones are the tabloid papers (*The Times, The Sun, The Daily Mail*). Compare the perimeter and area of the two types.

Ensuring progress

Supporting understanding

Support children who find drawing symmetrical shapes challenging by reminding them to count squares either side of the line of symmetry. To give children more practice draw a line (in any orientation) in the middle of a large sheet of paper to act as a line of symmetry. Provide them with coloured counters or pattern blocks to make symmetrical designs. They could copy their designs on to paper or take photographs of them.

Broadening understanding

In Step 4, challenge children to draw as many symmetrical shapes with an area of $10\,cm^2$ as they can. Encourage them to be systematic in their recording. Children with good understanding of the concept of area will be ready to use multiplication to find the area of rectangles because they appreciate that the squares are arranged in columns and rows.

✓ Concept mastered

Children can complete a simple symmetrical figure with respect to a specific line of symmetry. They can find the area of rectilinear shapes by counting squares.

Answers

Step 1			
a	12 cm²	c	15 cm²
b	12 cm²	d	6 cm²

Step 2

a   Irregular hexagon
(6, 1), (8, 2), (6, 3)

b   Irregular octagon
(7, 6), (6, 7), (7, 8)

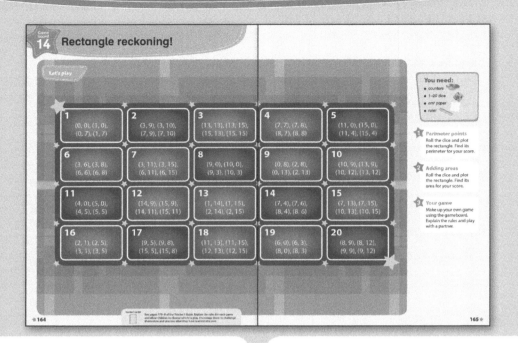

Game 1: Perimeter points

Each dice throw determines the coordinates of a rectangle. Children plot the rectangles, measure the perimeters and keep a running total to find their final score.

Maths focus

- Measure and calculate the perimeter of rectilinear figures in centimetres and metres

Resources

20 counters, 1–20 dice (1), cm² paper, rulers.

How to play

This is a game for two players. Before they begin, children should each draw a coordinate grid on squared paper with *x*- and *y*-axes labelled from zero to 15. Players then take it in turns to roll the dice, plot the rectangle for that number (from the gameboard) and calculate the perimeter. Their partner checks their answer. If they are correct, they score the numerical value of the perimeter and cover the number on the gameboard with a counter to show it has been plotted. If a player throws that number again, they miss that turn. The winner is the player with the higher total score when all 20 rectangles have been plotted.

Making it easier

Provide a prepared coordinate grid for children.

Making it harder

Challenge children to deduce the value of the perimeter from the coordinates before plotting the rectangle. If they are correct, they score double points.

Game 2: Adding areas

Each dice throw determines the coordinates of a rectangle. Children plot the rectangles, find the areas by counting squares and keep a running total to find their final score.

Maths focus

- Find the area of rectilinear shapes by counting squares

Resources

20 counters, 1–20 dice (1), cm² paper, rulers.

How to play

This is a game for two players. Before they begin, children should each draw a coordinate grid on squared paper with *x*- and *y*-axes labelled from zero to 15. Players then take it in turns to roll the dice, plot the rectangle for that number (from the gameboard) and find the area by counting squares. Their partner checks their answer. If they are correct, they score the numerical value of the area and cover the number on the gameboard with a counter to show it has been plotted. If a player throws that number again, they miss that turn. The winner is the player with the higher total score when all 20 rectangles have been plotted.

Making it easier

Provide a prepared coordinate grid for children.

Making it harder

Challenge children to deduce the value of the area from the coordinates before plotting the rectangle. If they are correct, they score double points.

Game 3: Your game

Children should invent their own game, designing rules that use the concepts covered in the unit. Challenge children to make their game easier or harder.

Rectangle reckoning!

Choose a game to play.

Game 1: Perimeter points

How to play

- Play with a partner.
- On cm² paper, each draw a coordinate grid with x- and y-axes labelled from zero to 15.
- Take turns to roll the dice.
  - ▶ Find the corresponding coordinates on the gameboard.
  - ▶ Plot the coordinates of the rectangle.
  - ▶ Calculate the perimeter of the rectangle. The number is your score.
  - ▶ Cover the number with a counter to show it has been plotted.
- Miss a turn if you throw a number that has already been plotted.
- The winner is the player with the higher score at the end of the game.

You need:

- 20 counters
- 1–20 dice
- cm² paper
- ruler

Game 2: Adding areas

How to play

- Play with a partner.
- On cm² paper, each draw a coordinate grid with x- and y-axes labelled from zero to 15.
- Take turns to roll the dice.
  - ▶ Find the corresponding coordinates on the gameboard.
  - ▶ Plot the coordinates of the rectangle.
  - ▶ Find the area of the rectangle by counting squares. The number is your score.
  - ▶ Cover the number with a counter to show it has been plotted.
- Miss a turn if you throw a number that has already been plotted.
- The winner is the player with the higher score at the end of the game.

You need:

- 20 counters
- 1–20 dice
- cm² paper
- ruler

Game 3: Your game

- Make up your own game using the gameboard.
- What are the rules for your game? Explain them to someone.

Please help your child by reading the instructions and playing the game together.

Assessment task 1

Resources

Squared paper, rulers.

Running the task

Ask children to tell you the perimeter and area of a 2 cm × 2 cm square. Ensure that they use the correct units and explain how they arrived at their answers. Repeat with other squares. Read through the task as a class. Children must calculate perimeters and find areas by counting squares and looking for patterns in the answers. Encourage children to work methodically through the squares. You could suggest that they record their results in a table to make it easier to spot patterns.

This task is completed with a partner so that children can compare and reason about their findings.

Evidencing mastery

Children demonstrate mastery when they can calculate the perimeters and areas and present them in a logical manner, perhaps in a table similar to the one shown below.

Area of flowerbed	1 m²	2 m²	3 m²	4 m²	5 m²
Perimeter of flowerbed	4 m	6 m	8 m	10 m	12 m
External perimeter of patio	12 m	14 m	16 m	18 m	20 m

Area of flowerbed	1 m²	2 m²	3 m²	4 m²	5 m²
Area of patio	8 m²	10 m²	12 m²	14 m²	16 m²
Total area	9 m²	12 m²	15 m²	18 m²	21 m²

They are then able to describe the patterns by looking at the differences. Children who show good understanding will always use square units for area.

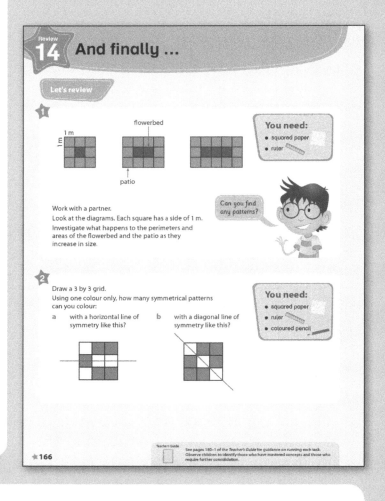

Assessment task 2

Resources

Squared paper, rulers, coloured pencils.

Running the task

Hold up some 2-D shapes and ask children to describe the line(s) of symmetry. Repeat the exercise with simple patterns, similar to those shown in the task in the Textbook. Ask children how they could check the lines of symmetry that they have identified.

Read through the task together. Ask children to identify the number of squares and discuss in what positions one square could be placed to have horizontal symmetry. Elicit that it could be placed in any of the three squares of the central row. Then ask where one square could be placed to have a diagonal line of symmetry (in any of the diagonal squares so that the line cuts the square in half from corner to corner). Encourage children to be systematic in their approach. Provide them with squared paper to record their findings.

When children have found all the possibilities for one, two, three and four squares they will actually have found all the possibilities. This is because if the four coloured squares are swapped to become blank and the blank five become coloured that gives the possibilities for five coloured squares. Swapping the patterns with three coloured squares to give three blank and six coloured gives the set for six squares, and so on.

Evidencing mastery

The task is accessible to all children. However children who are able to approach the task in a systematic manner and record the examples efficiently will clearly demonstrate mastery. Look for children who begin by drawing the possibilities for one coloured square, then two squares and so on. Some patterns are the same, just simply rotated through one or two right angles. Look for children who identify that these are identical and support any who seem unaware of this.

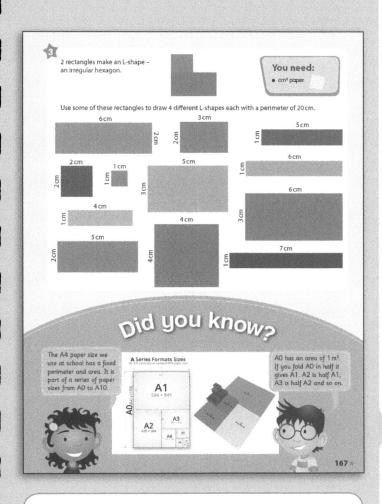

Concepts mastered

☑ Children can measure and calculate the perimeter of rectangles and squares in centimetres and metres. They can find the area of rectilinear shapes by counting squares and know that area is measured in cm² or m².

☑ Children can measure and calculate the perimeter of a rectilinear figure (including squares) in centimetres and metres. They can identify acute and obtuse angles and compare and order angles up to two right angles by size.

☑ Children can complete a simple symmetrical figure with respect to a specific line of symmetry. They can find the area of rectilinear shapes by counting squares.

Assessment task 3

Resources

cm² paper

Running the task

Before beginning the task, show children a range of rectilinear shapes and ask them to show you the perimeter. Then ask them to give you the rule for calculating the perimeter. Give a value to each length of each shape and ask them to find the perimeters. This is an opportunity to rehearse mental calculation strategies such as number bonds and sequencing. Read through the task with children to check understanding. Support those who find the task challenging by suggesting that they draw and cut out the rectangles, so that they can put them together and calculate the perimeter of the new rectilinear shape. This will make it easier for them to find possibilities. Provide further support by asking them what they should do if the perimeter is smaller or larger than the required 20 cm. When they have found one correct shape, encourage them to look at it carefully and think how they could change it to make another. You could extend the task by challenging children to make different shapes or different perimeters.

Evidencing mastery

If children are able to carry out this task independently and explain their thinking, they are demonstrating mastery of calculating the perimeter of rectilinear shapes. Look for children who choose one rectangle to draw and are able to visualise whether particular rectangles will work or not to make up the required perimeter. They may deduce that the two long sides of the L should add up to half the perimeter (10 cm) and choose the rectangles accordingly.

Did you know?

Children know that the paper size they use for their work and in printers is called A4 paper. Its exact size is 210 mm × 297 mm. They may also know A3 and A5 paper. In fact there is a whole series of sizes from A0 to A10 that is now used throughout most of the world, though not in North America and Canada:

- A0 has an area of 1 m²

- A1 is half the area A0, when the long side is folded in half

- A2 is half the area of A1, and so on.

This makes the series very practical and economical. The mathematics of the dimensions is rather advanced for Year 4 children, however, as the ratio of the length to the width is equal to the square root of two (1.4142).

A4 paper was only adopted in Britain in 1959. Before then the traditional file paper used in Europe and the Commonwealth was called foolscap and was longer and slightly wider (216 mm × 343 mm). Children may see this shape of paper in historical documents. Although the A paper series only became standard in the middle of the 20th century the advantages of such a system were first suggested in 1786!

1a Who reaches the end first?

- Draw the chart on paper so that counters will fit on the cells.
- Take it in turns to roll the dice once. Each player places a counter on the grid on the number they rolled.

  Now each player should:
  - ▶ roll the dice twice
  - ▶ add the numbers shown
  - ▶ multiply the result by 3
  - ▶ move the counter that many spaces.

  Example: If your dice shows 4 and 1, their sum is 5. You find the 5th multiple of 3, which is 15. Move the counter 15 spaces.

- Keep rolling the dice twice each. The winner is the player who reaches 144 first.

- Play the game again and count in multiples of 6. Repeat for multiples of 9.

You need:
- 1–6 dice
- 2 counters (or 5p coins)
- paper and pencil
- a partner

1	2	3	4	5	6	7	8	9	10	11	12
13	14	15	16	17	18	19	20	21	22	23	24
25	26	27	28	29	30	31	32	33	34	35	36
37	38	39	40	41	42	43	44	45	46	47	48
49	50	51	52	53	54	55	56	57	58	59	60
61	62	63	64	65	66	67	68	69	70	71	72
73	74	75	76	77	78	79	80	81	82	83	84
85	86	87	88	89	90	91	92	93	94	95	96
97	98	99	100	101	102	103	104	105	106	107	108
109	110	111	112	113	114	115	116	117	118	119	120
121	122	123	124	125	126	127	128	129	130	131	132
133	134	135	136	137	138	139	140	141	142	143	144

 Please help your child by reading the instructions and doing the activity together.

Rising Stars Mathematics Year 4 © Rising Stars UK Ltd 2016

1a Temperatures around the world

- Use the Internet to find 4 places in the world that have a temperature **below** 0°C today.

- Now find 4 places that have a temperature **above** 0°C today.

- Draw a line 40 squares long. Mark zero in the middle. Place each temperature on the number line.

- List the temperatures from the coldest to the hottest.

- What is the difference between the hottest and coldest temperatures in your number line?

- Now find the coldest place in the world today. Can you put that value on the number line? What about the hottest place in the world today? What is the difference between these values?

You need:
- Internet access
- squared paper
- ruler
- pencil

Please help your child by reading the instructions and doing the activity together.

Rising Stars Mathematics Year 4 © Rising Stars UK Ltd 2016

⭐ 1b Measuring at home

- Make a place-value grid like the one shown here.

1000	100	10	1	.	10th	100th	1000th

You need:
- kitchen scales
- various items of different sizes, e.g. bag of peas, bag of rice, a book
- paper and pencil
- a partner

- Choose an item that has a mass of less than 1 kg. Place it on the scales. Write its mass in grams on your place-value grid.

- Repeat for 7 different items that have a mass of up to 3 kg each.

- Write down the measurements in kilograms in a second place-value grid. Remember to include zero as a place holder in these numbers.

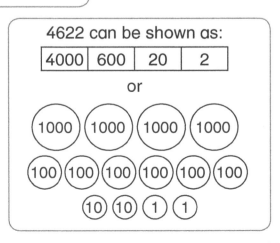

Please help your child by reading the instructions and doing the activity together.

⭐ 1b Egyptian numbers

5000 years ago Egyptians carved number symbols on their tombs.

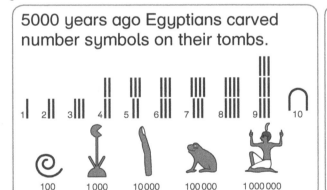

| 1 | 2 | 3 | 4 | 5 | 6 | 7 | 8 | 9 | 10 |

100 1000 10 000 100 000 1 000 000

A stone carving from Karnak Temple in Egypt shows the number 4622 like this:

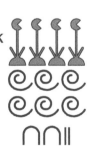

You need:
- paper and pencil
- a partner

- Use Egyptian symbols to write 3-digit numbers. Write 4 different numbers. List them in order of size.

- Ask your partner to read the numbers you have made.

- Repeat with 4-digit numbers.

Today we can represent numbers in many different ways.

- Show the numbers you made in at least 2 different ways.

4622 can be shown as:

4000	600	20	2

or

1000 1000 1000 1000

100 100 100 100 100 100

10 10 1 1

Please help your child by reading the instructions and doing the activity together.

2a Addition codes

A	B	C	D	E	F	G	H	I	J	K	L	M
3500	2601	3000	4200	5190	6111	7500	8200	1129	1300	1105	1352	4023
N	O	P	Q	R	S	T	U	V	W	X	Y	Z
1000	1340	2500	2222	3771	3880	3062	2800	3400	2350	5800	7000	6900

You need:
- paper and pencil
- a partner

- Complete the calculations below using a mental calculation strategy.

- The answers make a sentence. Use the code above to find it.

500 + 629

350 + 1002	1100 + 240	1200 + 2200	2005 + 3185

523 + 3500	4200 + 2800

1250 + 1250	3000 + 2190	1526 + 1536

- Make up an easy coded sentence for a friend using addition. Now make up a difficult question. Did they solve it using a mental or a written method?

 Please help your child by reading the instructions and doing the activity together.

2a Addition pyramids

Each block of the pyramid is completed by adding the 2 numbers below, e.g. 1000 + 850 = 1850.

- Use a written strategy to find the missing numbers.

You need:
- digit cards 0–9
- paper and pencil
- a partner

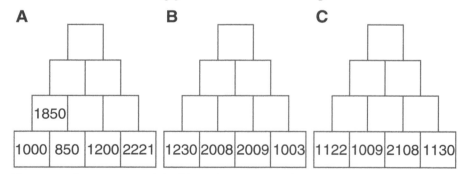

A

B

C

Row A: 1850 | 1000 | 850 | 1200 | 2221

Row B: 1230 | 2008 | 2009 | 1003

Row C: 1122 | 1009 | 2108 | 1130

Make an easy and a difficult addition pyramid. Can you solve them?

- Draw a few pyramids like the ones shown here.

- Place the digit cards face down on the table. Pick up 4 cards to make a 4-digit number. Do this 4 times and write the numbers in the bottom row of the pyramid.

- Take it in turns to find the missing numbers and to check each other's answers.

 Please help your child by reading the instructions and doing the activity together.

★184

2b Journeys

Transport	Cost	Departs from London at:	Arrives in Newcastle at:
Plane	£98.22	12:45	14:00
Train	£69.99	07:30	10:35
Coach	£44.80	11 p.m.	6 a.m.
Car	£72.00	6 a.m.	1:30 p.m.

Tom is visiting his grandparents. He must travel from London to Newcastle. The table shows the prices and times of the journey by plane, train, coach and car.

Use a mental subtraction method to answer these questions:

- How much cheaper is it to travel by coach than aeroplane?

- How much more expensive is it to travel by car than train?

- How long does each journey last?

- Do you think that Tom should travel by plane, train, coach or car? Why?

Hint: Before you start, change each value from pounds to pence.

You need:
- paper and pencil

Which mental method do you prefer? Why?

Rising Stars Mathematics Year 4 © Rising Stars UK Ltd 2016

2b Measuring your home

- Measure the length and width of your bedroom in centimetres.

- Measure the length and width of your kitchen in millimetres.

- What is the difference between the width of your kitchen and the width of your bedroom? What is the difference between the length of your kitchen and the width of your bedroom? Give your answers in millimetres.

- Write down the lengths and widths. How many different subtractions can you make? Use a mental or written method to calculate all the possible differences.

You need:
- metre stick or tape measure
- paper and pencil

Remember: 1 m = 1000 mm

3a Christmas tree

- Cut 4 lengths of ribbon: 3 cm, 6 cm, 9 cm and 12 cm.

- Make a Christmas tree by tying each ribbon onto a stick.

- If you placed all the pieces of ribbon together, how long would the ribbon be?

- Now make a bigger tree using 2 pieces of each length of ribbon: 3 cm, 6 cm, 9 cm and 12 cm. How long are the pieces of ribbon on this tree altogether?

- How much ribbon have you used altogether for both trees?

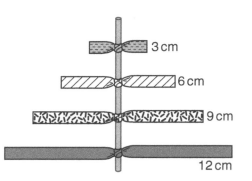

3 cm
6 cm
9 cm
12 cm

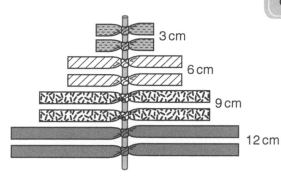

3 cm
6 cm
9 cm
12 cm

You need:
- short stick
- ribbon
- scissors
- a partner

If you do not have ribbon and a stick, try using strips of paper or card and glue.

Please help your child by reading the instructions and doing the activity together.

Rising Stars Mathematics Year 4 © Rising Stars UK Ltd 2016

3a Counting in sixes, nines and twelves

- Count in threes and shade the numbers in yellow.
- Count in sixes and circle the numbers in blue.
- Count in nines and circle the numbers in orange.
- Count in twelves and circle the numbers in purple.
- Which numbers are multiples of both 6 and 9?
- Which numbers are multiples of both 6 and 12?
- Which numbers are multiples of both 9 and 12?

1	2	3	4	5	6	7	8	9	10
11	12	13	14	15	16	17	18	19	20
21	22	23	24	25	26	27	28	29	30
31	32	33	34	35	36	37	38	39	40
41	42	43	44	45	46	47	48	49	50
51	52	53	54	55	56	57	58	59	60
61	62	63	64	65	66	67	68	69	70
71	72	73	74	75	76	77	78	79	80
81	82	83	84	85	86	87	88	89	90
91	92	93	94	95	96	97	98	99	100

You need:
- 4 different coloured pencils
- paper and pencil

What do you notice about these numbers?

Please help your child by reading the instructions and doing the activity together.

Rising Stars Mathematics Year 4 © Rising Stars UK Ltd 2016

3b Multiplication dice

You need:
- 1–6 dice
- timer
- paper and pencil
- a partner

- Take it in turns to roll the dice 3 times. Multiply your 3 numbers mentally.

- Pair and swap the numbers so that you can multiply your numbers in a different way. Can you find another way to multiply your numbers mentally?

- Repeat 5 times.

- Now take it in turns to throw the dice 4 times. Multiply the numbers you land on mentally as quickly as you can.

- Repeat 5 times.

- The winner is the player who calculates the products in as many ways as possible in 1 minute.

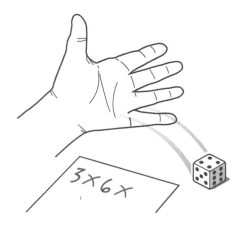

Please help your child by reading the instructions and doing the activity together.

Rising Stars Mathematics Year 4 © Rising Stars UK Ltd 2016

3b Multiplying puzzle

You need:
- paper and pencil

- The numbers hidden by each shape are multiplied to give the numbers in the last row and column.

- What number could each shape be?

⬭	△	45
◇	▭	6
◇	◇	△
45	54	

$$\text{⬭} \times \text{◇} \times \text{◇} = 45$$

- Make an easy multiplying puzzle with 2 unknown values and also a difficult multiplying puzzle with 3 unknown values. Why is it easy? Why is it difficult?

- Write 240 as the product of 2 factors. How many different ways can you find?

- How many ways are there of writing 240 as a product of 3 factors?

Please help your child by reading the instructions and doing the activity together.

Multiplication snap

You need:

- digit cards 1–9
- paper and pencil
- a partner

- Pick up 3 cards. Make a 2-digit number and a single-digit number.
- Multiply them like this:

- Write the calculation on paper. Replace the cards.
- Your partner picks up 3 cards and makes a new multiplication in the same way.
- If the two multiplications give the same product, say 'Snap!' first to win 10 points.
- Take turns and repeat 10 times. The winner has the most points.

Write all the different multiplications that gave the same result. How many can you find?

Please help your child by reading the instructions and doing the activity together.

Rising Stars Mathematics Year 4 © Rising Stars UK Ltd 2016

Multiplying choir

You need:

- paper and pencil

- There are 3 times as many boys as there are girls in the school choir. There are 28 girls. How many children are in the choir altogether?
- The choir gave a concert. This table shows the number of child and adult tickets sold. How much money did they take?

	Child tickets	**Adult tickets**
Price	£2	£9
Number of tickets sold	89	40

- The concert started at 10:20 a.m. The children sang 18 songs. Each song was 3 minutes long. The orchestra played 3 pieces. Each piece was 4 minutes long. There were no breaks. What time did the concert finish?

Please help your child by reading the instructions and doing the activity together.

Rising Stars Mathematics Year 4 © Rising Stars UK Ltd 2016

4a Investigating angles

- Complete the bar chart to show how many there are of each angle.
- Put all the acute angles in order of size. Start with the smallest.
- Put all the obtuse angles in order of size. Start with the smallest.

Are all right angles the same size?

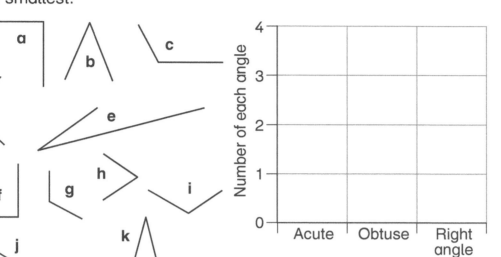

Please help your child by reading the instructions and doing the activity together.

4a Pizza angles

- Make 2 circular pizzas out of dough or plasticine.
- Cut the first pizza into 4 slices so that there is:
  - ▶ 1 right angle
  - ▶ 2 acute angles
  - ▶ 1 obtuse angle.
- Now cut the second pizza into 4 slices so that there is:
  - ▶ 1 acute angle
  - ▶ 2 obtuse angles
  - ▶ 1 right angle.

Draw all the angles you made.

Please help your child by reading the instructions and doing the activity together.

4b True triangles

- Are the following statements true or false?

  ▶ A scalene triangle cannot have a right angle.

  ▶ An isosceles triangle can only have 1 obtuse angle.

  ▶ The 3 angles in a scalene triangle can be: a right angle, an obtuse angle and an acute angle.

- Make up 2 more false statements about triangles. Explain to a partner why each statement is false.

You need:

- paper and pencil
- a partner

Explain your answers to a partner.

Please help your child by reading the instructions and doing the activity together.

Rising Stars Mathematics Year 4 © Rising Stars UK Ltd 2016

4b Making triangles

The ancient Egyptians were believed to make right-angled triangles using a rope which was knotted to make 12 equal sections.

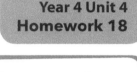

- Ask your friends or family members to help you. Make 12 knots in a rope.

- Hold 3 of the knots and keep the rope tight to make a triangle.

- Describe the angles of the triangle.

- Hold a different knot. How does this affect the triangle and its angles?

- Hold a different knot again and describe the difference.

- Draw the triangles you have made and sort them into 3 groups: equilateral, isosceles and scalene triangles.

You need:

- string or rope
- dotty paper
- ruler
- pencil
- friends or family

Please help your child by reading the instructions and doing the activity together.

Rising Stars Mathematics Year 4 © Rising Stars UK Ltd 2016

Making quadrilaterals

- Draw a line that is 2 cm long.
- Draw different quadrilaterals which have at least one side that is 2 cm long.
- Cut them out.
- Make new quadrilaterals by cutting 1 side of each shape.
- Explore how many cuts you must make to change a rectangle into a parallelogram.

You need:

- dotty paper
- ruler
- scissors
- pencil

Do you make the same number of cuts if you change a parallelogram into a rectangle?

Please help your child by reading the instructions and doing the activity together.

Straw quadrilaterals

- Make different quadrilaterals by cutting and joining 4 straws with tape.
- How many different quadrilaterals can you each make in 5 minutes?
- Collect 1 point for every quadrilateral you make. Repeat 4 times.
- Compare the shapes you made. What is the same? What is different?
- Copy the table and draw the shapes you made.

You need:

- straws
- scissors
- sticky tape
- ruler
- paper and pencil
- a partner

Shapes	Player 1	Player 2
Square		
Rectangle		
Rhombus		
Parallelogram		
Kite		
Irregular quadrilateral		
Total		

Please help your child by reading the instructions and doing the activity together.

Symmetry at home

You need:
- paper and pencil

- Look at the faces on objects around your home or garden. Find 2 objects to fit in each cell of the table below.
- Record your results in the table. Sketch each object. Insert the lines of symmetry where appropriate.

The face on this object has:					
1 line of symmetry	1 or more diagonal lines of symmetry	1 horizontal line of symmetry	1 vertical line of symmetry	2 or more lines of symmetry	no lines of symmetry

Please help your child by reading the instructions and doing the activity together.

Rising Stars Mathematics Year 4 © Rising Stars UK Ltd 2016

Triangle pictures

You need:
- paper or card
- glue
- coloured pencils
- scissors
- a partner

- Draw a picture using triangles with 1, 3 or no lines of symmetry.
- Try making your picture from paper or card.
- Ask a partner to identify how many of the triangles have 1, 3 or no lines of symmetry.
- Is their answer correct?
- Look closely at one of the triangles that has 3 lines of symmetry. What do you notice about the length of its sides?

This penguin is made out of different triangles. Some have 3 lines of symmetry. Some only have 1.

Please help your child by reading the instructions and doing the activity together.

Rising Stars Mathematics Year 4 © Rising Stars UK Ltd 2016

5a Holiday calculations

Can you help Ana solve these problems?

- I am visiting my grandparents for 4 weeks. How many days is that?

- My grandparents have 2 dogs. They are 5 years old and 6 years old. Their age in 'dog years' is 7 times bigger. How old are the dogs in 'dog years'?

- I take the dogs for a walk every day. We walk for 2 hours in the morning and 1 hour in the evening. How long do the dogs walk with me every week?

- My older brother works as a babysitter during the holidays. He charges £7 per hour. Last week he worked 2 hours per day on Monday, Tuesday and Wednesday. He worked 3 hours per day on Thursday and Friday. How much money did my brother earn last week?

- My brother saves £7 each day. He wants to buy a new bike that costs £100. How many days does he need to save to buy the bike?

You need:
- paper and pencil

Can you think of different ways to solve these problems?

 Please help your child by reading the instructions and doing the activity together.

5a Temperature game

- Both players start at 0°C.
- Take turns to roll the dice.
- If the number is 4, 5 or 6, the temperature falls. Move by as many degrees as the number on the dice in a negative direction. Put a pencil mark where you land.
- If the number is 1, 2 or 3, the temperature rises. Move in a positive direction and mark where you land.
- Write number statements to show each move you make.
- The winner reaches 20°C or –20°C first.

You need:
- 1–6 dice
- paper and pencil
- a partner

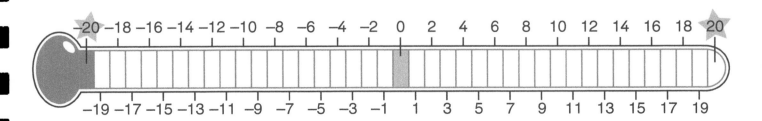

Please help your child by reading the instructions and doing the activity together.

5b Rounding masses

- Choose 10 items from your kitchen cupboard, e.g. pasta, bread, rice, flour, sugar, tea or coffee.

- Find the mass of each item using the scales. Measure in grams.

- Round each mass to the nearest 10, 100 and 1000. Explain your answers.

642.8 g

You need:

- kitchen weighing scales
- items from your kitchen cupboard
- paper and pencil

If you are unsure, draw a number line and place all the numbers there.

 Please help your child by reading the instructions and doing the activity together.

Rising Stars Mathematics Year 4 © Rising Stars UK Ltd 2016

5b Comparing masses

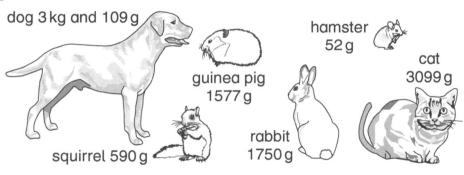

dog 3 kg and 109 g

hamster 52 g

cat 3099 g

guinea pig 1577 g

squirrel 590 g

rabbit 1750 g

You need:

- Internet access/ reference books
- paper and pencil

- Order the animals from heaviest to lightest. Write the names on the grid.

1 heaviest	2	3	4	5	6 lightest

- Write comparison statements for these measurements. Use both < and > for each. How many statements can you write?

- Use the Internet or books to find an animal that weighs more than the animal in box 5 but less than box 4. What animal did you find?

 Please help your child by reading the instructions and doing the activity together.

Rising Stars Mathematics Year 4 © Rising Stars UK Ltd 2016

5c Weekend times

Activity	Start		End	Duration
	11:05			
	13:45			
	15:05			
	5 p.m.			
	30 minutes past 6			
	20 minutes past 7			

You need:

- pencil

- What would you do on your perfect weekend? Would you see friends, make a cake, play football, or something else? List 6 of your chosen activities in the first column of the table.

- The table shows start times for each activity. Show the times on the clocks.

- Decide when each activity ends. Show this on the clocks.

- How long does each activity last? Which activity lasts the longest?

 Please help your child by reading the instructions and doing the activity together.

Rising Stars Mathematics Year 4 © Rising Stars UK Ltd 2016

5c Roman number game

- Roll the dice. Choose either a column or row with the number you rolled.

- Place the 6 numbers in your chosen column or row in order, starting with the smallest.

You need:

- conversion chart for Roman numerals
- 1–6 dice
- paper and pencil

	1	2	3	4	5	6
1	LV	XCV	XXXVIII	XLIII	CCIX	LXXXII
2	XCIX	XLII	LXII	XCIV	XXIX	CXXXV
3	LXIV	CCII	CXI	CII	CXII	CCL
4	CCL	CCCVIII	LXVIII	LXIII	LXIX	LXX
5	XXXI	LIV	XL	LXXVI	CCL	XVII
6	CCCL	LXX	CL	CIX	CIV	CVI

Which is the smallest number in the table? Which is the largest number?

 Please help your child by reading the instructions and doing the activity together.

Rising Stars Mathematics Year 4 © Rising Stars UK Ltd 2016 **195**

6a Using train timetables

This is the train timetable from Brighton to Reading.

	Train 1	Train 2	Train 3
Brighton	09:28	9:40	9:52
Burgess Hill		9:54	
Haywards Heath			
Gatwick Airport	09:52	10:12	10:15
Horley	09:57	10:17	
Reading	11:19	11:38	11:47

Train 1 is delayed by 10 minutes leaving Brighton. It is delayed by a further 5 minutes at Gatwick Airport.

Train 2 is delayed by 12 minutes leaving Gatwick Airport.

- Isabella needs to go from Brighton to Reading. She must arrive in Reading before 11:45 a.m. Which train should she choose? Explain your answer.

- Jake is travelling from Brighton to Gatwick Airport. He wants to take the fastest train. Which train will that be?

You need:
- paper and pencil

Please help your child by reading the instructions and doing the activity together.

6a Measuring lengths and widths

- Measure a table in your house in centimetres. You could measure your dining table, a coffee table or something else.

- Work out how much longer its length is than its width.

- Now work out the perimeter of the table.

- Measure the length and width of 2 rooms in your house in centimetres. Calculate:
  - ▶ the sum of the lengths
  - ▶ the sum of the widths
  - ▶ the difference in the lengths
  - ▶ the difference in the widths.

- Investigate how the sums and differences would change if the lengths and widths were:
  - ▶ 10 cm longer
  - ▶ 12 cm shorter.

- Explain your reasoning.

You need:
- metre stick or tape measure
- paper and pencil

What would happen if only one of the sides was 10 cm longer or shorter?

Please help your child by reading the instructions and doing the activity together.

6b Building pyramids

Each block of the pyramid is completed by finding the sum of the 2 numbers below, e.g. 800 + 200 = 1000.

● Build pyramids A and B by completing each row.

● Complete pyramid C so that the top row is 8500.

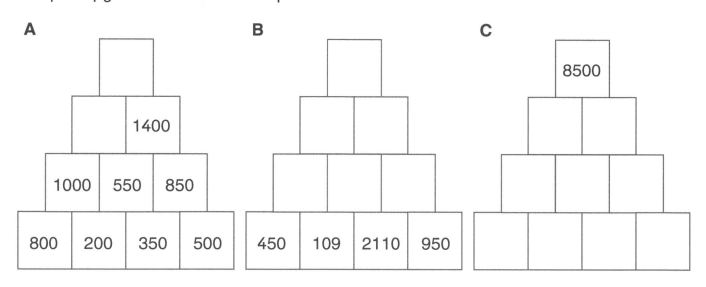

A

	1400		
1000	550	850	
800	200	350	500

B

C

8500

Please help your child by reading the instructions and doing the activity together.

Rising Stars Mathematics Year 4 © Rising Stars UK Ltd 2016

6b Recording time

● Measure in seconds how long it takes you to: eat an apple, eat dinner, complete your homework and tidy your room.

● Complete the bar chart to show your findings. It may help to record the information in a table first.

● How much longer did it take you to eat dinner than to eat an apple?

● How long in total did it take you to complete your homework and tidy your room?

● How long did you spend on all the activities in total? Which took the longest?

● Insert a new activity in the bar chart that takes less time than eating dinner. How long did you spend on all the activities in total now?

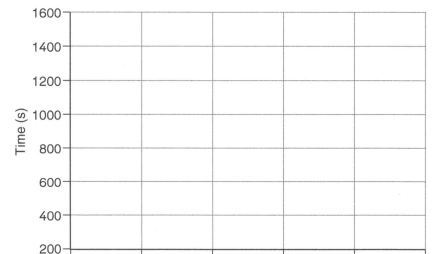

Please help your child by reading the instructions and doing the activity together.

Money problems

Book type	Price (£)
Storybook	4.50
Maths textbook	6.99
English textbook	7.99
Comic	1.99

You have £50 to spend on new books for the library.

- You buy 2 storybooks and 2 comics. How much more have you spent on the storybooks than the comics?

- How much money do you have left to spend?

- Do you have enough money to buy 2 maths textbooks and 2 English textbooks?

- Use the Internet or go to a bookshop to find the prices of other books you may wish to buy. How many books can you buy for £50? How much change would you receive?

You need:

- Internet access or bookshop
- paper and pencil

Write down any calculations needed.

Please help your child by reading the instructions and doing the activity together.

Rising Stars Mathematics Year 4 © Rising Stars UK Ltd 2016

Clever additions and subtractions

- On the 5 cards write 'mass', 'capacity', 'length', 'money', 'time'.

- Shuffle the cards. Place them face down in a pile. Pick up a card.

- Choose 2 values from the grid that represent the label on your card, e.g. if you pick 'mass', choose 2 values from the grid in kg or/and g.

- Add and subtract the values you choose. Remember to convert the measurements before adding or subtracting them.

- If the answer is correct, place a counter on top of both values.

- Take turns until all the counters have gone. The winner is the player with the most counters.

- Draw your own grid. Use different measurements and play the game again.

You need:

- 25 counters (or 5ps)
- 5 pieces of card or paper
- pencil
- a partner

£13.45	5 litres 200 ml	4 kg	3 km 176 m	1 hour 45 min
87 m	£6.28	$2\frac{1}{4}$ hours	4120 ml	$3\frac{1}{2}$ kg
$2\frac{1}{2}$ km	2 kg 300 g	134p	£15.73	$\frac{1}{2}$ hour
£3	1267 g	3 hours	50 m	236 ml
98p	3500 g	$1\frac{1}{2}$ litres	100 min	4 km

Please help your child by reading the instructions and doing the activity together.

Rising Stars Mathematics Year 4 © Rising Stars UK Ltd 2016

7a Quick fire fractions

- Roll the dice twice.
- The first number shows the row and the second number shows the column of the square you land on, e.g. if you roll 3 and 4, then read the fraction where the third row and fourth column meet ($\frac{10}{25}$).
- Colour the square yellow. In 60 seconds, find as many fractions as you can that are equal to the fraction you landed on. Colour them blue.
- Ask a partner to time you. How many seconds did it take you to complete the whole game? How many minutes is that?

You need:
- 1–6 dice
- timer
- yellow and blue coloured pencils
- paper and pencil
- a partner

	1	2	3	4	5	6
1	$\frac{7}{14}$	$\frac{9}{18}$	$\frac{16}{32}$	$\frac{3}{6}$	$\frac{20}{40}$	$\frac{5}{10}$
2	$\frac{7}{8}$	$\frac{28}{32}$	$\frac{14}{16}$	$\frac{6}{15}$	$\frac{1}{2}$	$\frac{12}{30}$
3	$\frac{27}{36}$	$\frac{14}{35}$	$\frac{30}{36}$	$\frac{10}{25}$	$\frac{77}{88}$	$\frac{3}{4}$
4	$\frac{4}{10}$	$\frac{5}{6}$	$\frac{21}{24}$	$\frac{4}{10}$	$\frac{2}{5}$	$\frac{6}{8}$
5	$\frac{12}{30}$	$\frac{10}{12}$	$\frac{12}{16}$	$\frac{70}{80}$	$\frac{18}{24}$	$\frac{20}{50}$
6	$\frac{20}{50}$	$\frac{22}{55}$	$\frac{36}{48}$	$\frac{35}{40}$	$\frac{50}{60}$	$\frac{15}{18}$

 Please help your child by reading the instructions and doing the activity together.

Rising Stars Mathematics Year 4 © Rising Stars UK Ltd 2016

7a Fractions code

- Find the answers.

You need:
- paper and pencil
- a friend or family member

$\frac{7}{9}$ subtract	$\frac{1}{7}$ more than	$\frac{1}{6}$ less than	Add $\frac{1}{4}$ to	Subtract $\frac{1}{12}$ from	Find the sum of $\frac{1}{8}$ and
a $\frac{1}{9} =$	**b** $\frac{6}{7} =$	**d** $1 =$	**f** $\frac{2}{4} =$	**h** $\frac{10}{12} =$	**j** $\frac{3}{8} =$
	c $\frac{5}{7} =$	**e** $\frac{3}{6} =$	**g** $\frac{1}{4} =$	**i** $\frac{7}{12} =$	**k** $\frac{2}{8} =$
					l $\frac{1}{8} =$

- Match your answers with the code below to find the name of an animal written backwards.

$\frac{6}{7} =$ **M**, $\frac{1}{2} =$ **P**, $\frac{3}{4} =$ **O**, $\frac{5}{6} =$ **A**, $\frac{1}{3} =$ **T**, $\frac{3}{8} =$ **I**, $1 =$ **U**, $\frac{2}{3} =$ **S**, $\frac{1}{4} =$ **H**

a   b   c   d   e   f   g   h   i   j   k   l

- Make addition and subtraction fraction questions into a code for a 4-letter word. Can your friend find the answer?

 Please help your child by reading the instructions and doing the activity together.

Rising Stars Mathematics Year 4 © Rising Stars UK Ltd 2016 **199**

7b Decimal and fraction equivalences

- Your partner picks up 1 or 2 digit cards and makes a decimal with either 1 or 2 digits. They also pick up a symbol card.

- You then find a fraction to make the number statement correct. You receive 1 point for every correct answer.

Example

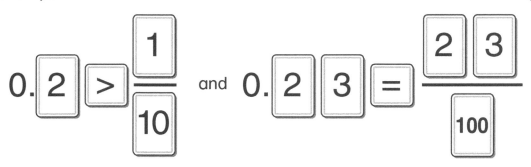

$$0.2 > \frac{1}{10} \quad \text{and} \quad 0.23 = \frac{23}{100}$$

Please help your child by reading the instructions and doing the activity together.

7b Stationery shopping

	Shop A price (£) for 1 packet of 100	Shop B price (£) for 1 packet of 10
Pencils	12.45	1.30
Rubbers	27.20	2.56
Rulers	35.08	3.58
Pens	54.60	5.20
Glue stick	65.21	7.10

- Your teacher is buying stationery items for Year 4. This is the price list from 2 shops. Which shop should she choose for each item?

- Describe the place value of each amount before and after your calculations. Use these words: 'whole number', 'tenth' and 'hundredth'.

There are many ways to solve this problem. You could find the cost of 1 item. You could find the cost of 10 items for Shop A, or find the cost of 100 items for Shop B.

Please help your child by reading the instructions and doing the activity together.

8a 7-day data

You need:
- soft toys
- pencil

- How long do you spend on the following activities?
  - ► How many hours do you sleep:
    each day? [ ] each week? [ ]
  - ► How many hours of TV do you watch:
    each day? [ ] each week? [ ]
  - ► How many hours do you spend playing:
    each day? [ ] each week? [ ]
  - ► How many hours do you spend studying at school:
    each day? [ ] each week? [ ]
- Use your soft toys to make a bar chart or pictogram showing how much time you spend on each activity in 1 week.
- Now draw your bar chart or pictogram here.

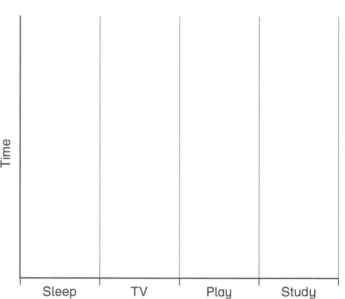

Time | Sleep | TV | Play | Study

Please help your child by reading the instructions and doing the activity together.

Rising Stars Mathematics Year 4 © Rising Stars UK Ltd 2016

8a Party planner

You need:
- Internet access, catalogue or shop
- paper and pencil

- You are preparing 11 party bags for your friends. Each bag contains: a ruler, a pen, a rubber, a pack of highlighters, a pack of felt tip pens and a pack of coloured pencils.
- Research the cost of each item. Record the costs in the table.
- Find the cost for 11 of each item. Record your answers in the table.
- What is the cost of all the items?

Item	Cost of 1 item	Cost of 11 items
Ruler		
Pen		
Rubber		
Highlighters		
Felt tip pens		
Pack of coloured pencils		
Total cost		

Please help your child by reading the instructions and doing the activity together.

Multiplying puzzle

• The shapes in the grid represent numbers. Find the missing numbers to make these calculations true. Read across, down and up, watching out for equals signs.

• Write all the calculations you make on a piece of paper.

◯	×	2	×	▢	=	96
=		=		=		=
4		2	×	6	=	◸
×		×		×		×
2	×	◇	×	◇	=	2
		×				×
0	=	1	×	△	×	4

Please help your child by reading the instructions and doing the activity together.

Rising Stars Mathematics Year 4 © Rising Stars UK Ltd 2016

Highest number

• Each player rolls the dice 3 times and multiplies their 3 numbers.

 × × =

• The player with the highest product wins 1 point.

• Repeat 6 times.

• Try a challenge! Take turns to roll the dice twice to make a 2-digit number. Find 3 numbers whose product is your 2-digit number. You can use the same number more than once.

Don't forget to use 1 if needed!

Please help your child by reading the instructions and doing the activity together.

Rising Stars Mathematics Year 4 © Rising Stars UK Ltd 2016

8c Market problems

- Huan bought 12 eggs for 9p each and 6 fresh rolls for 28p each. She paid with a £5 note. How much change did she get?

- Josh had nine 20p coins and seven 50p coins in his pocket. He wanted to buy 4 coffees and 4 cookies for his friends. The coffees were 95p each and cookies cost 50p each. Show that he did not have enough money. How much more did he need?

- Vicki works in the market. She makes fresh orange juice. She uses 6 fresh oranges to make 1 glass of juice.

  ▶ She made 98 glasses of juice in 1 day. How many oranges did she use that day?

  ▶ She sold each glass of juice for £3. How much money did she make that day?

- Sam sells sausage rolls in the market. He usually sells 57 sausages in 1 hour. On Saturday he worked from 7 a.m. to 4 p.m.

  ▶ How many sausage rolls did he sell in total?

  ▶ Each sausage roll costs £2. How much money did he make that day?

Please help your child by reading the instructions and doing the activity together.

8c Bouquet of flowers

- Design a bouquet of flowers for a friend or family member. You can spend up to £30. Your bouquet should include roses, lilies, carnations and daisies.

- Research the prices of these flowers at a local florist or online florist. Do not buy a readymade bouquet, but make one yourself.

- Choose how many of each flower you will include. Now draw your bouquet! Label each flower with its price.

- What will be the total cost of your bouquet?

Can you make a different bouquet for £30?

Please help your child by reading the instructions and doing the activity together.

8d What number?

- Find out what numbers Tom is thinking of. You could use the inverse operation to help you.

You need:
- paper and pencil

---

1 23 is half of the size of the number.
What is the number?

2 9 is $\frac{1}{12}$ of the size of a number.
What is the number?

3 7 is 7 times as large as a number.
What is the number?

4 51 is 1 more than half of the size of a number.
What is the number?

5 2 is $\frac{1}{10}$ of the size of a number.
What is the number?

Check your answer by putting the number back in the question. Does it work?

- Make up an easy question and a difficult question like these. Challenge an adult at home to answer them!

Please help your child by reading the instructions and doing the activity together.

Rising Stars Mathematics Year 4 © Rising Stars UK Ltd 2016

8d Cupcake recipe

- Work out the ingredients needed for:
  - ▶ 8 cupcakes
  - ▶ 16 cupcakes
  - ▶ 24 cupcakes.
- Show your calculations.
- Research the prices for all the ingredients. How much would it cost to make 8 cupcakes? 16? 24?

Cupcake recipe

makes 4 small cupcakes

Ingredients	Buttercream icing
1 egg white	50 g butter
42 g sugar	78 g icing sugar
40 g flour	12 ml milk
38 g butter	
17 ml milk	

You need:
- Internet access or shop
- recipe book
- paper and pencil

Work with an adult to make some cupcakes!

Please help your child by reading the instructions and doing the activity together.

Rising Stars Mathematics Year 4 © Rising Stars UK Ltd 2016

9a Trapezium: true or false?

- Read these statements about trapeziums. Is each one true or false?

- Draw trapeziums to explain your reasoning.

You need:
- squared paper
- ruler
- pencil

1 All trapeziums have 1 vertical line of symmetry.

2 A trapezium always has 2 parallel sides.

3 A trapezium can sometimes have 2 equal sides.

4 A trapezium cannot have a right angle.

- Make up 2 of your own statements about trapeziums. Are they true or false?

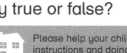 Please help your child by reading the instructions and doing the activity together.

9a Making a kite

1. Fold an A4 sheet of paper to make a kite shape.
2. Staple the folded corners in place.
3. Draw the kite's line of symmetry using a ruler. Fold it so that both sides meet.
4. Make a hole at the bottom of the kite. Tie string through the hole.
5. Unfold the kite. Test it on a windy day!

You need:
- A4 paper
- ruler
- stapler
- string
- pencil

Which kite flies best?

- Make this simple kite.

- Try to make a different kite that has longer sides.

- Describe the angles both your kites have.

- Now make a new kite with different size angles.

- Sketch all the kites you made.

Please help your child by reading the instructions and doing the activity together.

Coordinate stars

9b

- Copy this coordinate grid on squared paper. Add the stars.

- Roll the dice twice. The first number you roll gives the *x*-coordinate. The second number you roll gives the *y*-coordinate. Plot the numbers on the grid.

You need:

- 1–6 dice
- squared paper
- pencil
- a partner

- Each player gets 1 point for correctly plotting their coordinates. If you land on a star, you collect an extra 3 points.

- Each player has 4 turns. The person who gets the most points wins the game.

- Join the stars together to make a trapezium. Take it in turns to double each coordinate. Plot the new points and join them. What shape do they make?

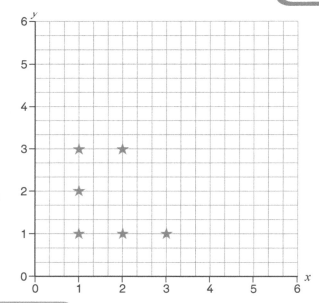

Please help your child by reading the instructions and doing the activity together.

Rising Stars Mathematics Year 4 © Rising Stars UK Ltd 2016

Moving around a grid

9b

- Draw a 20 × 20 grid on squared paper. Label both axes from 1 to 20.

- Plot these coordinates on the grid and join them: (3,4), (3,7), (6,1). These are 3 vertices of a trapezium.

- To draw a trapezium, the 4th coordinate could be (6,8). Find a different 4th point that will also make a trapezium. Join your coordinates and colour your trapezium.

- Shuffle the number cards and choose 2 cards. The first number shows how far your shape must move to the right. The second number shows how far the shape must move up.

You need:

- squared paper
- ruler
- number cards 1–10
- coloured pencils

- Draw the new shape and colour it. By how much have the *x*- and *y*-coordinates increased?

- Repeat with 2 different number cards. Can you state the coordinates of the new shape without drawing it? Now draw it to check your answer.

- What would happen if 1 corner of the shape was not translated the same distance as the other 3? Explain your answer.

Please help your child by reading the instructions and doing the activity together.

Rising Stars Mathematics Year 4 © Rising Stars UK Ltd 2016

10a Secret word!

You need:

- paper and pencil
- a friend or family member

- Find the answers to these questions.

1000 less than	1000 more than	Multiply by 25	
a 1175	**d** 2345	**g** 8	**i** 20
b 10110	**e** 9276	**h** 12	**j** 7
c 6789	**f** 17890		

- Match your answers with the code to find the name of a secret word written backwards.

  A = 3345, **E** = 9110, **F** = 18890, **K** = 5789, **L** = 10276, **N** = 500, **O** = 300, **S** = 175, **W** = 200

a	b	c	d	e	f	g	h	i	j

- This is the word WATER written backwards and the values of each letter. Each value is a multiple of 25.

R	E	T	A	W

  A = 225, **E** = 175, **R** = 75, **T** = 300, **W** = 150

Replace each letter with 5 questions about the multiples of 25. Give the code to a friend. Can they work out the backwards word?

 Please help your child by reading the instructions and doing the activity together.

10a Populations

You need:

- Internet access or reference books
- paper and pencil

Populations of some UK towns, as measured in 2011						
Uckfield	Wellington	North Ascot	Whittburn	Long Ashton	Kingsbridge	Dorchester
15213	11213	10227	10527	5254	6116	19060

- Write the populations in order of size from largest to smallest.

- Increase each population by 1000.

- Decrease each population by 1000.

- Use the Internet or books to find a town with a population of at least 10000 more people than Kingsbridge.

- Find a town with a population of at least 1000 fewer people than the population of Dorchester.

 Please help your child by reading the instructions and doing the activity together.

10b 4 cards!

- Pick up 4 cards. Write the 4 numbers in the 4 boxes given.
- Change the pounds into pennies, e.g. £21.37 = 2137p.
- Repeat 3 times. Write the values from the smallest to the largest.

You need:
- digit cards 1–9
- paper and pencil

£ ⬜⬜ . ⬜⬜ = _____ p   £ ⬜⬜ . ⬜⬜ = _____ p

£ ⬜⬜ . ⬜⬜ = _____ p   £ ⬜⬜ . ⬜⬜ = _____ p

- Now pick up 3 or 4 cards to write in these boxes. Change litres to millilitres, e.g. 3.56l = 3.560ml. Remember that 1 litre = 1000ml. Repeat 5 times. Write the values from the smallest to the largest.

⬜ . ⬜⬜ l = ⬜⬜⬜⬜ ml   ⬜⬜ . ⬜⬜ l = _____ ml

⬜ . ⬜⬜ l = ⬜⬜⬜⬜ ml   ⬜⬜ . ⬜⬜ l = _____ ml

Please help your child by reading the instructions and doing the activity together.

Rising Stars Mathematics Year 4 © Rising Stars UK Ltd 2016

10b TV guide

- Use a TV guide to find out the times of 6 of your favourite programmes for Saturday.

You need:
- Internet access or TV guide
- pencil

- Include a programme that lasts less than 1 hour, a programme that lasts longer than 1 hour and a programme that lasts longer than 90 minutes.

- Complete the table with the times, the names of the programmes and their duration.

- Find the difference in minutes between the 2 longest programmes in your table.

- Find the difference in minutes between the longest and the shortest programmes.

Time (from – to)	Programme's name	Duration

Please help your child by reading the instructions and doing the activity together.

Rising Stars Mathematics Year 4 © Rising Stars UK Ltd 2016

11a Money maze

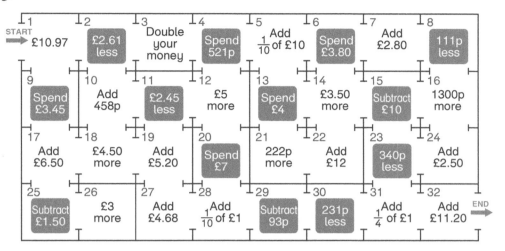

1 START £10.97	2 £2.61 less	3 Double your money	4 Spend 521p	5 Add $\frac{1}{10}$ of £10	6 Spend £3.80	7 Add £2.80	8 111p less
9 Spend £3.45	10 Add 458p	11 £2.45 less	12 £5 more	13 Spend £4	14 £3.50 more	15 Subtract £10	16 1300p more
17 Add £6.50	18 £4.50 more	19 Add £5.20	20 Spend £7	21 222p more	22 Add £12	23 340p less	24 Add £2.50
25 Subtract £1.50	26 £3 more	27 Add £4.68	28 Add $\frac{1}{10}$ of £1	29 Subtract 93p	30 231p less	31 Add $\frac{1}{4}$ of £1	32 Add £11.20 END

- Take it in turns to roll the dice. Move your counter the number of spaces shown on your dice, choosing a route to reach 'END'.

- Follow the instructions in the maze. Choose to use either a mental or written method.

- The winner is the person with the most money by the end of the game.

 Please help your child by reading the instructions and doing the activity together.

You need:
- 2 counters (or 5p coins)
- 1–6 dice
- paper and pencil
- a partner

Can you explain your choice of method?

11a Making dinner

- Work with an adult. You have the money above. You are cooking dinner and you need to buy pasta or rice, meatballs or prawns, cheese, carrots and tomatoes. Decide what you need to buy.

Pasta	Rice	Meatballs	Prawns	Cheese	Carrots	Tomatoes
70p for 500 g	£1.99 for 1 kg	£2.85 for 500 g	£2.99 for 350 g	£3.50 for 500 g	82p for 1 kg	99p for 150 g

- How much will your dinner cost? Make an estimate. Then use a written method to calculate the total cost. Use subtraction to check the answers.

- Will you have any money left?

Please help your child by reading the instructions and doing the activity together.

You need:
- Internet access or shop
- paper and pencil
- an adult

Check the prices of other items you might want to have for dinner.

11b Magic squares

- The numbers on each row, column and diagonal add up to the same number. Find the missing numbers using a mental method.

- Use a calculator to check your answers.

Hint: Add the numbers on the row or column where all the numbers are given. This will be the sum of every row, column and diagonal.

356		178
	445	
712	89	534

5600	100	7800
1200		3400

Please help your child by reading the instructions and doing the activity together.

Rising Stars Mathematics Year 4 © Rising Stars UK Ltd 2016

11b Calculating sales

This table shows the number of ice-creams and cakes sold at the busy Sunny Café.

Season	Month	Ice-creams	Cakes	Total
Winter	December	1750	3500	
	January	300	1500	1800
	February	280	1200	1480
Spring	March	290	1330	1620
	April	350	1800	2150
	May	2200	1780	
Summer	June	2500		4000
	July	3000		3780
	August	3800		5700
Autumn	September	1470		
	October	1000	1160	
	November	800	1230	

- Answer these questions.

1 How many more ice-creams were sold in the summer than in the winter?

2 How many more cakes than ice-creams were sold in spring?

3 There were 1200 more cakes than ice-cream sold in September. What were the total sales of ice-creams and cakes in September?

4 Complete the missing values in the table.

5 Which month had the highest total sales? Which month had the lowest total sales? What is the difference between the values?

- Make a 2-step problem of your own using the table. Ask a friend or family member to solve it.

- Can you think of another way to represent the data in the table?

Please help your child by reading the instructions and doing the activity together.

Rising Stars Mathematics Year 4 © Rising Stars UK Ltd 2016

12a True or false?

- Look at the grid below. Some of the calculations are true and some are false. Write T or F beside each one.
- Check your answers using a calculator.

You need:
- calculator
- paper and pencil

$\frac{2}{5} = \frac{24}{60}$	$\frac{5}{15} = \frac{8}{24}$	$\frac{1}{4} = \frac{3}{14}$	$\frac{11}{22} = \frac{33}{55}$
$\frac{6}{8} = \frac{12}{16}$	$\frac{1}{3} = \frac{2}{5}$	$\frac{15}{20} = \frac{5}{10}$	$\frac{1}{4} + \frac{2}{4} = \frac{6}{8}$
$\frac{1}{4} + \frac{3}{4} = 1\frac{1}{4}$	$\frac{5}{6} - \frac{3}{6} = \frac{1}{6}$	$\frac{3}{10} + \frac{5}{10} = \frac{8}{10} = \frac{4}{5}$	$\frac{3}{9} - \frac{1}{9} = \frac{1}{4}$
$1\frac{1}{4} + \frac{1}{4} = 1\frac{1}{2}$	$1\frac{7}{8} + 2\frac{3}{8} = 3\frac{1}{4}$	$3\frac{1}{8} - 1\frac{3}{8} = \frac{5}{8}$	$\frac{3}{5} + \frac{3}{5} = 1\frac{1}{5}$
$\frac{10}{60} = \frac{30}{80}$	$1\frac{1}{2} - 1\frac{1}{4} = \frac{1}{4}$	$\frac{14}{49} = \frac{6}{21} = \frac{2}{7}$	$1 - \frac{2}{8} = \frac{1}{8}$

 Please help your child by reading the instructions and doing the activity together.

12a Fractions and decimals memory game

- Cut the grid below into 24 cards. Place them all face down.
- Turn over 2 cards at a time. If they are equal to each other, then this is a match and you keep the cards. If they are not equal, place them back face down.
- Take turns. The winner is the one who finds the most matching cards.

You need:
- scissors
- paper and pencil
- a partner

$\frac{1}{5}$	$\frac{2}{10}$	$\frac{6}{30}$	0.2	0.25	$\frac{25}{100}$	$\frac{1}{4}$
$\frac{1}{2}$	$\frac{10}{20}$	0.5	$\frac{16}{32}$	0.16	$\frac{16}{100}$	$\frac{8}{50}$
0.08	$\frac{8}{100}$	$\frac{4}{50}$	$\frac{2}{25}$	0.06	$\frac{6}{100}$	$\frac{3}{50}$
$\frac{3}{10}$	0.3	$\frac{15}{50}$	$\frac{30}{100}$	$\frac{2}{8}$	$\frac{4}{25}$	$\frac{12}{200}$

 Please help your child by reading the instructions and doing the activity together.

12b Bigger or smaller?

14.2 cm

15 cm

This shoe is 142 mm long
or 14.2 cm.

This shoe is 150 mm long
or 15 cm. **15 > 14.2**

- Measure the lengths of your slippers, sandals, trainers and another pair of shoes that you have at home. Record the lengths to the nearest millimetre. Change these 4 lengths to centimetres.

- Use <, > or = to compare the values you recorded. How many comparisons can you make?

- Now round the lengths to the nearest centimetre. Record these beside the actual lengths. Check which is bigger. Use <, > or = to show each statement.

- Do this activity again with shoes belonging to your family. Write 6 statements using <, > or =.

- Place 1 shoe on a piece of paper. Make a pencil mark where the shoe starts and where it ends. Join these 2 points with a line and then measure it.

1 m = 1000 mm,
1 m = 100 cm,
1 cm = 10 mm

Please help your child by reading the
instructions and doing the activity together.

Rising Stars Mathematics Year 4 © Rising Stars UK Ltd 2016

12b Rounding

- Count the coins your family member has in their purse each day for 5 days.

- Round the total each day to the nearest £.

- Record the data in the table.

	Money – actual value (£)	Money – rounded to the nearest £
Day 1		
Day 2		
Day 3		
Day 4		
Day 5		

- Draw a number line and insert the actual and rounded values from your table on it. At what number does your number line start and finish?

- Look in your fridge. Ask your family member the prices of 3 items, e.g. milk, bread and butter. Can you insert these values on your number line?

- Round these values too. Are you rounding up or down? Explain your answer using the number line.

Please help your child by reading the
instructions and doing the activity together.

Rising Stars Mathematics Year 4 © Rising Stars UK Ltd 2016

13a Mental maze

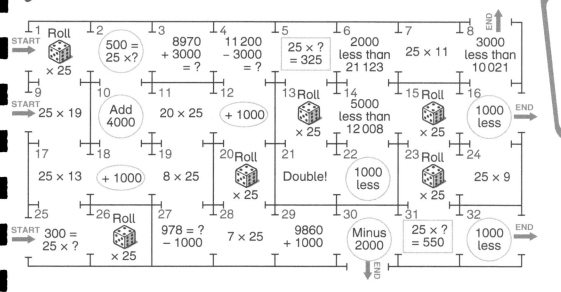

START 1 Roll ×25 | 2 500 = 25 ×? | 3 8970 + 3000 = ? | 4 11 200 − 3000 = ? | 5 25 × ? = 325 | 6 2000 less than 21 123 | 7 25 × 11 | 8 3000 less than 10 021 END

START 9 25 × 19 | 10 Add 4000 | 11 20 × 25 | 12 + 1000 | 13 Roll ×25 | 14 5000 less than 12 008 | 15 Roll ×25 | 16 1000 less END

17 25 × 13 | 18 + 1000 | 19 8 × 25 | 20 Roll ×25 | 21 Double! | 22 1000 less | 23 Roll ×25 | 24 25 × 9

START 25 300 = 25 × ? | 26 Roll ×25 | 27 978 = ? − 1000 | 28 7 × 25 | 29 9860 + 1000 | 30 Minus 2000 END | 31 25 × ? = 550 | 32 1000 less END

- Choose your starting point. Choose a route to reach an end point.

- Take turns to roll the dice. Move your counter the number of spaces shown on the dice.

- Carry out the action shown on the spaces you land on. The answer is your score.

- The winner has the highest score at the end of the game.

Rising Stars Mathematics Year 4 © Rising Stars UK Ltd 2016

You need:
- 1–6 dice
- 2 counters (or 5p coins)
- paper and pencil
- a partner

13a Alien problems

- On Planet Baba, dogs have 7 legs and cats have 6 legs. There are 66 legs. How many dogs and cats are there?

$$\boxed{} \times 7 + \boxed{} \times 6 = 66$$

- Females on Planet Baba have 3 eyes and males have 7 eyes. If there are 52 eyes in a room, how many male and females are there? Can you find any different answers?

- On Planet Baba, birds have 3 wings and butterflies have 8 wings. If there are 105 wings fluttering, how many birds and butterflies are there?

- Spiders have 11 legs and ants have 14 legs on Planet Baba. There are the same number of ants as spiders. There are 100 legs altogether. How many spiders and ants are there?

You need:
- paper and pencil

Make up an easy and a difficult multiplying word problem for a friend. What makes one easy and the other difficult?

13b At the cinema

- Vijay went to the cinema with his family. Help him to solve these problems about his visit. Use your knowledge of multiplying, adding and subtracting.

- Change all the values to pence first.

Make up an easy and a difficult question for a friend. Why is it easy? Why is it difficult?

1 Mum bought 2 adult tickets for £9.20 each and 4 children's tickets for £5.65 each. How much did she pay in total?

2 Vijay bought 6 packets of mints. Each packet cost 124p! He paid with a £10 note. How much change did he get?

3 Dad ordered some popcorn and a bottle of water for everyone. The cost for popcorn and water was £5.99 per person. Dad had £30 cash in his pocket. Was this enough to pay for the popcorn and drinks for 6 people? Explain your answer.

4 The cinema gallery had 9 rows of seats. There were 34 seats in each row. How many seats were there altogether in the gallery?

5 The main cinema was almost full. There were 400 seats and only 2 rows with 17 seats each were empty. How many people were there in the main cinema?

Please help your child by reading the instructions and doing the activity together.

13b Largest and smallest product

- Measure the height of someone in your family who is taller than 1 m.

- Think about their height in centimetres. Write this 3-digit number.

- Multiply this 3-digit number by your age.

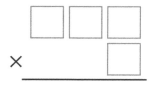

- Now rearrange all 4 numbers to make a different 3-digit number and a single-digit number so they have the largest product possible.

- Rearrange all 4 numbers to make a 3-digit number and a single-digit number so they have the smallest product possible.

- Write all the multiplications possible. Check each other's answers.

⭐214

Please help your child by reading the instructions and doing the activity together.

13c Shopping

- My last shopping receipt was torn, so I cannot see what I spent on broccoli and grapes.

- I buy 4 times less broccoli than carrots each week. How much broccoli do I buy each week?

- If broccoli costs £2 per kg, how much do I spend on broccoli each week?

- If I buy 1 kg of broccoli, how many kilograms of carrots would I buy?

- The mass of the oranges I buy each week is twice the mass of the grapes I buy each week. If I buy 2 kg of oranges, what is the mass of the grapes I buy? Grapes cost £1.99 for 500 g. How much do I spend on grapes?

- Look through your food shopping receipt and pretend it is enough food for 4 people. What would the food shopping receipt show if it was for only 1 person? For 6 people? For 8 people?

You need:
- food shopping receipt
- calculator
- paper and pencil

RECEIPT

4 tins of beans	£2.40
Apples (2 kg)	£2.10
6 eggs	£1.40
Carrots (1 kg)	80p
Bacon (300 g)	£1.99
Potatoes (2.5 kg)	£3.00
Bread (800 g)	£1.20
Oranges (2 kg)	£2.50
Cheese (500 g)	£3.00
Bananas (1 kg)	70p
Grapes	
Broccoli	

 Please help your child by reading the instructions and doing the activity together.

Rising Stars Mathematics Year 4 © Rising Stars UK Ltd 2016

13c Play date

- Write the names of 4 friends you could invite over to play.

- You could play in your bedroom, in your living room or outside.

- You could build with bricks, play an imaginary game, do some craft or play with a ball.

- How many combinations are there, e.g. with Jan play with the bricks in the living room, and so on?

Make up your own problem, e.g. use the letters in your name and your friends' names to make different words. How many different words with 5 letters can you make with them?

 Please help your child by reading the instructions and doing the activity together.

14a Making a den!

- Clear out a corner in the shape of a rectangle in your bedroom or in another room, with help from an adult.

- Measure the length and width of the rectangle. Calculate its perimeter and area.

- Use some pieces of furniture (e.g. sofa, table and chairs) to build the den. Turn chairs so they face outward to make more space in the den. Place a sheet over the furniture. Use heavy books to keep the sheet in place.

- Can you predict the perimeter and area of your sheet? Measure its length and width and calculate the exact perimeter and area. Were your predictions close?

- To make the den more comfortable, put 2 different size pillows or cushions inside it. Choose pillows that have rectangle faces. Measure their sides and calculate their area and perimeter.

- Make a sketch of your den on squared paper. Can you rearrange the furniture to make a different den with the same area? Sketch the new den and calculate its perimeter.

Please help your child by reading the instructions and doing the activity together.

You need:

- furniture for den making
- metre stick or tape measure
- squared paper
- paper and pencil
- an adult

Rising Stars Mathematics Year 4 © Rising Stars UK Ltd 2016

14a Lengths and widths of rectangles

Pattern 1

☐ 1 cm

- Look at the shapes in Pattern 1. What is the width and length of each shape? What do you notice?

- Find the perimeter and area of each shape. Write the values in the table.

- Is there a pattern? Can you predict what the 5th shape will be? And the 10th?

You need:

- paper and pencil

	Shape 1	Shape 2	Shape 3	Shape 4	Shape 5	Shape 10
Perimeter (cm)	4					
Area (cm²)	1					

Pattern 2

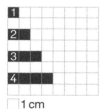

- Look at the shapes in Pattern 2. What is the width and length of each shape? What do you notice?

- Find the perimeter and area of each shape. Write the values in a table like the one for Pattern 1.

- Is there a pattern? Can you predict what the 5th shape will be? And the 10th?

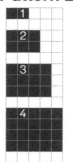

Please help your child by reading the instructions and doing the activity together.

Rising Stars Mathematics Year 4 © Rising Stars UK Ltd 2016

14b Making angles

- Fold a piece of paper so that you make 2 straight lines. Cut the paper.

- Look at the 3 shapes you made. Can you name them?

- Describe the angles in each polygon. Place a letter on each angle. Write them in order starting with the smallest.

Example

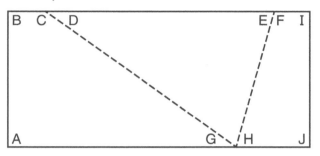

- Cut another piece of paper so that the new shapes have only right angles.

- Next try to cut a piece of paper so that the new shapes have no right angles.

 Please help your child by reading the instructions and doing the activity together.

Rising Stars Mathematics Year 4 © Rising Stars UK Ltd 2016

14b Collage calendar

You need:
- ruler
- old magazines/ wrapping paper
- calendar tabs (or similar)
- scissors
- glue
- A4 paper and pencil

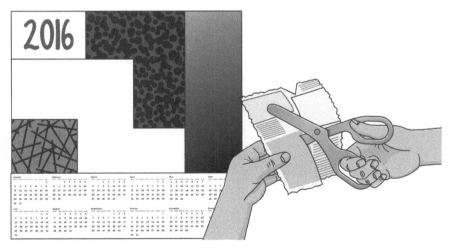

- Cut different size rectangles out of old magazines.

- Measure their perimeters.

- Place the rectangles on an A4 sheet of paper to make rectilinear shapes.

- Calculate the perimeters of each rectilinear shape. Is it the same as the sum of the perimeter of the rectangles that it was made of? Explain your answer.

- Make a calendar out of the rectilinear shapes. Leave enough space for the year and months.

 Please help your child by reading the instructions and doing the activity together.

Aliens

You need:
- cm squared paper
- paper and pencil
- a partner

- Each square has an area of 1 cm squared. Place the aliens in order starting with the one that has the smallest area.

- Work out the perimeter of each alien.

- Draw any lines of symmetry on each alien.

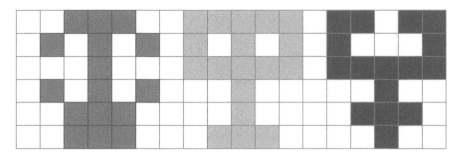

- Take it in turns to draw half of an alien that has an area of 24 squares. Does your alien have a vertical or a horizontal line of symmetry or both?

- Your partner must complete the drawing and state the perimeter of your alien.

 Please help your child by reading the instructions and doing the activity together.

Rising Stars Mathematics Year 4 © Rising Stars UK Ltd 2016

Investigating areas

You need:
- cm squared paper
- scissors
- pencil

- 4 rectangles have been cut out of a square piece of paper which is 16 cm long. Each rectangle has a length of 12 cm and the length is 3 times longer than the width. Find the area of each rectangle.

- Find the total area of all 4 rectangles.

- Find the area of the white square in the middle of the paper. Is there another way to do this?

- Cut out the 4 rectangles. Make different shapes by using some or all the 4 rectangles and the white square so that each shape has at least 1 line of symmetry.

- Draw all the shapes. What is their area?

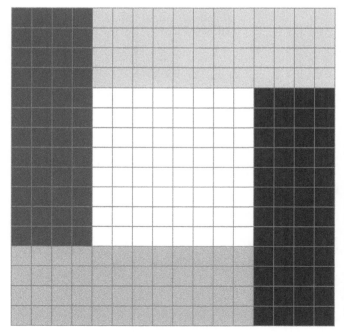

Please help your child by reading the instructions and doing the activity together.

Rising Stars Mathematics Year 4 © Rising Stars UK Ltd 2016

Homework sheets answers

Homework 5 2a

Addition codes

500 + 629 = 1129

350 + 1002 = 1352, 1100 + 240 = 1340,
1200 + 2200 = 3400, 2005 + 3185 = 5190

523 + 3500 = 4023, 4200 + 2800 = 7000

1250 + 1250 = 2500, 3000 + 2190 = 5190, 1526 + 1536 = 3062

I love my pet.

Homework 6 2a

Addition pyramids

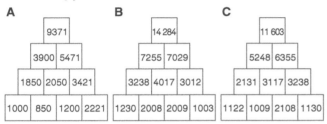

Homework 7 2b

Journeys

Difference between plane and coach: 9822 – 4480 = 5342p or
£98.22 – £44.80 = £53.42; difference between train and car: 7200 – 6999 = 201p
or £72.00 – £69.99 = £2.01; length of each journey: plane 1 h 15 min,
train 3 h 5 min, coach 7 h, car 7 h 30 min

Homework 9 3a

Christmas tree

30 cm, 60 cm, 90 cm

Homework 10 3a

Counting in sixes, nines and twelves

1	2	3	4	5	(6)	7	8	(9)	10
11	(12)	13	14	15	16	17	(18)	19	20
21	(22)	23	(24)	25	26	(27)	28	29	(30)
31	32	33	34	35	(36)	37	38	39	(40)
41	(42)	43	44	(45)	46	47	(48)	49	50
51	52	53	(54)	55	56	(57)	58	59	(60)
61	62	(63)	64	65	(66)	67	68	69	70
71	(72)	73	74	75	76	77	(78)	79	80
(81)	82	83	(84)	85	86	87	88	89	(90)
91	92	(93)	94	95	(96)	97	98	(99)	100

Multiples of both 6 and 9: 18, 36, 54, 72, 90; multiples of both 6 and 12: 12,
24, 36, 48, 60, 72, 84, 96; multiples of both 9 and 12: 36, 72

Homework 12 3b

Multiplying puzzle

(5)	(9)	45
<3>	[2]	6
<3>	<3>	(9)
45	54	

Possible answers include: 240 = 10 × 24, 5 × 48, 40 × 6, 8 × 30, 120 × 2;
240 = 2 × 3 × 40 . There are 10 ways for 2 factors and 33 ways for 3 factors.

Homework 14 3c

Multiplying choir

112, £538, 11:26 a.m.

Homework 15 4a

Investigating angles

Acute

Obtuse

Right angle

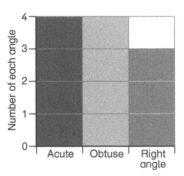

All right angles are equal. Not all acute and obtuse angles are equal as they can
be many different sizes.

Homework 16 4a

Pizza angles

Example answers:

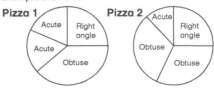

Homework 17 4b

True triangles

false, true, false

Homework 22 4d

Triangle pictures

Triangles that have 3 lines of symmetry have equal sides.

Homework 23 5a

Holiday calculations

28 days, 35 and 42 years old, 21 hours, £84, 15 days

Homework 26 5b

Comparing masses

1 heaviest	2	3	4	5	6 lightest
dog	cat	rabbit	guinea pig	squirrel	hamster

Homework 29 6a

Using train timetables

Isabella Train 1. Jake Train 3.

Homework 31 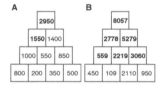 6b

Building pyramids

A

| 2950 |
1550	1400
1000	550	850
800	200	350	500

B

| 8057 |
2778	5279
559	2219	3060
450	109	2110	950

C There are various ways to get to 8500.

Homework 33 6c

Money problems

£5.02; £37.02; yes

Homework 35 7a

Quick fire fractions

Equivalences:

$\frac{7}{14} = \frac{9}{18} = \frac{3}{6} = \frac{20}{40} = \frac{5}{10} = \frac{14}{28} = \frac{16}{32} = \frac{1}{2}$

$\frac{27}{36} = \frac{18}{24} = \frac{12}{16} = \frac{3}{4} = \frac{6}{8} = \frac{36}{48}$

$\frac{7}{8} = \frac{14}{16} = \frac{35}{40} = \frac{70}{80} = \frac{21}{24} = \frac{28}{32} = \frac{77}{88}$

$\frac{2}{5} = \frac{6}{15} = \frac{4}{10} = \frac{10}{25} = \frac{12}{30} = \frac{14}{35} = \frac{20}{50} = \frac{22}{55}$

$\frac{5}{6} = \frac{10}{12} = \frac{15}{18} = \frac{30}{36} = \frac{50}{60}$

Homework 36 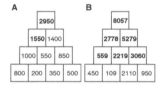 7a

Fractions code

a $\frac{6}{9}$ or $\frac{2}{3}$

b $\frac{7}{7}$ or 1

c $\frac{6}{7}$

d $\frac{5}{6}$

e $\frac{2}{6}$ or $\frac{1}{3}$

f $\frac{3}{4}$

g $\frac{1}{2}$ or $\frac{2}{4}$

h $\frac{9}{12}$ or $\frac{3}{4}$

i $\frac{6}{12}$ or $\frac{1}{2}$

j $\frac{4}{8}$ or $\frac{1}{2}$

k $\frac{3}{8}$

l $\frac{2}{8}$ or $\frac{1}{4}$

HIPPOPOTAMUS

Homework 38 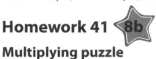 8b

Stationery shopping

Pencils – Shop A; Rubbers – Shop B;
Rulers – Shop A; Pens – Shop B; Glue – Shop A

Homework 41 8b

Multiplying puzzle

8	×	2	×	6	=	96
=		=		=		=
4		2	×	6	=	12
×		×		×		×
2	×	1	×	1	=	2
		×				×
0	=	1	×	0	×	4

Homework 43 8c

Market problems

Huan: £2.24; Josh: no, he had 180 + 350 = 530p and spent (95 × 4) + (50 × 4) = 580p so needed 50p more; Vicki: 588 oranges, £294; Sam: 513 sausage rolls, £1026

Homework 45 8d

What number?

1 46

2 108

3 1

4 100

5 20

Homework 46 8d

Cupcake recipe

Number of cupcakes	Eggs	Sugar (g)	Flour (g)	Butter (g)	Milk (ml)	Icing butter (g)	Icing sugar (g)	Icing milk (ml)
8	2	84	80	76	34	100	156	24
16	4	168	160	152	68	200	312	48
24	6	252	240	228	102	300	468	72

Homework 47 9a

Trapeziums: true or false?

1 false

2 true

3 true

4 false

Homework 51 10a

Secret word!

a 175

b 9110

c 5789

d 3345

e 10 276

f 18 890

g 200

h 300

i 500

j 175

SNOWFLAKES

Homework 52

Populations

	Dorchester	Uckfield	Wellington	Whittburn	North Ashton	Kingsbridge	Long Ashton
Size order	19 060	15 213	11 213	10 527	10 227	6116	5254
+1000	20 060	16 213	12 213	11 527	11 227	7116	6254
−1000	18 060	14 213	10 213	9527	9227	5116	4254

Homework 57

Magic squares

356	**801**	178
267	445	**623**
712	89	534

5600	100	7800
6700	**4500**	**2300**
1200	**8900**	3400

Homework 58

Calculating sales

Season	Month	Ice-creams	Cakes	Total
Winter	December	1750	3500	5250
	January	300	1500	1800
	February	280	1200	1480
Spring	March	290	1330	1620
	April	350	1800	2150
	May	2200	1780	3980
Summer	June	2500	1500	4000
	July	3000	780	3780
	August	3800	1900	5700
Autumn	September	1470	2670	4140
	October	1000	1160	2160
	November	800	1230	2030

1 6970 more ice-creams

2 2070

3 4140

4 see table

5 August highest sales = 5700,
February lowest sales = 1480,
difference = 4220

Homework 59

True or false?

$\frac{2}{5} = \frac{24}{60}$	**T**	$\frac{5}{15} = \frac{8}{24}$	**T**	$\frac{1}{4} = \frac{3}{14}$	**F**	$\frac{11}{22} = \frac{33}{55}$	**F**
$\frac{6}{8} = \frac{12}{16}$	**T**	$\frac{1}{3} = \frac{2}{5}$	**F**	$\frac{15}{20} = \frac{5}{10}$	**F**	$\frac{1}{4} + \frac{2}{4} = \frac{6}{8}$	**T**
$\frac{1}{4} + \frac{3}{4} = 1\frac{1}{4}$	**F**	$\frac{5}{6} - \frac{3}{6} = \frac{1}{6}$	**F**	$\frac{3}{10} + \frac{5}{10} = \frac{8}{10} = \frac{4}{5}$	**T**	$\frac{3}{9} - \frac{1}{9} = \frac{1}{4}$	**F**
$1\frac{1}{4} + \frac{1}{4} = 1\frac{1}{2}$	**T**	$1\frac{7}{8} + 2\frac{3}{8} = 3\frac{1}{4}$	**F**	$3\frac{1}{8} - 1\frac{3}{8} = \frac{5}{8}$	**F**	$\frac{3}{5} + \frac{3}{5} = 1\frac{1}{5}$	**T**
$\frac{10}{60} = \frac{30}{80}$	**F**	$1\frac{1}{2} - 1\frac{1}{4} = \frac{1}{4}$	**T**	$\frac{14}{49} = \frac{6}{21} = \frac{2}{7}$	**T**	$1 - \frac{2}{8} = \frac{1}{8}$	**F**

Homework 60

Fractions and decimals memory game

$\frac{1}{5} = \frac{2}{10} = \frac{6}{30} = 0.2$

$\frac{1}{2} = \frac{10}{20} = 0.5 = \frac{16}{32}$

$0.08 = \frac{8}{100} = \frac{4}{50} = \frac{2}{25}$

$\frac{3}{10} = 0.3 = \frac{15}{50} = \frac{30}{100}$

$0.25 = \frac{25}{100} = \frac{1}{4} = \frac{2}{8}$

$0.16 = \frac{16}{100} = \frac{8}{50} = \frac{4}{25}$

$0.06 = \frac{6}{100} = \frac{3}{50} = \frac{12}{100}$

Homework 64

Alien problems

6 dogs and 4 cats; 1 female and 7 males or 15 females and 1 male; 27 birds and 3 butterflies; 4 spiders and 4 ants

Homework 65

At the cinema

1 £41

2 £2.56

3 No, he needed £5.94 more

4 306

5 366

Homework 67

Shopping

250 g, 50p, 4 kg, 1 kg, £3.98

Homework 68

Play date

There are 12 combinations for each friend and there are 4 friends and the host, so 60 combinations in total.

Homework 70

Lengths and widths of rectangles

Pattern 1

	Shape 1	Shape 2	Shape 3	Shape 4	Shape 5	Shape 10
Perimeter (cm)	4	6	8	10	12	22
Area (cm²)	1	2	3	4	5	10

Pattern 2

	Shape 1	Shape 2	Shape 3	Shape 4	Shape 5	Shape 10
Perimeter (cm)	6	10	14	18	22	42
Area (cm²)	2	6	12	20	30	110

Homework 73

Aliens

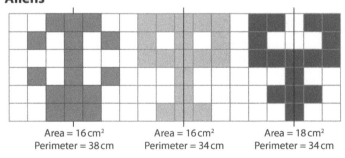

Area = 16 cm²
Perimeter = 38 cm

Area = 16 cm²
Perimeter = 34 cm

Area = 18 cm²
Perimeter = 34 cm

Homework 74

Investigating areas

Area of each rectangle = 48 cm², 4 rectangles = 192 cm²,
area of white square = 64 cm², total area = 256 cm²

Glossary of mathematical terms

1, 2, 3

2-dimensional (2-D)
Points in 2-dimensional space lie on a flat surface.

3-dimensional (3-D)
Points in 3-dimensional space occupy a space or a volume.

5, 10, 15... minutes past
Ways of counting minutes on an analogue clock. The minute hand takes five minutes to move between each hour mark on the clock face. See also *analogue clock*.

12-hour time
Counting hours of the day in two blocks of twelve. 12.01-12 noon as a.m. and 12.01-12 midnight as p.m. Often told on a 12-hour clock and known as analogue time.

24-hour time
Counting hours of the day from 0-24. Used on digital clocks. 2 p.m. is written as 14:00.

A

a.m.
From Latin ante-meridian, meaning before midday. See also *12-hour time*.

above/below zero
Temperatures are measured relative to 0°C – the freezing point of water, e.g. 4° below zero is –4°C.

acute angle
An angle between 0° and 90°. See also *obtuse, reflex angle*.

add
A mathematical operation to increase one number (the augend) by another to give the sum.

addend
The number being added in an addition calculation. See also *augend*.

addition
A mathematical operation combining two or more numbers to find a total. Augend + addend = sum (or total).

addition fact
An addition statement likely to be frequently used, so worth memorising.

algebra
Generalised calculation using symbols (variables) instead of numbers. It can be used to prove statements and show general relationships.

analogue clock
A dial with hands used to show time. The dial shows 12 hours in a full circle. The minute hand moves one complete turn every hour. Times on these clocks are read, e.g. 20 past five or five to four.

angle
The amount of turn between two straight lines that meet at a point. Usually measured in degrees. Symbol: °. See also *acute, obtuse, reflex angle*.

anticlockwise
A rotation or turn in the opposite direction to the movement of the hands on a clock. See also *clockwise*.

approximate, approximately
A number that is not exact, e.g. 2028 is approximately 2000. Symbol: ≈.

arc
Part of the circumference of a circle.

area
The 2-D measure of the size of a surface. Measured in 'square' units: mm², cm², m², km².

array
An arrangement of numbers, shapes or objects in rows of equal size and columns of equal size, used to find out how many altogether.

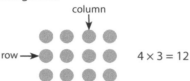

$4 \times 3 = 12$

ascending/descending order
Ascending order: rank values from smallest to largest.
Descending order: rank values from largest to smallest.

associative law
A mathematical law or rule where numbers can be grouped in different ways when adding or multiplying, without changing the total, e.g. $(a + b) + c = a + (b + c)$ and $(a \times b) \times c = a \times (b \times c)$.

augend
The number being added to in an addition calculation. See also *addend*.

average
The middle value of a set of numbers. It is found by adding all the numbers together and dividing by how many numbers there are. See also *mean*.

axis, axes
Scale lines, usually vertical and horizontal, used to define positions of points on a grid or graph.

axis of symmetry
An axis of symmetry divides the shape into two identical parts. Also called a mirror line.

B

balance
Things are balanced when both sides have equal value, e.g. 1000 g = 1 kg, 3 + 6 = 10 – 1.

bar chart
A statistical diagram using bars to show the frequency of outcomes.

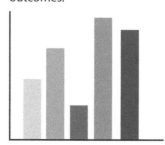

bar line chart
A statistical diagram using lines to show the frequency of discrete outcomes.

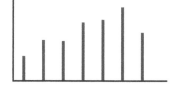

base, square-based
The flat surface underneath a 3-D shape. A square-based pyramid has one square base and four triangular faces.

Base 10 system
This is another name for the decimal number system. It increases and decreases by powers of 10. When we multiply a number by, e.g. 10, the digits move one place to the left because the number is made ten times bigger. When we divide by, e.g. 100, the number is 100 times smaller and the digits move two places to the right.

block diagram
A diagram showing statistical information. Each block stands for one object or event.

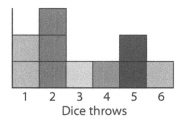
Dice throws

breadth
The same as width.

C

calendar
A list of the days of the year, arranged by month, week and day.

capacity
The amount a container can hold, e.g. the capacity of a 2 l bottle is 2 litres, the capacity of a football stadium is the amount of people it will hold. See also *volume*.

Carroll diagram
A Carroll diagram sorts objects according to a criteria and not that criteria. Can be several criteria but always the criteria and not the criteria, e.g. odd numbers/not odd numbers, multiples of 5/not multiples of 5, dogs/not dogs.

category
A group of elements or numbers all with the same property, e.g. dogs, cats, rats are all in the category 'animals'.

Celsius
A scale used to measure temperature. Sometimes called Centigrade. Units are °C.

centilitre
One hundredth of a litre. Symbol: cl. 100 cl = 1 l.

centimetre
A unit of length, $\frac{1}{100}$ of 1 metre. Symbol: cm.

centre
A point at the exact middle of a shape. The centre of a circle is the same distance from all points on its circumference.

century
100 years.

change
The money left over when buying something with a note or coin bigger than the amount needed. The change is given back to the buyer.

chart
A statistical diagram.

circle, circular
A set of points that are all a fixed distance (the radius) from a point (the centre). Like a circle.

circumference
The perimeter of a circle. The set of points a fixed distance from the centre of a circle. See also *arc*.

clock, clock face, hands
A clock is used to show and record time. It can have a circular face with revolving hands to mark hours and minutes, or it can have a digital display.

clockwise
A rotation or turn in the same direction as the movement of the hands on a clock. See also *anticlockwise*.

column
A vertical list of elements or numbers, usually in a table or an array.

combinations
Different combinations made from a selection, e.g. the various different outfits which can be made by choosing one hat and one coat to wear from three hats and four coats.

commutative
Addition and multiplication are commutative. It doesn't matter which way you add or multiply in, the answer is always the same. Same answer, different calculation, e.g. $3 + 4 = 4 + 3$. But subtraction and division are not commutative, e.g. $7 - 2 \neq 2 - 7$.

compound number
A number that is not a prime number.

compound shape
A compound shape consists of two or more simple shapes such as a triangle placed on a square or oblong on top of a square. Also known as a composite shape.

concentric
Circles which share the same centre.

cone
A 3-D shape with a flat, circular face and a curved face. It has one apex directly above the circular base.

congruent
Shapes are congruent if they are exactly the same shape and size.

consecutive
Numbers that follow each other in a linear pattern, e.g. 3, 4, 5; 60, 70, 80; 17, 19, 21.

Glossary

construct

To draw a shape accurately using a ruler, compasses and a protractor.

coordinate

An ordered pair of (x, y) values that define the position of a point on a Cartesian plane. In 3-D (x, y, z).

corner

A point on a 2-D shape where sides meet. Properly called a vertex (plural, vertices).

cube

A 3-D shape made from six identical squares which all meet at right angles, e.g. a cube of sugar.

cube number, cubed

Formed when a number is multiplied by itself and then by itself again. 2 cubed = $2 \times 2 \times 2 = 8$. The cube numbers are a sequence $1^3, 2^3, 3^3$ and so on, which gives the numbers 1, 8, 27, 64, 125 and so on. See also *square number*.

cubic millimetres (mm³), cubic centimetres (cm³), cubic metres (m³), cubic kilometres (km³)

Metric measurements of liquid and solid volume. 1 mm³ is the volume enclosed in a cube of length 1 mm, etc.

cuboid

A 3-D shape made from six rectangles. Two or four of the rectangles could be squares, e.g. a cereal box. A cube is a special sort of cuboid.

currency

A money system. In the UK, the currency is pounds sterling (£). In the EU, the currency is the euro (€).

curved

A line that is not straight, e.g. a circle, or a surface that is not flat, e.g. an egg.

curved surface

A surface of a 3-D shape which is not flat, e.g. the surface of a sphere or cylinder.

cylinder, cylindrical

A 3-D object with circular ends and a uniform cross-section. The top is vertically above the base. Like a cylinder.

D

data

Numbers collected from a questionnaire or survey. Pieces of information usually represented in a special way, e.g. on bar charts and pie charts.

database

A method of storing data, often in large tables on a computer.

date

How we record the passing of time. Usually given as day of the month, month and then year, e.g. 3rd April 2015.

decimal, decimal fraction, decimal point, decimal place, decimal equivalent

Fractions as tenths, hundredths and so on represented as digits after a decimal point, e.g. 0.253 is equivalent to $\frac{2}{10} + \frac{5}{100} + \frac{3}{1000}$ or $\frac{253}{1000}$.

degree

Symbol: °. A unit used to measure the size of an angle. There are 360° in one complete turn. Also a unit of temperature.

denominator

The number underneath the vinculum in a fraction. Also called the divisor.

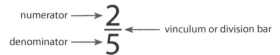

numerator ⟶ $\frac{2}{5}$ ⟵ vinculum or division bar
denominator ⟶

diagonal

A straight line inside a shape that goes from one corner to another (but not an edge).

diagram

A sketch or accurate drawing of a mathematical shape or problem.

diameter

A line passing across a circle, or a sphere, which passes through the centre. See also *radius*.

difference

The result of a subtraction. The difference between 12 and 5 is 7. See also *minuend, subtrahend*.

digit

A symbol from 0–9 in the decimal system. Used to show value. The value of each digit depends on its position, e.g. in 200, the digit 2 represents two hundreds.

digit total/sum

The sum of all the digits in a number, e.g. the digit sum of 435 is $4 + 3 + 5 = 12$. This carries on to $1 + 2 = 3$, so the digit total of 435 is 3.

digital clock, digital time

A system that shows the time as numbers. It can use the 12-hour or the 24-hour clock. 6 o'clock in the evening would show as 06.00 p.m. or 18:00.

discount

A reduction offered on the price of an item for sale.

distance apart ... between ... to ... from

The length of the shortest line joining two points.

distribution

In statistics. The distribution of a set of values.

distributive law

When adding or multiplying, the numbers can be rearranged to support calculating, e.g. $2 \times 13 \times 5 = (2 \times 5) \times 13 = 10 \times 13 = 130$ and $a(b + c) = ab + ac$.

dividend

The number that is divided in a division calculation, e.g. in $12 \div 6 = 2$, 12 is the dividend. See also *denominator, division bracket, divisor, quotient*.

dividing

The process of division.

divisibility

Whether a number can be divided without remainder. All even numbers are divisible by 2.

division

A mathematical operation which groups a number into a given number of parts, e.g. $12 \div 4$ is 12 divided into four parts each of value 3. It is the inverse operation to multiplication.

division bracket

The half box around the dividend in a division. See also *dividend*.

division fact

A division statement likely to be frequently used, so worth memorising.

division (on a scale)
The intervals on a scale, on a ruler or a graph axis.

divisor
The number that is used to divide in a division sum, e.g. in 12 ÷ 6 = 2, 6 is the divisor. See also *denominator, dividend, quotient.*

dodecahedron
A 3-D polyhedron with 12 faces. A regular dodecahedron has pentagonal faces.

double
To multiply by 2.

E

edge
The line made where two faces of a 3-D shape meet.
See also *face, vertex.*

eighths
The fraction of a whole obtained when it is shared into eight equal pieces.

equal sharing
To divide a number or set of items into equal parts.

equals
Symbol: =. Is the same as and equivalent to, e.g. 5 + 3 = 7 + 1.

equation
A mathematical statement showing an equality,
e.g. $10 \times 2 = 4 \times 5$ or $2x + 6 = 16$.

equilateral triangle
A triangle with three equal sides and three equal angles of 60°.

equivalent, equivalent to
Symbol: ≡. Two numbers or expressions that are equal, but which can be in a different form, e.g. £1 ≡ 100p.

equivalent fractions
Fractions with the same value, e.g. $\frac{1}{4} = \frac{2}{8} = \frac{3}{12}$. These are equivalent fractions.

estimate
An approximate answer, often used to check a complex calculation.

even
A whole number which is divisible by 2. It is a multiple of 2. See also *odd.*

F

face
A flat surface of a 3-D shape. See also *edge* and *vertex.*

factor
Numbers that divide exactly into a number are its factors, e.g. the factors of 12 are 1, 2, 3, 4, 6, 12.

factor pair
Two factors that multiply together to give the number. The factor pairs of 12 are $1 \times 12, 2 \times 6, 3 \times 4$.

factorise
To write a number or algebraic expression as a product of two or more factors.

flat
In 2-D and faces of 3-D shapes, not curved.

foot, feet
An imperial unit of length, approximately 30 cm.
12 inches = 1 foot and 3 feet = 1 yard.

formula, formulae
A mathematical sentence using letters or symbols (variables),
e.g. area of a rectangle = length × width or $a = l \times w$.

fraction
Part of a whole, written as one number divided by another. In the fraction $\frac{3}{5}$, the numerator 3 is above the vinculum and the denominator 5 is below.

frequency table
A statistical table listing various outcomes and the frequency that they occur.

G

gallon
An imperial measure of capacity. 1 gallon is approximately 4.5 litres. See also *pint.*

gram
Symbol: g. A unit of mass. There are 1000 grams in a kilogram. See also *kilogram.*

graph
A diagram showing the relationship between two sets of numbers.

greater than
Also called more than. Symbol: >. Used when comparing the size of two quantities or measures. 10 is greater than 7, or 10 > 7. See also *less than.*

greater than or equal to
Symbol: ≥. An inequality showing the lowest value a number can take. $n \geq 7$ means n can have any value from 7 upwards. See also *less than or equal to.*

greatest value, least value
The highest or lowest value that can occur.

grouping
To divide, objects and numbers can be shared or grouped. Grouping is putting objects or numbers into groups of a particular size.

H

half
When a whole is divided into two equal parts.

half past
A measure of time. Half (an hour) past, so half past 5 is the same as 5:30 and 30 minutes past 5. See also *o'clock.*

halfway between
The midpoint between two values, e.g. 15 is halfway between 10 and 20.

heavier than, lighter than
Comparing two masses or weights, e.g. 4 kg is heavier than 3 kg, 3 kg is lighter than 4 kg.

heaviest, lightest
Comparing two or more masses or weights, e.g. of 5 kg, 6 kg and 10 kg, 5 kg is the lightest, 10 kg is the heaviest.

heavy, light
Words used to compare mass or weight.

Glossary

hemisphere
Half of a sphere.

heptagon, heptagonal
A 2-D shape with seven straight sides.

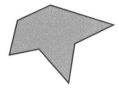

hexagon, hexagonal
A 2-D shape with six straight sides.

hollow
Having an outline or surface that curves inwards, e.g. the inside of a hemisphere.

horizontal
Parallel to the horizon. See also *vertical*.

hour
Symbol: h. A measure of time. There are 24 hours in a day and 60 minutes in one hour. See also *minute*, *second*.

hour hand
The hand on a clock that measures the hours. One complete revolution takes 12 hours. See also *minute hand*.

hundred
One hundred, 100, is ten tens or one more than 99.

hundred thousand
100 000.

hundreds
The position in a number where the digit represents hundreds, e.g. in 278 there is a digit 2 in the hundreds place, so there are 2 hundreds.

hundreds boundary
When counting from tens to hundreds, the hundreds boundary is crossed.

hundredths
A fraction $\frac{1}{100}$ or 0.01.

I

imperial unit
A non-metric unit of measure, e.g. inches, yards, miles, pints. Many are still in common use.

in every, for every
A way of expressing proportion (in every) and ratio (for every), e.g. One in every ten pupils has a dog; For every teacher there are 15 students. See also *ratio*.

inch, inches
An imperial unit of length, approximately 2.5 cm. 12 inches = 1 foot.

integer, positive, negative
An integer is a whole number which can be positive or negative, e.g. –4, –2, 4, 100.

intersecting, intersection
Where two lines or curves cross.

inverse
Inverse operations leave the original value unchanged. The inverse of + 4 is – 4. The inverse of × 4 is ÷ 4 or × $\frac{1}{4}$. The inverse 'undoes' the action.

irregular
Not regular. A shape with sides and angles that are not equal.

isosceles triangle
A triangle with two equal sides and two equal base angles. A right-angled isosceles triangle has one right angle.

K

kilogram
Symbol: kg. A unit of mass. There are 1000 grams in a kilogram. See also *gram*.

kilometre
A metric measure of distance. 1 km = 1000 m.

kite
A quadrilateral with two pairs of equal adjacent sides.

L

least popular, least common
In statistics. The value or outcome that happens least often. See also *most common*.

length, height, width, depth
Words used to describe lengths of lines and shapes, e.g. a cuboid has length 5 cm, width 3 cm and height 6 cm.

less than
Used when comparing the size of two quantities or measures, e.g. 7 is less than 10. See also *more than*.

less than or equal to
Symbol: ≤. An inequality showing the highest value a number can take. $n \leq 7$ means n can have any value up to and including 7. See also *greater than or equal to*.

line
A line is straight. It has no thickness and extends in both directions without ending.

line graph
A statistical graph with a continuous line showing the trend or variation in a value.

line segment
Part of a line that has a starting and ending point.

line symmetry
A 2-D object has line symmetry if it can be folded into two identical halves along a mirror line. Each half is a mirror image of the other.

line of symmetry

linear number sequence
A sequence of numbers that increases by a constant difference, e.g. 9, 13, 17, 21, 25, and so on.

litre
Symbol: l. A measure of capacity. 1000 millilitres = 1 litre.

long, longer, longest
A comparison of lengths, e.g. a line is 3 cm, 3 cm is longer than 2 cm. Three lines are 4 cm, 6 cm and 8 cm. The longest length is 8 cm.

M

mass
A metric measure of the amount of matter in an object. Measured in grams (g), kilograms (kg) or tonnes (t). The mass of an object does not change, but its weight alters with any changes in the force of gravity.

maximum/minimum value
The largest/smallest value a number or variable can take.

mean
A measure of average. Mean = total of all data values ÷ number of data points. See also *median, range*.

measure, measurement
The size of a unit, e.g. we can measure area in square metres. Also means the act of measuring something.

measuring cylinder
A graduated cylinder for measuring volume and capacity accurately.

measuring scale
A way of measuring using a line or a dial with equal divisions, like on a ruler.

median
A measure of average. The middle number or value when all the elements of the data set are in ascending (or descending) order. If there is no middle value, then the mean of the two middle values. See also *mean, mode, range*.

mental calculation
Doing a calculation in your head, but perhaps with jottings.

metre
Symbol: m. A unit of length equal to 100 centimetres. 100 centimetres = 1 metre.

metric unit
Any unit used to measure on a metric scale, e.g. kilograms, centimetres, litres. All based on the decimal system.

mile
An imperial measure of distance. Used in the UK and US to measure distances between places. 5 miles is approximately equivalent to 8 kilometres.

millennium
A thousand years (10 centuries).

millilitre
Symbol: ml. A measure of capacity. 1000 millilitres = 1 litre.

millimetre
One thousandth of a metre. 1000 mm = 1 m.

million
1 000 000.

minuend
The starting number in a subtraction calculation, e.g. 10 (the minuend) – 3 (the subtrahend) = 7 (the difference). See also *subtrahend, difference*.

minus
Symbol. Another word for subtract.

minute
Symbol: min. A measure of time. See also *second, hour*.

minute hand
The hand on a clock face that measures the minutes. One complete revolution takes 60 minutes (one hour). See also *hour hand*.

mixed number
A number with both a whole number part and a fractional part, e.g. $3\frac{1}{2}$.

money
Coins and notes used to buy goods and services.

more than
Also called greater than. Symbol: >. Used when comparing the size of two quantities or measures. 10 is more than 7 or 10 > 7. See also *less than*.

more than or equal to
Symbol: ≥. An inequality showing the lowest value a number can take. $n \geq 7$ means n can have any value from 7 upwards. See also *less than or equal to*.

most common
In statistics. The most frequently occurring outcome. See also *least common*.

multiple, multiple of
A multiple is the product of two numbers, e.g. the multiples of 7 are 7, 14, 21, 28 and so on.

multiplicand
A number to be multiplied, e.g. in $6 \times 3 = 18$, 6 is the multiplicand. See also *multiplier*.

multiplication
A mathematical operation.

multiplication fact
A multiplication statement likely to be frequently used, so worth memorising, e.g. the multiplication table.

multiplication table
A list of multiplication facts for a given multiple, often learned by heart.

multiplier
The multiplying number, e.g. in $6 \times 3 = 18$, 3 is the multiplier. See also *multiplicand*.

multiply
Symbol: ×. A mathematical process equivalent to repeated addition, e.g. $2 \times 4 = 2 + 2 + 2 + 2 = 8$ or repeated grouping.

N

negative numbers
Numbers below zero on the number line. Read as negative 1, negative 2 and so on. See also *integer*.

net (open, closed)
The compound shape resulting from opening out a 3-D shape to show its 2-D faces and how they are connected. A one-piece set of connected 2-D shapes which can be folded to make a 3-D shape.

nth term
An algebraic expression that gives the value of any term in a sequence from its position in the sequence. An unknown value.

number
A label given to a quantity, using numerals. There are many different types of number, including counting numbers 0, 1, 2, 3 and so on; fractions; negative numbers; ordinal numbers.

Glossary

number bonds/pairs
Pairs of numbers with a particular total, e.g. the number bonds for 10 are all pairs of whole numbers, like 2 and 8, which add up to 10.

number statement
A mathematical statement using numbers, also called a number sentence, e.g. 4 + 5 − 1 = 8.

numeral
A symbol used to represent a number. We use arabic numerals 0-9, but there are also Roman numerals and other systems.

numerator
The number above the vinculum in a fraction.

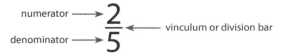

numerator ⟶ $\frac{2}{5}$ ⟵ vinculum or division bar
denominator ⟶

 O

oblong
An irregular rectangle. A 2-D shape with two pairs of opposite sides that are equal and the angles are 90°. See also *square*.

obtuse angle
An angle between 90° and 180°. See also *acute, reflex angle*.

octagon, octagonal
A 2-D shape with eight straight sides.

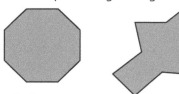

o'clock
A way of describing an exact hour time, e.g. 5 o'clock means the time is 5:00. See also *half past*.

octahedron, octahedral
A 3-D shape with eight triangular faces.

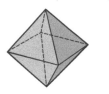

odd
A whole number which has a remainder of 1 when divided by 2. It is not a multiple of 2. See also *even*.

one hundred less/more
A number one hundred whole units more or less than another number. 900 is a hundred less than 1000 and 100 more than 800.

one less
The number one whole before that number on an number line, e.g. 9 is one less than 10.

one more
The number one whole after that number on a number line, e.g. 9 is one more than 8.

one third
A fraction obtained when a whole is divided into three equal parts.

ones
When counting individual items, the next counting number is allocated to the set each time one more is counted. 9 is the largest number of ones. See also *single-digit*.

ones boundary
When counting from a decimal to a whole number, the ones boundary is crossed. See also *tenths boundary*.

ordinal number
A number that tells the order of something, e.g. in a list 1st, 2nd, 3rd, and so on.

ounce
An imperial measure of mass. Symbol: oz. 1 ounce is approximately 28 g. 16 oz = 1 pound.

outcome
One of the possible results from a statistical experiment or trial, e.g. when tossing a coin there are two equally-likely outcomes: heads or tails.

P

p.m.
From Latin post-meridian, meaning after midday. 14:00 on the 24-hour clock is 2:00 p.m. See also *12-hour time*.

parallel
Lines that are the same distance apart and never meet.

parallelogram
A 2-D shape with two pairs of opposite sides that are equal and parallel. A rectangle is a special parallelogram, with all the angles 90°.

parts of a whole
A fraction of a whole number or object. If there are five equal parts of a whole then each part is $\frac{1}{5}$.

pattern
A regular arrangement of shapes or numbers that follows a rule.

pentagon, pentagonal
A 2-D shape with five straight sides.

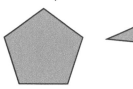

percentage, per cent, %
A fraction or mixed number expressed as hundredth parts, e.g. $\frac{1}{2} = \frac{50}{100} = 50\%$.

perimeter
The total distance measured around the outside of a 2-D shape or area. Calculated by adding the lengths of all the sides.

perpendicular
At right-angles to. Horizontal lines are always perpendicular to vertical lines.

pictogram
A picture to show statistical information. A picture is used to represent one or a number of elements.

pie chart
A statistical diagram that shows proportions of quantities as slices of a circle (a pie).

pint
An imperial measure of capacity. There are 8 pints in 1 gallon. 1 litre is approximately 1.75 pints.

place, place value
Place value has several aspects to it. One is positional, which is where the digit of a number is placed, e.g. in 345, the digit 3 is positioned in the hundreds. Another is multiplicative, which is when we multiply the digit by its position to get its true value. So the 3 in 345 is multiplied by 100 to give 300. A third is additive. This is when all the individual values of the digits are added together to give the whole number, e.g. $300 + 40 + 5 = 345$.

plane
A flat surface.

polygon
The general name for 2-D shapes with three or more straight sides. Includes triangle (three sides), quadrilateral (four sides), pentagon (five sides), and so on.

polyhedron
The general name for 3-D shapes with straight sides. Plural polyhedra. Includes tetrahedron, prisms, pyramids.

pound
An imperial measure of mass. Symbol: lb. 2.2 lb is approximately 1 kg. See also *ounce*.

prime factor
A factor of a number that is also a prime number, e.g. the prime factors of 12 are 2 and 3, since $12 = 2 \times 2 \times 3 = 2^2 \times 3$.

prime number
A number with only two factors, itself and 1. 1 is not a prime number.

prism
A 3-D shape with two identical and parallel ends, joined by rectangular faces. The cross-section of a prism is always the same shape and size as the ends.

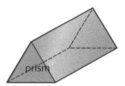

product
The result of multiplying two numbers, e.g. the product of 4 and 3 is $4 \times 3 = 12$.

profit, loss
The money made or lost in a financial transaction. Can be expressed as a money value or as a percentage.

proper/improper fraction
A proper fraction is a fraction that is less that 1, with the numerator less than the denominator, e.g. $\frac{2}{5}$. In an improper fraction, the numerator is larger than the denominator, e.g. $\frac{5}{2}$.

pyramid, square-based
A 3-D shape with a square base and four triangular faces.

Q

quadrant
One of the four regions formed by the x- and y-axes on a Cartesian graph.

quadrilateral
A 2-D shape with four straight sides.

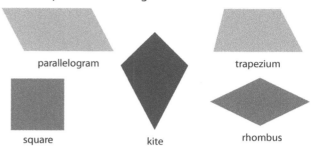

parallelogram

square

kite

trapezium

rhombus

quarter
When a whole is divided into four equal parts.

quarter past, quarter to
15 minutes past the hour or 15 minutes before the hour, e.g. quarter to 12 is 11:45, quarter past 12 is 12:15.

questionnaire
A set of questions given to people to fill in, in order to collect data for analysis. See also *survey, data*.

quotient
The answer to a division calculation, e.g. in $12 \div 6 = 2$, 2 is the quotient. See also *denominator, dividend, divisor*.

R

radius
Any straight line segment from the centre of a circle to the edge (circumference). The radius is half of the diameter. See also *diameter*.

range
A measure of statistical spread. The difference between the highest and lowest values in a set of data. See also *mean, median*.

ratio
A comparison of parts, usually expressed in its simplest form, using a colon, e.g. 12 boys and 15 girls expressed as a ratio is 12:15 or 4:5.

rectangle, rectangular
A four-sided 2-D shape with four right angles and equal opposite sides. A square is a regular rectangle with all four sides equal. An oblong is an irregular rectangle.

rectilinear
A rectangular shape.

reduced to, simplify
To reduce or simplify a fraction or ratio, divide both numbers by the highest common factor, e.g. $\frac{6}{9} = \frac{2}{3}$.

reflect, reflection
To transform an object by reflecting it in a mirror line. The image is the same shape and size as the object.

reflective symmetry
A figure or object has reflective symmetry if there is a line (2-D) or a plane (3-D) which divides the shape into two identical parts.

line of symmetry

Glossary

reflex angle
An angle greater than 180°. See also *acute, obtuse angle*.

regular
A 2-D shape with all the sides equal length and equal angles.

remainder
The number left over after a division sum, e.g. 13 ÷ 3 = 4 remainder 1.

rhombus
A 2-D shape with four equal sides and equal opposite angles.

right angle
A quarter of a full turn. 90°.

right-angled triangle
A triangle with one right angle. Can be isosceles or scalene.

Roman numerals
Numbers used by the Romans. Digits have no place value, e.g. II = 2 , VI = 6, LX = 60.

rotate, rotation
To transform an object by turning it a given direction and angle round a fixed point. The image is the same shape and size as the object.

round up, round down
A method of approximation. 37 rounds up to the nearest 10 so gives an approximation of 40, but 34 rounds down to the nearest 10 so gives an approximation of 30. Digits 4 or less round down and digits 5 or more round up, so 750 to the nearest 100 is 800.

row
A horizontal arrangement of, e.g. objects, shapes or numbers. See also *array*.

rule
An instruction for carrying out a mathematical operation or continuing a pattern. It can be written using symbols or words. See also *sequence*.

S

scalene triangle
A triangle with no equal sides or angles.

scales
A way of measuring using a line with equal divisions, like on a ruler. Also a device for measuring weight.

second
Symbol: s. A measure of time. There are 60 seconds in one minute. See also *minute, hour*.

semi-circle
Half of a circle, made from half of the curved circumference and a diameter.

sequence
A set of numbers made by following a given rule, e.g. the multiples of 3 are 3, 6, 9 and so on.

sevenths
The fraction of a whole obtained when it is cut into seven equal pieces.

shape
A 2-D or 3-D object.

sharing
A model for division, e.g. 10 ÷ 2 = 5 is 10 shared between 2, giving 5 each. Links closely with fractions, e.g. 10 shared between 2 is 5, so 5 is half of 10.

short, shorter, shortest
Words used when comparing lengths or height, e.g. a line is 3 cm, 2 cm is shorter than 3 cm, three lines are 4 cm, 6 cm and 8 cm. The shortest length is 4 cm.

side
A 2-D shape or figure has sides which are line segments. These line segments form the boundary of the shape. See also *corner*.

single-, 2-, 3-digit numbers
The number of digits in a number, e.g. 3 is a single-digit number, 13 is a 2-digit number and 213 is a 3-digit number.

sixths
The fraction of a whole obtained when it is cut into six equal pieces.

sorting
Classifying objects, shapes or numbers into groups according to their properties.

sphere, spherical
A 3-D shape where every point on the surface is the same distance from the centre, like a ball.

square
A regular quadrilateral where all the sides are equal.

square millimetre (mm²), square centimetre (cm²), square metre (m²)
Metric units of measure of area equivalent to a square 1 mm by 1 mm, a square 1 cm by 1 cm or a square 1 m by 1 m. Symbols: mm², cm² and m².

square number, squared
The square numbers are a sequence $1^2, 2^2, 3^2$, formed by multiplying each number by itself. This gives the numbers 1, 4, 9, 16, 25 and so on. See also *cube number*.

statement
A number sentence, e.g. 2 + 4 = 6.

statistics
The branch of mathematics which studies the collection, representation and interpretation of data.

subtract
To do a subtraction calculation.

subtraction
A subtraction finds the difference between two numbers. Also called taking away, e.g. 10 (the minuend) – 3 (the subtrahend) = 7 (the difference). See also *minuend*.

subtraction fact
A subtraction statement likely to be frequently used, so worth memorising.

subtrahend
The number that is subtracted from the minuend.

sum
The answer to an addition calculation. The sum of 4 and 5 is 9. See also *total*.

surface
The face or faces of a 3-D shape. They can be flat like the face of a cube or curved like a sphere.

survey
A survey collects data for analysis. See also *questionnaire, data*.

symmetry, symmetrical
A figure has line symmetry if it can be folded along a mirror line into two halves which are mirror images of each other. It has rotational symmetry if it can be rotated to give an identical shape.

line of symmetry

T

table
An arrangement of numbers or objects in rows and columns. See also *array*.

take away
Another name for subtraction. See also *subtraction*.

tall, taller, tallest
A comparison of two or more heights, e.g. Janet is 130 cm tall and John is 128 cm tall. Janet is taller than John, but Sam is the tallest.

tally
A set of marks used for quick and accurate counting. Usually counting in sets of 5 with four downward strokes and the 5th stroke is a diagonal line across the four downward strokes.

tally chart
A table used to collect information using tally counting.

temperature
A measure of hotness. Usually in degrees Celsius or degrees Fahrenheit. Symbol: °C or °F.

ten less
The number ten before that number on a number line, e.g. 40 is ten less than 50.

ten more
The number ten after that number on a number line, e.g. 50 is ten more than 40.

ten thousand
10 000.

tens boundary
When counting from ones to tens, the tens boundary is crossed.

tenths
The fraction of a whole obtained when it is cut into ten equal pieces. The basis for the decimal system of counting.

tenths boundary
When counting from a hundredth to a tenth, the tenths boundary is crossed. See also *ones boundary*.

tetrahedron
A 3-D shape with four triangular faces.

thousand less/more
The number one thousand whole units more or less than another number. 9000 is a thousand less than 10 000 and 11 000 is a thousand more than 10 000.

thousandths
$\frac{1}{1000} = 0.001$.

three-quarters
A fraction of a whole. Three parts of a whole that has been divided into four equal parts.

timetable
A table listing start and finish or arrival and departure times of activities or events, e.g. a school timetable or a public transport timetable.

title
A sentence to describe or explain a chart, graph or diagram.

tonne
A metric measure of mass. 100 kilograms = 1 tonne.

total
The answer to an addition calculation. The total of 4, 3 and 5 is 12. See also *sum*.

translate, translation
To transform an object by moving it a given distance and direction. The image is the same shape and size as the object and in the same orientation.

trapezium
A quadrilateral with one pair of parallel sides. It can also be isosceles.

triangle, triangular
A 2-D shape with three straight sides.

triangular prism
A 3-D shape with two identical and parallel triangular ends, joined by three rectangular faces.

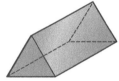

turn (whole turn, half turn, quarter turn, three-quarter turn)
A rotation about a point or line, like a hand around the clock face or a door about the join to the door frame. A whole turn is one complete revolution.

U

units
The standard measures, e.g. the units of length are metres, centimetres.

unknowns
Numbers to be found by solving equations and formulae. Represented by letters or shapes.

V

variable
A quantity that can take a range of different values. Represented by letters.

Venn diagram
A diagram of interlocking circles, used to sort numbers or objects by category.

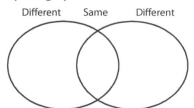

Different   Same   Different

Glossary

vertex, vertices
The point where two sides meet on a 2-D shape and where three or more faces meet on a 3-D shape. See also *face, edge*.

vertical
At right-angles (90°) to the horizontal plane.
See also *perpendicular*.

vinculum
The line that separates the numerator from the denominator.

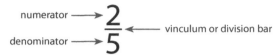

volume
Liquid volume is the amount of liquid in a container, e.g. 250 ml of water in a 2 l bottle. Measured in cubic ml, litres and so on.

Solid volume is the space a 3-D object takes up, e.g. a fridge in the kitchen. Measured in cubic mm, cm, metres and so on.

See also *capacity*.

W

weight
The force exerted on a mass by gravity. The units are units of force (Newtons). Often confused with mass.

whole-part relationship
How the parts are related to the whole, often illustrated with bars. This can be used when describing relationships between, e.g. addition and subtraction, fractions, percentages and ratio.

written calculation
A mathematical operation using a particular method.

X

x-axis
The horizontal line on a graph or coordinate grid that runs through zero.

Y

y-axis
The vertical line on a graph or coordinate grid that runs through zero.

yard
An imperial unit of length, approximately 90 cm. Symbol: yd. 36 inches = 3 feet = 1 yard. See also *foot, feet, inch, inches*.

Alexander, R. (2008). *Essays on pedagogy*. Abingdon: Routledge.

Alexander, R. (2012). *Neither national nor a curriculum?* York: Cambridge Primary Review.

Askew, M., Brown, M., Rhodes, V., Johnson, D., and Wiliam, D. (1997). *Effective teachers of numeracy*. London: King's College.

Askew, M., Hodgen, J., Hossain, S. and Bretscher, N. (2010). Theme 10 Textbooks. *Values and variables: mathematics education in high-performing countries*. London: Nuffield Foundation. 34-35.

Barber, M. and Mourshed, M. (2007). *How the world's best-performing school systems come out on top*. McKinsey Education.

Barmby, P., Bilsborough, L., Harries, T. and Higgins, S. (2009). *Primary mathematics: teaching for understanding*. Maidenhead: Open University Press.

Barmby, P., Harries, A.V. and Higgins, S.E. (2010). Teaching for understanding/understanding for teaching. Thompson, I. (Ed.) *Issues in teaching numeracy in primary schools*. Buckingham: Open University Press. 45-57. http://dro.dur.ac.uk/7939/1/7939.pdf

Benton, T. (2014). *A re-evaluation of the link between autonomy, accountability and achievement in PISA 2009*. Cambridge: Cambridge Assessment.

Carpenter, T.P. et al. (1999). *Children's mathematics: cognitively guided instruction*. Portsmouth NH: Heinemann.

DfE. (2011). *The National Strategies 1997-2011: A brief summary of the impact and effectiveness of the National Strategies*. https://www.gov.uk/government/uploads/system/uploads/attachment_data/file/175408/DFE-00032-2011.pdf

DfE. (2014). *National Curriculum in England: mathematics programmes of study*. https://www.gov.uk/government/publications/national-curriculum-in-england-mathematics-programmes-of-study

Drury, H. (2014). *Mastering mathematics: teaching to transform achievement*. Oxford: Oxford University Press.

Fan, L., Zhu, Y., and Miao, Z. (2013). Textbook research in mathematics education: development status and directions. *ZDM: The International Journal on Mathematics Education*, 45: 633-646.

Goldin, G.A. (1998). Representational systems, learning and problem solving in mathematics. *Journal of Mathematical Behavior*, 17(2): 137-65.

Gu, L., Huang, R., and Marton, F. (2004). Teaching with variation: a Chinese way of promoting effective mathematics learning. Lianghuo, F., Ngai-Ying, W., Jinfa, C., and Shiqi, L. (Eds.) *How Chinese learn mathematics: perspectives from insiders*. Singapore: World Scientific Publishing Co. Pte. Ltd. 309-347.

Haggerty, L., and Pepin, B. (2002). An investigation of mathematics textbooks and their use in English, French and German classrooms: who gets an opportunity to learn what? *British Educational Research Journal*, 28(4): 567-590.

Harries, T., and Sutherland, R. (1999). Primary school mathematics textbooks: an international comparison. Thompson, I. (Ed.) *Issues in teaching numeracy in primary schools*. Buckingham: Open University Press. 1-66.

Hiebert, J. and Carpenter, T.P. (1992). Learning and teaching with understanding. Grouws, D.A. (Ed.) *Handbook of Research on Mathematics Teaching and Learning*. New York: Macmillan. 66-97.

Hodgen, J., Brown, M., Coe, R. and Kuchemann, D. (2012). Why have educational standards changed so little over time: the case of school mathematics in England. Paper presented at the *British Educational Research Association* (BERA) annual conference. Institute of Education, University of London.

Howson, G. (2013). The development of mathematics textbooks: historical reflections from a personal perspective. *ZDM: The International Journal on Mathematics Education*, 45(5): 647-658.

Hoyles, C., Morgan, C. and Woodhouse, G. (1999). *Rethinking the maths curriculum*. London: Falmer Press.

Jianhua, L. (2004). Thorough understanding of the textbook: a significant feature of Chinese teacher manuals. Lianghuo, F., Ngai-Ying, W., Jinfa, C., and Shiqi, L. (Eds.) *How Chinese learn mathematics: perspectives from insiders*. Singapore: World Scientific Publishing Co. Pte. Ltd. 262-280.

Lai, M.Y. and Murray, S. (2012). Teaching with procedural variation: a Chinese way of promoting deep understanding of mathematics. *International Journal for Mathematics Teaching and Learning*. Retrieved on 12th May 2015 from http://www.cimt.plymouth.ac.uk/journal/default.htm

Lo, M.L., and Marton, F. (2012). Towards a science of the art of teaching: using variation theory as a guiding principle of pedagogical design. *International Journal of Lesson and Learning Studies*, 1(1): 7-22.

Macintyre, T. and Hamilton, S. (2010). Mathematics learners and mathematics textbooks: a question of identity? Whose curriculum? Whose mathematics? *Curriculum Journal*, 21(1): 3-23.

Maclellan, E. (1997). The role of concrete materials in constructing mathematical meaning. *Education 3-13*, 25(3): 31-35.

Mason, J. and Johnston-Wilder, S. (Eds.) (2004). Learners powers. *Fundamental constructs in Mathematics Education*. London: Routledge Falmer. 115-142.

McCulloch, J. (2011). *Subject to change: should primary schools structure learning around subjects or themes?* London: Pearson Centre for Policy and Learning.

Merttens, R. (2012). The "concrete-pictorial-abstract" heuristic. *Mathematics Teaching*, 228: 33-38.

Morris, P. and Adamson, B. (2010). *Curriculum, schooling and society in Hong Kong*. Hong Kong: Hong Kong University Press.

Morris, P. and Auld, E. (2013). Comparative education, the 'new paradigm' and policy borrowing: constructing knowledge for educational reform. *Comparative Education*, 13th August 2013.

National Centre for Excellence in the Teaching of Mathematics. (2010). Developing mathematics in primary schools. Headteachers talk about creating and sustaining excellence in the teaching of mathematics. *National Centre for Excellence in the Teaching of Mathematics*, 24.

National Centre for Excellence in the Teaching of Mathematics. (2014). *Mastery approaches to mathematics and the new National Curriculum*. https://www.ncetm.org.uk/public/files/19990433/Developing_mastery_in_mathematics_october_2014.pdf

National Centre for Excellence in the Teaching of Mathematics. (2015). *NCETM Mathematics Textbook Guidance*. https://www.ncetm.org.uk/files/21383193/NCETM+Textbook+Guidance.pdf

Nisbet, I. (2013). Is there a place for China's wise laoshi? *TES*, 14th June 2013.

Nuñes, T., Bryant, P. and Watson, A. (2009). *Key understandings in mathematics learning*. London: The Nuffield Foundation.

Oates, T. (2010). *Could do better: using international comparisons to refine the National Curriculum in England*. Cambridge: Cambridge Assessment.

Oates, T. (2014). *Why textbooks count: a policy paper*. Cambridge: Cambridge Assessment.

OECD. (2010). *Strong performers and successful reformers in education: lessons from PISA for the United States*. Paris: Organisation for Economic Co-operation and Development.

Ofsted (Office for Standards in Education). (2011). *Good practice in primary mathematics: evidence from successful schools*. London: Ofsted. https://www.gov.uk/government/publications/good-practice-in-primary-mathematics-evidence-from-successful-schools

Ofsted (Office for Standards in Education). (2008). *Mathematics: understanding the score*. London: Ofsted. https://www.gov.uk/government/publications/mathematics-made-to-measure

Ofsted (Office for Standards in Education). (2012). *Mathematics: made to measure*. London: Ofsted. https://www.gov.uk/government/publications/mathematics-made-to-measure

Rabel, S. and Wooldridge, I. (2013). Exploratory talk in mathematics: what are the benefits? *Education 3-13*, 41(1): 15-22.

Raiker, A. (2002). Spoken language and mathematics. *Cambridge Journal of Education*, 32(1): 45-60.

Reynolds, D. and Farrell, S. (1996). *Worlds apart? A review of international studies of educational achievement involving England*. London: HMSO for OFSTED.

Rowland, T., Huckstep, P. and Thwaites, A. (2003). The knowledge quartet. *Proceedings of the British Society for Research into Learning Mathematics*, 23(3): 97-103.

Shulman, L.S. (1986). Those who understand: knowledge growth in teaching. *Educational Researcher*, 15(2): 4-14.

Sierpinska, A. (1994). *Understanding in mathematics*. London: Falmer Press.

Sowell, E.J. (1989). Effects of manipulative materials in mathematics education. *Journal for Research in Mathematics Education*, 20(5): 498-505.

Sun, X. (2011). "Variation problems" and their roles in the topic of fraction division in Chinese mathematics textbook examples. *Educational Studies in Mathematics*, 76: 65-85.

White, R. and Gunston, R. (1992). *Probing understanding*. London: Falmer Press.

Williams, P. (2008). Independent review of mathematics teaching in Early Years settings and primary schools. *Department for Children, Schools and Families*, 90.

Xu, B. (2013). The development of school mathematics textbooks in China since 1950. *ZDM: The International Journal on Mathematics Education*, 45(5): 725-736.

Yan, Z. and Lianghuo, F. (2006). Focus on the representation of problem types in intended curriculum: a comparison of selected mathematics textbooks from mainland China and the United States. *International Journal of Science and Mathematics Education*, 4(4): 609-626.

Yang, D.C. and Huang, F.Y. (2004). Relationships among computational performance, pictorial representation, symbolic representation and number sense of sixth-grade students in Taiwan. *Educational Studies*, 30(4): 373-389.

IMPORTANT INFORMATION REGARDING YOUR PURCHASE

Your Rising Stars Mathematics Online Resource Bank

Your purchase includes one year's FREE access to a wealth of digital resources for all of the teachers in your school to access.

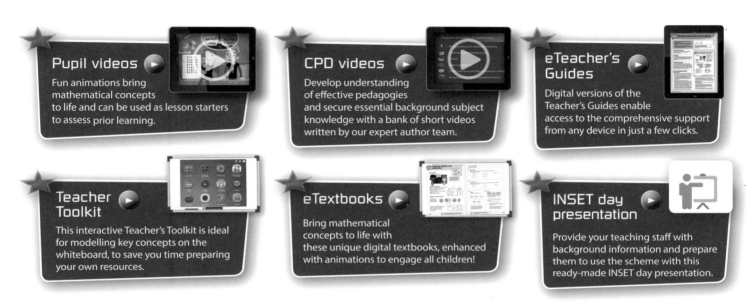

Pupil videos ▶
Fun animations bring mathematical concepts to life and can be used as lesson starters to assess prior learning.

CPD videos ▶
Develop understanding of effective pedagogies and secure essential background subject knowledge with a bank of short videos written by our expert author team.

eTeacher's Guides ▶
Digital versions of the Teacher's Guides enable access to the comprehensive support from any device in just a few clicks.

Teacher Toolkit ▶
This interactive Teacher's Toolkit is ideal for modelling key concepts on the whiteboard, to save you time preparing your own resources.

eTextbooks ▶
Bring mathematical concepts to life with these unique digital textbooks, enhanced with animations to engage all children!

INSET day presentation ▶
Provide your teaching staff with background information and prepare them to use the scheme with this ready-made INSET day presentation.

How to access your resources

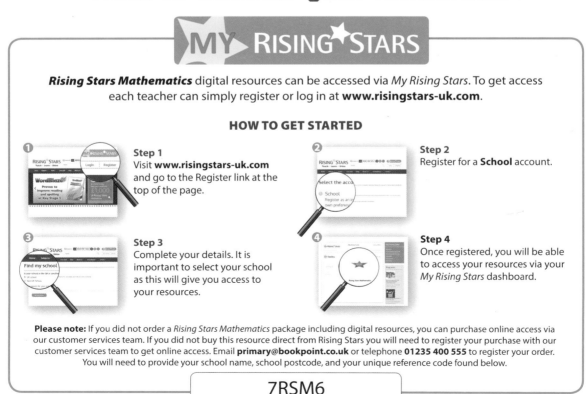

MY RISING STARS

Rising Stars Mathematics digital resources can be accessed via *My Rising Stars*. To get access each teacher can simply register or log in at **www.risingstars-uk.com**.

HOW TO GET STARTED

Step 1
Visit **www.risingstars-uk.com** and go to the Register link at the top of the page.

Step 2
Register for a **School** account.

Step 3
Complete your details. It is important to select your school as this will give you access to your resources.

Step 4
Once registered, you will be able to access your resources via your *My Rising Stars* dashboard.

Please note: If you did not order a *Rising Stars Mathematics* package including digital resources, you can purchase online access via our customer services team. If you did not buy this resource direct from Rising Stars you will need to register your purchase with our customer services team to get online access. Email **primary@bookpoint.co.uk** or telephone **01235 400 555** to register your order. You will need to provide your school name, school postcode, and your unique reference code found below.

7RSM6

Rising Stars Mathematics Year 6: 9781786002648